GEOS the pearson custom library for geography & geology

Geol-1000/1002
Lab Manual (Revised)

Cal State University, East Bay

Pearson Learning Solutions

New York   Boston   San Francisco
London   Toronto   Sydney   Tokyo   Singapore   Madrid
Mexico City   Munich   Paris   Cape Town   Hong Kong   Montreal

Senior Vice President, Editorial and Marketing: Patrick F. Boles
Executive Marketing Manager: Nathan L. Wilbur
Sponsoring Editor: Debbie Coniglio
Operations Manager: Eric M. Kenney
Development Editor: Christina Martin
Production Manager: Jennifer Berry
Art Director: Renée Sartell
Cover Designer: Kristen Kiley

Cover Art: Courtesy of Photoubrary.com, Robert Harding World Imagery, Getty Images/Photodisc.

This special edition published in cooperation with Pearson Learning Solutions.

Printed in the United States of America.

Please visit our web site at *www.prenhall.com/geos*

Attention bookstores: For permission to return any unsold stock, contact us at *pe-uscustomreturns@pearson.com*.

Pearson Learning Solutions, 501 Boylston Street, Suite 900, Boston, MA 02116
A Pearson Education Company
www.pearsoned.com

ISBN 10: 0-558-72875-8
ISBN 13: 978-0-558-72875-5

CONTENTS

EXERCISE

1

The Study of Minerals

The ability to identify minerals using the simplest of
techniques is a necessity for the Earth scientist, especially those scientists working in the field. In this exercise you will become familiar with the common
physical properties of minerals and learn how to use
these properties to identify minerals (Figure 1). In
order to understand the origin, classification, and al-
teration of rocks, which are for the most part aggregates (mixtures) of minerals, you must first be able to
identify the minerals that comprise them.

Figure 1 Quartz crystals. Slender, six-sided, transparent crystals
that will scratch glass. The shape of the crystals and their hardness
are two physical properties used to identify this mineral. (Photo by
E. J. Tarbuck)

Objectives

After you have completed this exercise, you should be
able to:

1. Recognize and describe the physical properties
   of minerals.
2. Use a mineral identification key to name minerals.
3. Identify several minerals by sight.
4. List the uses of several minerals that are mined.

Materials

hand lens

Materials Supplied by Your Instructor

mineral samples	dilute hydrochloric acid
streak plate	set of quartz crystals
magnet	(various sizes)
glass plate	contact goniometer
binocular microscope	crystal growth solution(s)

Terms

mineral	translucent	cleavage plane
rock-forming	transparent	direction of
mineral	color	cleavage
luster	streak	fracture
metallic luster	hardness	specific gravity
nonmetallic	crystal form	magnetism
luster	contact goniometer	striations
opaque	cleavage	tenacity

Introduction

A **mineral** is a naturally occurring, inorganic solid
with an orderly internal arrangement of atoms (called
crystalline structure) and a definite, but not fixed, chemical composition. Some minerals, such as gold and diamond, are single chemical elements. However, most
minerals are compounds consisting of two or more elements. For example, the mineral halite is composed

Table 1 Mineral Uses

MINERAL	USE
Chalcopyrite	Mined for copper
Feldspar	Ceramics and porcelain
Fluorite	Used in steel manufacturing
Galena	Mined for lead
Graphite	Pencil "lead," lubricant
Gypsum	Drywall, plaster of paris, wallboard
Halite	Table salt, road salt, source of sodium and chlorine
Hematite	Mined for iron
Magnetite	Mined for iron
Pyrite	Mined for sulfur and iron
Quartz	In the pure form, for making glass
Sphalerite	Mined for zinc
Talc	Used in ceramics, paint, talcum powder

of the elements sodium and chlorine. The distinctive crystalline structure and chemical composition of a mineral give it a unique set of physical properties such as its luster, its hardness, and how it breaks. The fact that each mineral has its own characteristic physical and chemical properties can be used to distinguish one mineral from another.

Of the nearly 4,000 known minerals, only a few hundred have any current economic value. An example would be the mineral gypsum, used for making drywall and wallboard. Table 1 lists a few of the minerals that are mined as well as their uses. Of the remaining minerals, no more than a few dozen are abundant. Collectively, these few often occur with each other in the rocks of Earth's crust and are classified as the **rock-forming minerals**.

Physical Properties of Minerals

The physical properties of minerals are those properties that can be determined by observation or by performing some simple tests. The primary physical properties that are determined for all minerals include optical properties (in particular, luster, the ability to transmit light, color, and streak), hardness, crystal form, cleavage or fracture, and specific gravity. Secondary (or "special") properties, including magnetism, taste, feel, striations, tenacity, and the reaction with dilute hydrochloric acid, are also useful in identifying certain minerals.

Optical Properties

Of the many optical properties of minerals, four—luster, the ability to transmit light, color, and streak—are frequently determined for hand specimens.

Luster Luster describes the manner in which light is reflected from the surface of a mineral. Any mineral that shines with a metal-like appearance has a **metallic luster**. Those minerals that do not have a metallic lus-

ter are termed **nonmetallic** and may have one of a variety of lusters that include vitreous (glassy), pearly (like a pearl), or earthy (dull, like soil or concrete). In general, many minerals with metallic luster produce a dark gray, black, or other distinctively colored powder when they are rubbed on a hard porcelain plate (this property, called *streak,* will be investigated later).

Observe the mineral photographs shown in Figures 2 through 13. The minerals illustrated in Figures 5 and 6 have definite metallic lusters. The minerals in Figure 9 have nonmetallic, vitreous (glassy) lusters. Some minerals, such as hematite (Figure 7), occur in both metallic and nonmetallic varieties.

Transmission of Light The ability of a mineral to transmit light can be described as either **opaque**, when no light is transmitted (e.g., Figure 3); **translucent**, when light but not an image is transmitted; or, **transparent**, when an image is visible through the mineral (e.g., Figure 1). In general, most minerals with a metallic luster are opaque, while vitreous minerals are either translucent or transparent.

Examine the mineral specimens provided by your instructor, and answer the following questions.

1. How many of your specimens can be grouped into each of the following luster types?
   Metallic: _____   Nonmetallic-glassy: _____
2. How many of your specimens are transparent, and how many are opaque?
   Transparent: _____   Opaque: _____

Color Color, although an obvious feature of minerals, may also be misleading. For example, slight impurities in a mineral may result in one sample of the mineral having one color while a different sample of the same mineral may have an entirely different color. *Thus, color is one of the least reliable physical properties.*

3. Observe the minerals in Figure 8. Both of the minerals shown are varieties of the same mineral, quartz. What is the reason for the variety of colors that quartz exhibits?

   _____

   _____

4. Examine the mineral specimens supplied by your instructor, and describe those that appear to be the same mineral but with variable colors.

   _____

   _____

Streak The streak of a mineral is the color of the fine powder of a mineral obtained by rubbing a corner across a piece of unglazed porcelain—called a *streak plate.* Whereas the color of a mineral may vary from sample to sample, its streak usually does not and is therefore the more reliable property (see Figure 7). In

Figure 2   Fluorite (left), halite (center), and calcite (right) exhibit smooth cleavage planes that are produced when the mineral is broken. (Photo by GeoScience Resources/American Geological Institute).

Figure 5   Galena. An ore of lead with a high specific gravity.

Figure 3   Sphalerite. An ore of zinc.

Figure 6   Pyrite. A brassy-yellow mineral with a metallic luster that is commonly known as "fool's gold."

Figure 4   Graphite. A soft silver-gray mineral.

Figure 7   Hematite. An ore of iron that has both a metallic (right) and nonmetallic (left) form.

Figure 8 Two varieties of the mineral quartz. Rose quartz (right) and smoky quartz (left).

Figure 11 Augite. A dark green to black, rock-forming, pyroxene mineral.

Figure 9 Biotite mica (black) and muscovite mica (light color) are similar in appearance, except for color.

Figure 12 Potassium feldspar, variety microcline.

Figure 10 Hornblende. A generally green to black, rock-forming, amphibole mineral.

Figure 13 Plagioclase feldspar, variety labradorite.

many cases, the color of a mineral's streak may not be the same as the color of the mineral. [*Note:* Minerals that have about the same hardness as, or are harder than, a streak plate (about 7 on Mohs scale of hardness), may not powder or produce a streak.]

5. Select three of the mineral specimens provided by your instructor. Do they exhibit a streak? If so, is the streak the same color as the mineral specimen?

	COLOR OF SPECIMEN	STREAK
Specimen 1:	_____	_____
Specimen 2:	_____	_____
Specimen 3:	_____	_____

Hardness

Hardness, one of the most useful diagnostic properties of a mineral, is a measure of the resistance of a mineral to abrasion or scratching. It is a relative property in that a harder substance will scratch, or cut into, a softer one.

In order to establish a common system for determining hardness, Friedrich Mohs (1773–1839), a German mineralogist, developed a reference scale of mineral hardness. The Mohs scale of hardness (Figure 14), widely used today by geologists and engineers, uses 10 index minerals as a reference set to determine the hardness of other minerals. The hardness value of 1 is assigned to the softest mineral in the set, talc, and 10 is assigned to the hardest mineral, diamond. Higher-numbered minerals will scratch lower-numbered minerals. For example, quartz, with a hardness of 7, will scratch calcite, which has a hardness of 3. It should be remembered that Mohs scale is a *relative ranking* and does *not* imply that mineral number 2, gypsum, is twice as hard as mineral 1, talc.

Most people do not have a set of Mohs reference minerals available. However, by knowing the hardness of some common objects, such as those listed on Mohs scale in Figure 14, a hardness value can be assigned to a mineral. For example, a mineral that has a hardness greater than 5.5 will scratch glass. Table 2 can serve as a guide for determining the hardness of a mineral.

6. Test the hardness of several of the mineral specimens provided by your instructor by rubbing any two together to determine which are hard (the minerals that do the scratching) and which are soft (the minerals that are scratched). Doing this will give you an indication of what

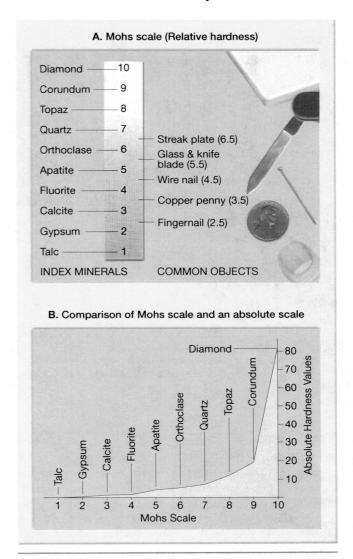

Figure 14 Hardness scales. **A.** Mohs scale of hardness, with the hardness of some common objects. **B.** Relationship between Mohs relative hardness scale and an absolute hardness scale.

is meant by the term "relative hardness" of minerals.

7. Use the hardness guide in Table 2 to find an example of a mineral supplied by your instructor that falls in each of the three categories.

Table 2　Hardness guide

HARDNESS	DESCRIPTION
Less than 2.5	A mineral that can be scratched by your fingernail (hardness = 2.5).
2.5 to 5.5	A mineral that cannot be scratched by your fingernail (hardness = 2.5), and cannot scratch glass (hardness = 5.5).
Greater than 5.5	A mineral that scratches glass (hardness = 5.5).

Figure 15 Atomic arrangement, crystal form, and cleavage of the mineral halite. Halite (NaCl) contains sodium and chlorine atoms arranged in a one-to-one ratio forming a cube. The internal, orderly arrangement of atoms produces the external cubic crystal form of the mineral. Planes of weak bonding between atoms in the internal crystalline structure are responsible for halite's cubic cleavage.

Crystal Form

Crystal form is the external appearance or shape of a mineral that results from the internal, orderly arrangement of atoms (Figure 15). Most inorganic substances consist of crystals. The flat external surfaces on a crystal are called *crystal faces*. A mineral that forms without space restrictions will exhibit well-formed crystal faces. However, most of the time, minerals must compete for space, and the result is a dense intergrown mass in which crystals do not exhibit their crystal form, especially to the unaided eye.

8. At the discretion of your instructor, you may be asked to grow crystals by evaporating prepared concentrated solutions. Following the specific directions of your instructor, and after you have completed your experiment(s), write a brief paragraph summarizing your observations.

_____

_____

_____

One of the most useful instruments for measuring the angle between crystal faces on large crystals is the **contact goniometer** (Figure 16).

9. The mineral shown in Figure 1 has a well-developed crystal form with six faces that intersect at

about 120° and come to a point. Two varieties of the same mineral are shown in Figure 8. Why do those in Figure 8 not exhibit crystal form?

_____

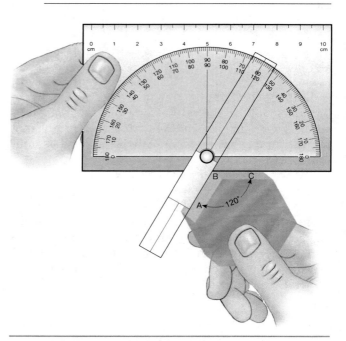

Figure 16 Contact goniometer. To use the instrument, hold the straight edge of the protractor in contact with one crystal face and the edge of the celluloid strip in contact with the other face. The angle is read where the fine line on the celluloid strip overlaps the degrees on the protractor. For example, the angle between the adjacent crystal faces on the mineral illustrated (angle ABC) is 120°.

10. Select one of the photographed minerals, other than Figure 1, that exhibits its crystal form and describe its shape.

    Figure _____ : _____

11. Observe the various size crystals of the mineral quartz on display in the lab. Use the contact goniometer to measure the angle between similar, adjacent crystal faces on several crystals. Then write a statement relating the angle between adjacent crystal faces to the size of the crystal.

    _____

    _____

Cleavage and Fracture

Cleavage is the tendency of some minerals to break along regular planes of weak bonding between atoms in the internal crystalline structure (see Figure 15). When broken, minerals that exhibit cleavage produce smooth, flat surfaces, called **cleavage planes**.

Cleavage is described by (1) noting the number of **directions of cleavage**, which is the number of different sets of planes that form the surfaces of a mineral crystal when it cleaves, and (2) the angle(s) at which the directions of cleavage meet (see Figure 15). Each cleavage plane of a mineral crystal that has a different orientation is counted as a different direction of cleavage. When two or more cleavage planes are parallel or line up with each other, they are counted only once, as one direction of cleavage. Minerals may have one, two, three, four, or more directions of cleavage (Figure 17).

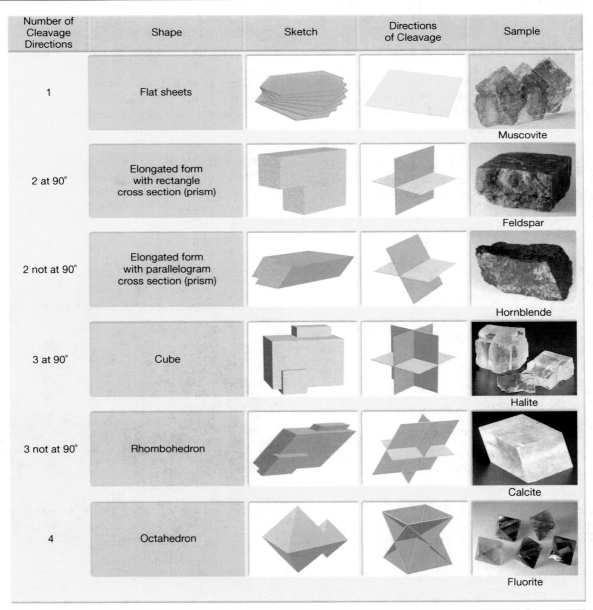

Number of Cleavage Directions	Shape	Sketch	Directions of Cleavage	Sample
1	Flat sheets			Muscovite
2 at 90°	Elongated form with rectangle cross section (prism)			Feldspar
2 not at 90°	Elongated form with parallelogram cross section (prism)			Hornblende
3 at 90°	Cube			Halite
3 not at 90°	Rhombohedron			Calcite
4	Octahedron			Fluorite

Figure 17 Common cleavage directions of minerals.

Observe the minerals shown in Figures 5 and 15. These minerals have broken with regularity and exhibit cleavage. The specimens shown are in the form of a cube. Although there are six planes of cleavage surrounding each specimen, each exhibits only three directions of cleavage: top and bottom form one parallel set of planes—hence the first direction of cleavage; the two sides are a second parallel set—a second direction of cleavage; and the front and back form the third direction of cleavage. The cleavage of both minerals is described as three directions of cleavage that intersect at 90° (also commonly called *cubic cleavage*) (see Figure 17).

Cleavage and crystal form are *not* the same. Some mineral crystals cleave while others do not. Cleavage is determined by the bonds that hold atoms together, while crystal form results from the internal, orderly arrangement of the atoms. The best way to determine whether or not a mineral cleaves is to break it and carefully examine the results.

Minerals that do not exhibit cleavage when broken are said to **fracture** (see Figure 4). Fracturing can be irregular, splintery, or conchoidal (smooth curved surfaces resembling broken glass). Some minerals may cleave in one or two directions and also exhibit fracturing (see Figure 12).

12. The minerals shown in Figure 9 have one direction of cleavage. Describe the appearance of a mineral that exhibits this type of cleavage.

   _____

13. Observe the photograph of calcite, the mineral on the right in Figure 2. Several smooth, flat planes result when the mineral is broken.

   a. How many planes of cleavage are present on the specimen?

   _____ planes of cleavage

   b. How many directions of cleavage are present on the specimen?

   _____ directions of cleavage

   c. The cleavage directions meet at (90° angles, angles other than 90°). Circle your answer.

14. Select one mineral specimen supplied by your instructor that exhibits cleavage. Describe its cleavage by completing the following statement.

   _____ directions of cleavage at _____ degrees

Specific Gravity

Specific gravity is a number that represents the ratio of the weight of a mineral to the weight of an equal volume of water. For example, the mineral quartz, Figures 1 and 8, has a specific gravity of 2.65; this means it weighs 2.65 times more than an equal volume of water. The mineral galena, Figure 5, with a specific gravity of 7.4, feels heavy when held in your hand. With a little practice, you can estimate the specific gravity of a mineral by hefting it in your hand. The average specific gravity of minerals is about 2.7, but some metallic minerals have a specific gravity two or three times greater than the average.

15. Find a mineral specimen supplied by your instructor that exhibits a high specific gravity by giving each mineral a heft in your hand.

Other Properties of Minerals

Luster, the ability to transmit light, hardness, color, streak, crystal form, cleavage or fracture, and specific gravity are the most basic and common physical properties used to identify minerals. However, other special properties can also be used to identify certain minerals. These other properties include:

Magnetism   Magnetism is characteristic of minerals, such as magnetite, that have a high iron content and are attracted by a magnet. A variety of magnetite called *lodestone* is itself actually magnetic and will pick up paper clips (Figure 18).

Figure 18   Magnetite, variety lodestone, has polarity like a magnet and will attract iron objects.

Specimen Number	Luster	Hardness	Color	Streak	Fracture or Cleavage (number of directions and angle of intersection)	Other Properties	Name	Economic Use or Rock-forming

Figure 19 Mineral identification chart.

Specimen Number	Luster	Hardness	Color	Streak	Fracture or Cleavage (number of directions and angle of intersection)	Other Properties	Name	Economic Use or Rock-forming

Figure 19 Mineral identification chart (*continued*)

Taste   The mineral halite (Figure 2, center) has a "salty" taste.

CAUTION: Do not taste any minerals or other materials without knowing it is *absolutely* safe to do so.

Feel   The mineral talc often feels "soapy," while the mineral graphite (Figure 4) has a "greasy" feel.

Striations   Striations are closely spaced, fine lines on the crystal faces of some minerals. They resemble the surface of a phonograph record but are straight. Certain plagioclase feldspar minerals often exhibit striations on one cleavage surface (see Figure 13).

Tenacity   Tenacity is the manner in which a substance resists breaking. Terms like *flexible* (a thin piece of plastic) and *brittle* (glass) are used to describe this property.

Reaction to Dilute Hydrochloric Acid   A very small drop of dilute hydrochloric acid, when placed on a freshly exposed surface of some minerals, will cause them to "fizz" (effervesce) as the gas carbon dioxide is released. The test is often used to identify a group of minerals called the *carbonate minerals*. The mineral calcite, Figure 2 (right), (chemical name: calcium carbonate) is the most common carbonate mineral and is frequently found in rocks.

CAUTION: Hydrochloric acid can discolor, decompose, and disintegrate mineral and rock samples. Use the acid only after you have received specific instructions on its use from your instructor. Never taste minerals that have had acid placed on them.

16. Following the directions given by your instructor, examine the mineral specimens to determine if any exhibit one or more of the special properties listed above.

Identification of Minerals

Having investigated the physical properties of minerals, you are now prepared to proceed with the identification of the minerals supplied by your instructor.

To identify a mineral, you must first determine, using available tools, as many of its physical properties as you can. Next, knowing the properties of the mineral, you proceed to a mineral identification key, which often functions like an outline, to narrow down the choices and arrive at a specific name. *As you complete*

the exercise, remember that the goal is to learn the procedure for identifying minerals through observation and not simply to put a name on them.

Arrange your mineral specimens by placing them on a numbered sheet of paper. Locate the mineral identification chart, Figure 19, and write the numbers of your mineral specimens, in order, under the column labeled "Specimen Number."

Using a Mineral Identification Key

Figure 20 is a mineral identification key that uses the property of luster as the primary division of minerals into two groups, those with metallic lusters and those with nonmetallic lusters. Color (either dark- or light-colored) is used as a secondary division for the nonmetallic minerals. Examine the mineral identification key closely to see how it is arranged.

17. Use the mineral identification key (Figure 20). What would be the name of the mineral with these properties: nonmetallic luster, light-colored, softer than a fingernail, produces small, thin plates or sheets when scratched by a fingernail, white color, and a "soapy" feel?

    Mineral name:

    (Check your answer with your instructor before proceeding.)

18. Complete the mineral identification chart, Figure 19, by listing the properties of each of the mineral specimens supplied by your instructor. Use the mineral identification key, Figure 20, to determine the name of each of the minerals.

19. Use Table 1, *Mineral Uses*, to determine which of the minerals you identify have an economic use.

    List their use in the column to the right of their name on the mineral identification chart, Figure 19.

20. The mineral photographs, Figure 2 (right, calcite) and Figures 8 through 13, show some of the most common rock-forming minerals. If your mineral specimens include examples of these minerals, indicate that they are rock-forming in the column to the right of their name on your mineral identification chart.

Minerals on the Internet

Apply the concepts from this exercise to an investigation of the mineral resources in your home state by completing the corresponding online activity on the *Applications & Investigations in Earth Science* website at http://prenhall.com/earthsciencelab

METALLIC MINERALS

Hardness	Streak	Other Diagnostic Properties	Name (Chemical Composition)
Harder than glass	Black	Black; magnetic; hardness = 6; specific gravity = 5.2; often granular	Magnetite (Fe_3O_4)
	Greenish-black	Brass yellow; hardness = 6; specific gravity = 5.2; generally an aggregate of cubic crystals	Pyrite (FeS_2)-fool's gold
	Red-brown	Gray or reddish brown; hardness = 5–6; specific gravity = 5; platy appearance	Hematite (Fe_2O_3)
Softer than glass but harder than a finger nail	Greenish-black	Golden yellow; hardness = 4; specific gravity = 4.2; massive	Chalcopyrite ($CuFeS_2$)
	Gray-black	Silvery gray; hardness = 2.5; specific gravity = 7.6 (very heavy); good cubic cleavage	Galena (PbS)
	Yellow-brown	Yellow brown to dark brown; hardness variable (1–6); specific gravity = 3.5–4; often found in rounded masses; earthy appearance	Limonite ($Fe_2O_3 \cdot H_2O$)
	Gray-black	Black to bronze; tarnishes to purples and greens; hardness = 3; specific gravity = 5; massive	Bornite (Cu_5FeS_4)
Softer than your fingernail	Dark gray	Silvery gray; hardness = 1 (very soft); specific gravity = 2.2; massive to platy; writes on paper (pencil lead); feels greasy	Graphite (C)

NONMETALLIC MINERALS

Hardness		Cleavage	Other Diagnostic Properties	Name (Chemical Composition)
Dark colored	Harder than glass	Cleavage Present	Greenish black to black; hardness = 5–6; specific gravity = 3.4; fair cleavage, two directions at nearly 90 degrees	Augite (Ca, Mg, Fe, Al silicate)
			Black to greenish black; hardness = 5–6; specific gravity = 3.2; fair cleavage, two directions at nearly 60 degrees and 120 degrees	Hornblende (Ca, Na, Mg, Fe, OH, Al silicate)
			Red to reddish brown; hardness = 6.5–7.5; conchoidal fracture; glassy luster	Garnet (Fe, Mg, Ca, Al silicate)
		Cleavage not prominent	Gray to brown; hardness = 9; specific gravity = 4; hexagonal crystals common	Corundum (Al_2O_3)
			Dark brown to black; hardness = 7; conchoidal fracture; glassy luster	Smoky quartz (SiO_2)
			Olive green; hardness = 6.5–7; small glassy grains	Olivine $(Mg, Fe)_2SiO_4$

Figure 20   Mineral identification key.

NONMETALLIC MINERALS

	Hardness	Cleavage	Other Diagnostic Properties	Name (Chemical Composition)
Dark colored (continued)	Softer than glass but harder than a fingernail	Cleavage present	Yellow brown to black; hardness = 4; good cleavage in six directions, light yellow streak that has the smell of sulfur	Sphalerite (ZnS)
			Dark brown to black; hardness = 2.5–3, excellent cleavage in one direction; elastic in thin sheets; black mica	Biotite mica (K, Mg, Fe, OH, Al silicate)
		Cleavage absent	Generally tarnished to brown or green; hardness = 2.5; specific gravity = 9; massive	Native copper (Cu)
	Softer than your fingernail	Cleavage not prominent	Reddish brown; hardness = 1–5; specific gravity = 4–5; red streak; earthy appearance	Hematite (Fe_2O_3)
			Yellow brown; hardness = 1–3; specific gravity = 3.5; earthy appearance; powders easily	Limonite ($Fe_2O_3 \cdot H_2O$)
Light Colored	Harder than glass	Cleavage present	Pink or white to gray; hardness = 6; specific gravity = 2.6; two directions of cleavage at nearly right angles	Potassium feldspar ($KAlSi_3O_8$) (pink)
				Plagioclase feldspar ($NaAlSi_3O_8$ to $CaAl_2Si_2O_8$) (white to gray)
		Cleavage absent	Any color; hardness = 7; specific gravity = 2.65; conchoidal fracture; glassy appearance; varieties: milky (white), rose (pink), smoky (gray), amethyst (violet)	Quartz (SiO_2)
	Softer than glass but harder than a finger nail	Cleavage present	White, yellowish to colorless; hardness = 3; three directions of cleavage at 75 degrees (rhombohedral); effervesces in HCl; often transparent	Calcite ($CaCO_3$)
			White to colorless; hardness = 2.5; three directions of cleavage at 90 degrees (cubic); salty taste	Halite (NaCl)
			Yellow, purple, green, colorless; hardness = 4; white streak; translucent to transparent; four directions of cleavage	Fluorite (CaF_2)
	Softer than your fingernail	Cleavage present	Colorless; hardness = 2–2.5; transparent and elastic in thin sheets; excellent cleavage in one direction; light mica	Muscovite mica (K, OH, Al silicate)
			White to transparent, hardness = 2; when in sheets; is flexible but not elastic; varieties: selenite (transparent, three directions of cleavage); satin spar (fibrous, silky luster); alabaster (aggregate of small crystals)	Gypsum ($CaSO_4 \cdot 2H_2O$)
		Cleavage not prominent	White, pink, green; hardness = 1–2; forms in thin plates; soapy feel; pearly luster	Talc (Mg silicate)
			Yellow; hardness = 1–2.5	Sulfur (S)
			White; hardness = 2; smooth feel; earthy odor; when moistened, has typical clay texture	Kaolinite (Hydrous Al silicate)
			Pale to dark reddish brown; hardness = 1–3; dull luster; earthy; often contains spheroidal-shaped particles; not a true mineral	Bauxite (Hydrous Al oxide)

Figure 20   Mineral identification key (*continued*)

Notes and calculations.

The Study of Minerals

Date Due: _____

Name: _____

Date: _____

Class: _____

After you have finished this exercise, complete the following questions. You may have to refer to the exercise for assistance or to locate specific answers. Be prepared to submit this summary/report to your instructor at the designated time.

1. Describe the procedure for identifying a mineral and arriving at its name.

_____

_____

_____

2. Name the physical property of a mineral that is described by each of the following statements.

PHYSICAL PROPERTY

Breaks along smooth planes: _____

Scratches glass: _____

Shines like a metal: _____

A red-colored powder on unglazed porcelain:

_____

3. Describe the shape of a mineral that has three directions of cleavage that intersect at 90°.

_____

4. Name two minerals you identified that have good cleavage. Describe the cleavage of each mineral.

MINERAL   **CLEAVAGE**

_____ : _____

_____ : _____

5. Select five minerals you identified, and list their names and physical properties.

_____ : _____

_____

_____

_____ : _____

_____

_____

_____ : _____

_____

_____

_____ : _____

_____

_____

_____ : _____

_____

_____

6. Name one mineral that you identified that has an economic use.

MINERAL   **MINED FOR**

_____ : _____

7. List the name and hardness of two minerals you identified.

   MINERAL   HARDNESS

   _____ : _____

   _____ : _____

8. How many directions of cleavage do the feldspar minerals—potassium feldspar and plagioclase feldspar—have?

   ___ directions of cleavage

9. What was your conclusion concerning the angles between similar crystal faces on different size crystals of the same mineral?

   _____

10. List the name(s) of the minerals you identified that had a special property such as magnetism or feel. Write the special property that you observed next to the name of the mineral.

    MINERAL   SPECIAL PROPERTY

    _____ : _____

    _____ : _____

    _____ : _____

11. What physical property most distinguishes biotite mica from muscovite mica?

    _____

12. Selecting from the minerals illustrated in Figures 1 through 13, list, by name, one mineral that exhibits each of the following:

    one direction of cleavage: _____

    striations: _____

    multiple colors: _____

    cubic cleavage: _____

    nonmetallic, vitreous luster: _____

    fracture: _____

    metallic luster: _____

A.   B.

Figure 21   Two mineral specimens for use with question 13.

13. Referring to the minerals illustrated in Figure 21, list the physical properties of each mineral that can be determined from its photograph.

    A: _____

    _____

    _____

    _____

    B: _____

    _____

    _____

    _____

14. The mineral identification key, Figure 20, uses the property of luster as its primary division of minerals. Develop and describe an alternative classification key that uses another property, or properties, to divide minerals into groups.

    _____

    _____

    _____

    _____

    _____

    _____

    _____

Common Rocks

To an Earth scientist, rocks represent much more than usable substances. They are the materials of the Earth; understanding their origin and how they change allows us to begin to understand Earth and its processes. It is often said that "the history of Earth is written in the rocks"—we just have to be smart enough to read the "words."

In this exercise, you will investigate some of the common rocks that are found on and near Earth's surface. The criteria used to classify a rock as being of either igneous, sedimentary, or metamorphic origin are examined, as well as the procedure for identifying rocks within each of these three families.

Objectives

After you have completed this exercise, you should be able to:

1. Examine a rock and determine if it is an igneous, sedimentary, or metamorphic rock.

2. List and define the terms used to describe the textures of igneous, sedimentary, and metamorphic rocks.

3. Name the dominant mineral(s) found in the most common igneous, sedimentary, and metamorphic rocks.

4. Use a classification key to identify a rock.

5. Recognize and name some of the common rocks by sight.

Materials

metric ruler   hand lens

Materials Supplied by Your Instructor

igneous rocks   dilute hydrochloric acid
sedimentary rocks   streak plate

metamorphic rocks   glass plate
hand lens or binocular   copper penny
   microscope

Terms

rock	weathering	composition
rock cycle	sediment	detrital material
igneous rock	lithification	chemical material
magma	metamorphic	foliation
sedimentary rock	rock	texture

Introduction

Most **rocks** are aggregates (mixtures) of minerals. However, there are some rocks that are composed essentially of one mineral found in large impure quantities. The rock limestone, consisting almost entirely of the mineral calcite, is a good example.

Rocks are classified into three types, based on the processes that formed them. One of the most useful devices for understanding rock types and the geologic processes that transform one rock type into another is the **rock cycle**. The cycle, shown in Figure 1, illustrates the various Earth materials and uses arrows to indicate chemical and physical processes. As you examine the rock cycle and read the following definitions, notice the references to the origin of each rock type.

The three types of rock are igneous, sedimentary, and metamorphic.

Igneous Igneous rocks (Figures 2–9) are the solidified products of once molten material called **magma**. The distinguishing feature of most igneous rocks is an interlocking arrangement of mineral crystals that forms as the molten material cools and crystals grow. *Intrusive* igneous rocks form below the surface of Earth, while those that form at the surface from lava are termed *extrusive*.

Sedimentary These rocks (Figures 10–17) form at or near Earth's surface from the accumulated products of

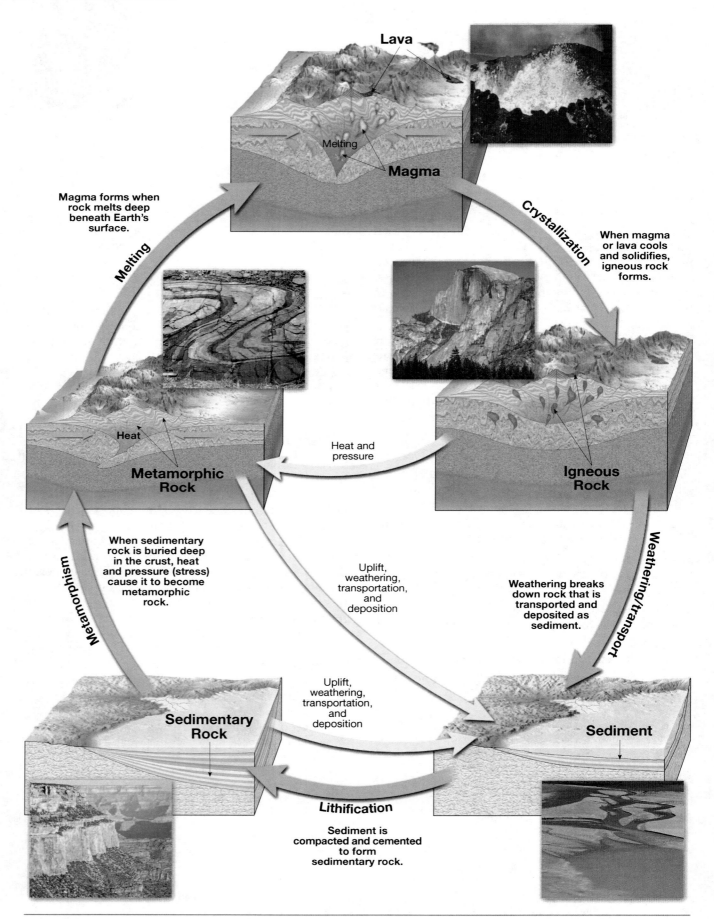

Figure 1 The rock cycle illustrating the role of the various geologic processes that act to transform one rock type into another.

weathering, called **sediment**. These products may be solid particles or material that was formerly dissolved and then precipitated by either inorganic or organic processes. The process of **lithification** transforms the sediment into hard rock. Since sedimentary rocks form at, or very near. Earth's surface, they often contain organic matter, or fossils, or both. The layering (or bedding) that develops as sediment is sorted by, and settled out from, a transporting material (usually water or air) helps make sedimentary rocks recognizable.

Metamorphic These rocks (Figures 18–25) form below Earth's surface where high temperatures, pressures, and/or chemical fluids change preexisting rocks without melting them.

Minerals are identified by using their physical and chemical properties. However, rock types and the names of individual rocks are determined by describing their *textures* and *compositions*. The key to success in rock identification lies in learning to accurately determine and describe these properties.

Texture refers to the shape, arrangement, and size of mineral grains in a rock. The shape and arrangement of mineral grains help determine the type (igneous, sedimentary, or metamorphic) of rock. Mineral grain size is often used to separate rocks within a particular type. Each rock type uses different terms to describe its textures.

Composition refers to the minerals that are found in a rock. Often the larger mineral grains can be identified by sight or by using their physical properties. In some cases, small mineral grains may require the use of a hand lens or microscope. Occasionally, very small grains cannot be identified with the normal magnification of a microscope. Practice and increased familiarity with the minerals will make this assessment easier.

Comparing Igneous, Sedimentary, and Metamorphic Rocks

One of the first steps in the identification of rocks is to determine the rock type. Each of the three rock types has a somewhat unique appearance that helps to distinguish one type from the other.

Examine the specimens of the three rock types supplied by your instructor, as well as the photographs of the rocks in Figures 2–25. Then answer the following questions.

1. Which two of the three rock types appear to be made primarily of intergrown crystals?

   _____ rocks and _____ rocks

2. Which one of the two rock types you listed in question 1 has the mineral crystals aligned or arranged so that they are oriented in the same direction in a linear, linelike manner?

3. Which one of the two rock types you listed in question 1 has the mineral crystals in most of the rocks arranged in a dense interlocking mass with no alignment?

   _____

4. Of the three rock types, (igneous, sedimentary, metamorphic) rocks often contain haphazardly arranged pieces or fragments, rather than crystals. Circle your answer.

Igneous Rock Identification

Igneous rocks form from the cooling and crystallization of magma. The interlocking network of mineral crystals that develop as the molten material cools gives most igneous rocks their distinctive crystalline appearance.

Textures of Igneous Rocks

The rate of cooling of the magma determines the size of the interlocking crystals found in igneous rocks. The slower the cooling rate, the larger the mineral crystals. The five principal textures of igneous rocks are:

Coarse Grained (or *phaneritic*) The majority of mineral crystals are of a uniform size and large enough to be identifiable without a microscope. This texture occurs when magma cools slowly inside Earth.

Fine Grained (or *aphanitic*) Very small crystals, which are generally not identifiable without strong magnification, develop when molten material cools quickly on, or very near, the surface of Earth.

Porphyritic Two very contrasting sizes of crystals are caused by magma having two different rates of cooling. The larger crystals are termed *phenocrysts;* and the smaller, surrounding crystals are termed *groundmass* (or *matrix*).

Glassy No mineral crystals develop because of very rapid cooling. This lack of crystals causes the rock to have a glassy appearance. In some cases, rapidly escaping gases may produce a frothy appearance similar to spun glass.

Fragmental The rock contains broken, angular fragments of rocky materials produced during an explosive volcanic eruption.

Examine the igneous rock photographs in Figures 2–9. Then answer the following questions.

5. The igneous rock illustrated in Figure 2 is made of large mineral crystals that are all about the same size. The rock formed from magma that cooled (slowly, rapidly) (inside, on the surface of) Earth. Circle your answers.

Igneous Rocks

Figure 2 Granite, a common coarse-grained, intrusive igneous rock.

Figure 6 Basalt, a fine-grained igneous rock.

Figure 3 Rhyolite, a fine-grained, extrusive rock.

Figure 7 Gabbro, a coarse-grained, intrusive igneous rock.

Figure 4 Diorite, a coarse-grained igneous rock.

Figure 8 Obsidian, an igneous rock with a glassy texture.

Figure 5 Andesite porphry, an igneous rock with a porphyritic texture.

Figure 9 Pumice, a glassy rock containing numerous tiny voids.

Sedimentary Rocks

Figure 10   Conglomerate, a detrital sedimentary rock.

Figure 11   Sandstone, a common detrital sedimentary rock.

Figure 12   Shale, a detrital sedimentary rock composed of very fine grains.

Figure 13   Breccia, a detrital sedimentary rock containing large, angular fragments.

Figure 14   Fossiliferous limestone, a biochemical sedimentary rock.

Figure 15   Coquina, a biochemical limestone consisting of visible shells and shell fragments, loosely cemented.

Figure 16   Rock salt, a chemical sedimentary rock formed as water evaporates.

Figure 17   Bituminous coal, a sedimentary rock composed of altered plant remains.

Metamorphic Rocks

Figure 18   Slate, a fine-grained, foliated metamorphic rock.

Figure 19   Phyllite, a foliated metamorphic rock with barely visible grains.

Figure 20   Schist, a foliated metamorphic rock with visible grains (variety: garnet-mica schist).

Figure 21   Gneiss, a foliated-banded metamorphic rock that often forms during intensive metamorphism.

Figure 22   Schist, variety mica schist.

Figure 23   Marble, a nonfoliated metamorphic rock that forms from the metamorphism of the sedimentary rock limestone.

Figure 24   Quartzite, a nonfoliated metamorphic rock composed of fused quartz grains.

Figure 25   Anthracite coal, often called hard coal, forms from the metamorphism of bituminous coal.

6. The rock shown in Figure 6 is made of mineral crystals that are all small and not identifiable without a microscope. The rock formed from magma that cooled (slowly, rapidly) (inside, on/near the surface of) Earth. Circle your answers.

7. The igneous rock in Figure 5 has a porphyritic texture. The large crystals are called _____, and the surrounding, smaller crystals are called _____.

8. The rocks in Figures 2 and 3 have nearly the same mineral composition. What fact about the mineral crystals in the rocks makes their appearances so different? What caused this difference?

_____

_____

Select a coarse-grained rock from the igneous rock specimens supplied by your instructor and examine the mineral crystals closely using a hand lens or microscope.

9. Sketch a diagram showing the arrangement of the mineral crystals in the igneous rock specimen you examined in the space provided below. Indicate the scale of your sketch by writing the appropriate length within the ( ) provided on the bar scale.

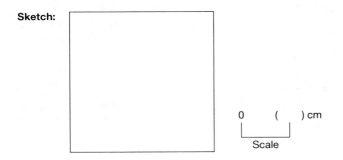

Sketch:

0   (   ) cm

Scale

Composition of Igneous Rocks

The specific mineral composition of an igneous rock is ultimately determined by the chemical composition of the magma from which it crystallized. However, the minerals found in igneous rocks can be arranged into four groups. Each group can be identified by observing the proportion of dark-colored minerals compared to light-colored minerals. The four groups are

Felsic (or *granitic*) Composed mainly of the light-colored minerals quartz and potassium feldspars. Dark-colored minerals account for less than 15% of the minerals in rocks found in this group.

Intermediate (or *andesitic*) A mixture of both light-colored and dark-colored minerals. Dark minerals comprise about 15% to 45% of these rocks.

Mafic (or *basaltic*) Dark-colored minerals such as pyroxene and olivine account for over 45% of the composition of these rocks.

Ultramafic Composed almost entirely of the dark-colored minerals pyroxene and olivine, these rocks are rarely observed on Earth's surface. However, the ultramafic rock peridotite is believed to be a major constituent of Earth's upper mantle.

10. Estimate the percentage of dark minerals contained in the igneous rock in Figure 4. (You may find the color index at the top of Figure 26, *Igneous & Rock Identification Key,* helpful.) The rock's color is (light, medium, dark, very dark). Circle your answer.

11. The rocks shown in Figures 3 and 6 have the same texture. What fact about the mineral crystals makes their appearances so different?

_____

Using an Igneous Rock Identification Key

The name of an igneous rock can be found by first determining its texture and color (an indication of mineral composition), identifying visible mineral grains, and then using an igneous rock identification key such as the one shown in Figure 26 to determine the name.

For example, the igneous rock shown in Figure 2 has a coarse-grained texture and is light-colored (quartz and potassium feldspar dominant). Intersecting the light-colored column with the coarse-grained row on the igneous rock identification key, Figure 26, determines that the name of the rock is "granite."

12. Place each of the igneous rocks supplied by your instructor on a numbered piece of paper. Then complete the igneous rock identification chart, Figure 27, for each rock. Use the igneous rock identification key, Figure 26, to determine each specimen's name.

Sedimentary Rock Identification

Sedimentary rocks, Figures 10–17, form from the accumulated products of weathering called *sediment*. Sedimentary rocks can be made of either, or a combination of, detrital or chemical material.

Detrital material consists of mineral grains or rock fragments derived from the process of mechanical weathering that are transported and deposited as solid particles (sediment). Rocks formed in this manner are called *detrital sedimentary rocks.* The mineral pieces that make

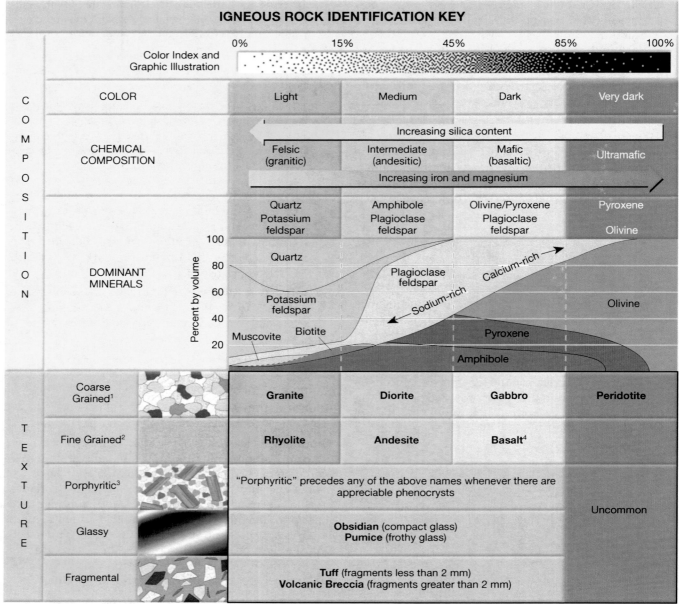

IGNEOUS ROCK IDENTIFICATION KEY

[1] Also called phaneritic. Crystals generally 1-10 mm (1 cm). The term pegmatite is added to the rock name when crystals are greater than 1 cm; e.g. granite-pegmatite.

[2] Also called aphanitic. Crystals generally less than 1 mm.

[3] For example, a granite with phenocrysts is called porphyritic granite.

[4] Basalt with a cinder-like appearance that develops from gas bubbles trapped in cooling lava (a texture referred to as vesicular) is called scoria.

Figure 26 Igneous rock identification key. Color, with associated mineral composition, is shown along the top axis. Each rock in a column has the color and composition indicated at the top of the column. Texture is shown along the left side of the key. Each rock in a row has the texture indicated for that row. To determine the name of a rock, intersect the appropriate column (color and mineral composition) with the appropriate row (texture) and read the name at the place of intersection.

up a detrital sedimentary rock are called *grains* (or *fragments* if they are pieces of rock). The identification of a detrital sedimentary rock is determined primarily by the size of the grains or fragments. Mineral composition of the rock is a secondary concern.

Chemical material was previously dissolved in water and later precipitated by either inorganic or organic processes. Rocks formed in this manner are called *chemical sedimentary rocks*. If the material is the result of the life processes of water-dwelling organisms—for example, the formation of a shell—it is said to be of biochemical origin. Mineral composition is the primary consideration in the identification of chemical sedimentary rocks.

Sedimentary rocks come in many varieties that have formed in many different ways. For the purpose of examination, this investigation divides the sedimentary rocks into the two groups, *detrital* and *chemical*, based upon the type of material found in the rock.

Specimen Number	Texture	Color (light-intermediate-dark)	Dominant Minerals	Rock Name

Figure 27 Igneous rock identification chart.

Examining Sedimentary Rocks

Examine the sedimentary rock specimens supplied by your instructor. Separate those that are made of pieces or fragments of mineral, rock material, or both. They are the detrital sedimentary rocks. Do *not* include any rocks that have abundant shells or shell fragments. You may find the photographs of the detrital sedimentary rocks in Figures 10–13 helpful. The remaining sedimentary rocks, those with shells or shell fragments and those that consist of crystals, are the chemical rocks.

Pick up each detrital rock specimen and rub your finger over it to feel the size of the grains or fragments.

13. How many of your detrital specimens feel rough like sand? How many feel smooth like mud or clay?

_____ specimens feel rough and _____ feel smooth.

Use a hand lens or microscope to examine the grains or fragments of several coarse detrital rock specimens. Notice that they are not crystals.

14. Sketch the magnified pieces and surrounding material, called *cement* (or *matrix*), of a coarse detrital rock in the space provided on the following page. Indicate the scale of your sketch by writing the appropriate length within the ( ) provided on the bar scale.

Sketch:

0   (   ) cm
Scale

a. Observe the material surrounding the grains or fragments in the rock specimen closely with a hand lens or microscope. The material is (course, fine). Circle your answer.

b. Write a brief description of the detrital rock specimen you have examined.

_____

_____

Two of the minerals that often comprise the grains of detrital sedimentary rocks are quartz, a hard (hardness = 7) mineral with a glassy luster, and clay, a soft, fine mineral that consists of microscopic platy particles. The difference in appearance and hardness of quartz and clay is helpful in distinguishing them.

15. How many of your detrital specimens are made of quartz, and how many appear to be made of clay?

_________ specimens have quartz grains and

_________ have clay grains.

As a result of their method of formation, many chemical sedimentary rocks are fine-to-coarse crystalline, while others consist of shells or shell fragments.

16. How many of your chemical sedimentary rocks are crystalline, and how many contain abundant shells or shell fragments?

_________ specimens are crystalline and

_________ contain shells or shell fragments.

Limestones, Figures 14 and 15, are the most abundant chemical sedimentary rocks. They have several origins and many different varieties; however, one thing that all limestones have in common is that they are made of the calcium carbonate mineral called *calcite.* Calcite can precipitate directly from the sea to form limestone or can be used by marine organisms to make shells. After the organisms die, the shells become sediment and eventually the sedimentary rock limestone.

Calcite is a mineral that reacts with dilute hydrochloric acid and effervesces (fizzes) as carbon dioxide gas is released. Most limestones react readily when a small drop of acid is placed on them, thus providing a good test for identifying the rock. Many limestones also contain fragments of seashells, which also aid in their identification.

17. Follow the directions of your instructor to test the specified sedimentary rock(s) with the dilute hydrochloric acid provided and observe the results. [*Note:* Several detrital sedimentary rocks have calcite surrounding their grains or fragments (calcite cement) that will effervesce with acid and give a *false* test for limestone. Observe the acid reaction closely.]

Using a Sedimentary Rock Identification Key

The sedimentary rock identification key in Figure 28 divides the sedimentary rocks into detrital and chemical types. Notice that the primary subdivisions for the detrital rocks are based upon grain size, whereas composition is used to subdivide the chemical rocks.

Detrital Sedimentary Rocks

Texture (particle size)	Sediment Name	Rock Name
Coarse (over 2 mm)	Gravel (rounded particles)	**Conglomerate**
Coarse (over 2 mm)	Gravel (angular particles)	**Breccia**
Medium (1/16 to 2 mm)	Sand (if abundant feldspar is present the rock is called **Arkose**)	**Sandstone**
Fine (1/16 to 1/256 mm)	Mud	**Siltstone**
Very fine (less than 1/256 mm)	Mud	**Shale**

Chemical Sedimentary Rocks

Composition	Texture	Rock Name	
Calcite, $CaCO_3$ (effervesces in HCl)	Fine to coarse crystalline	**Crystalline Limestone**	
		Travertine	
	Visible shells and shell fragments loosely cemented	**Coquina**	**Biochemical Limestone**
	Various size shells and shell fragments cemented with calcite cement	**Fossiliferous Limestone**	
	Microscopic shells and clay	**Chalk**	
Quartz, SiO_2	Very fine crystalline	**Chert** (light colored) **Flint** (dark colored)	
Gypsum $CaSO_4 \cdot 2H_2O$	Fine to coarse crystalline	**Rock Gypsum**	
Halite, NaCl	Fine to coarse crystalline	**Rock Salt**	
Altered plant fragments	Fine-grained organic matter	**Bituminous Coal**	

Figure 28 Sedimentary rock identification key. Sedimentary rocks are divided into two groups, detrital and chemical, depending upon the type of material that composes them. Detrital rocks are further subdivided by the size of their grains, while the subdivision of the chemical rocks is determined by composition.

Specimen Number	Detrital or Chemical	Texture (grain size)	Sediment Name or Composition	Rock Name

Figure 29 Sedimentary rock identification chart.

18. Place each of the sedimentary rocks supplied by your instructor on a numbered piece of paper. Then complete the sedimentary rock identification chart, Figure 29, for each rock. Use the sedimentary rock identification key, Figure 28, to determine each specimen's name.

Sedimentary Rocks and Environments

Sedimentary rocks are extremely important in the study of Earth's history. Particle size and the materials from which they are made often suggest something about the place, or environment, in which the rock formed. The fossils that often are found in a sedimentary rock also provide information about the rock's history.

Reexamine the sedimentary rocks and think of them as representing a "place" on Earth where the sediment was deposited.

19. Figure 11 is the rock sandstone that formed from sand. Where on Earth do you find sand, the primary material of sandstone, being deposited today?

_____

Figure 30 shows a few generalized environments (places) where sediment accumulates. Often, an environment is characterized by the type of sediment and life forms associated with it.

20. Use Figure 30 to name the environment(s) where, in the past, the sediment for the following sedimentary rocks may have been deposited.

ORIGINAL SEDIMENT   ENVIRONMENT(S)

Sandstone: (sand)

Shale: (mud)

Limestone: (coral, shells)

Metamorphic Rock Identification

Metamorphic rocks were previously igneous, sedimentary, or other metamorphic rocks that were changed by any combination of heat, pressure, and chemical fluids during the process of **metamorphism**. They are most often located beneath sedimentary rocks on the continents and in the cores of mountains.

During metamorphism new minerals may form, and/or existing minerals can grow larger as metamorphism becomes more intense. Frequently, mineral crystals that are elongated (like hornblende) or have a sheet structure (like the micas—biotite and muscovite) become oriented perpendicular to compressional forces. The resulting parallel, linear alignment of mineral crystals perpendicular to compressional forces (differential stress) is called **foliation** (Figure 31). Foliation is unique to many metamorphic rocks and gives them a layered or banded appearance.

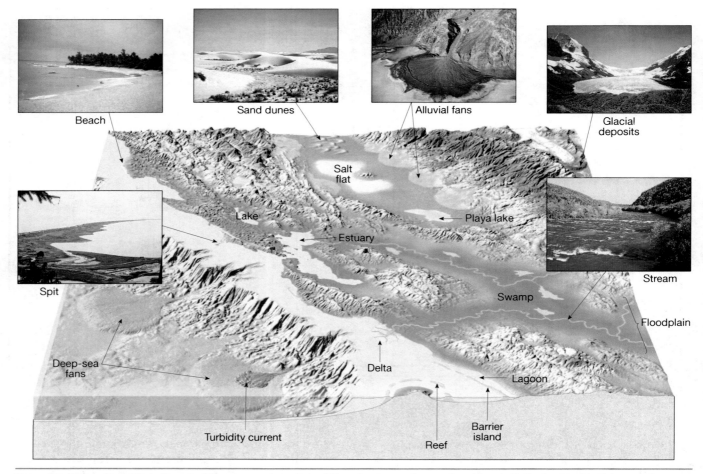

Beach

Sand dunes

Alluvial fans

Glacial deposits

Salt flat

Lake

Playa lake

Estuary

Spit

Stream

Swamp

Floodplain

Deep-sea fans

Delta

Lagoon

Turbidity current

Reef

Barrier island

Figure 30   Generalized illustration of sedimentary environments. Although many environments exist on both the land and in the sea, only some of the most important are represented in this idealized diagram. (Photos by E. J. Tarbuck, except alluvial fan, by Marli Miller)

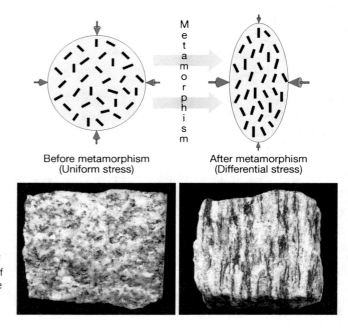

Before metamorphism (Uniform stress)

After metamorphism (Differential stress)

Figure 31   Under directed pressure, planar minerals, such as the micas, become reoriented or recrystallized so that their surfaces are aligned at right angles to the stress. The resulting planar orientation of mineral grains is called **foliation** and gives the rock a foliated texture. If the coarse-grained igneous rock (granite) on the left underwent intense metamorphism, it could end up closely resembling the metamorphic rock on the right (gneiss). (Photos by E. J. Tarbuck)

Metamorphic rocks are divided into two groups based on texture—foliated and nonfoliated. These textural divisions provide the basis for the identification of metamorphic rocks.

Foliated Metamorphic Rocks

The mineral crystals in foliated metamorphic rocks are either elongated or have a sheet structure and are arranged in a parallel or "layered" manner. *During metamorphism, increased heat and pressure can cause the mineral crystals to become larger and the foliation more obvious.* (Figure 32) The metamorphic rocks in Figures 18–22 exhibit foliated textures.

21. From the rocks illustrated in Figures 18 and 20, the (slate, schist) resulted from more intensive heat and pressure. Circle your answer.

22. From the metamorphic rocks in Figures 19 and 21, the (phyllite, gneiss) shows the minerals separated into light and dark bands. Circle your answer. (The foliated-banded texture of the rock that you have selected often results

from the most intensive heat and pressure during metamorphism.)

Select several of the foliated metamorphic rock specimens supplied by your instructor that have large crystals and examine them with a hand lens or microscope.

23. Sketch the appearance of the magnified crystals of one foliated metamorphic rock in the space provided below. Indicate the scale of your sketch by writing the appropriate length within the ( ) provided on the bar scale.

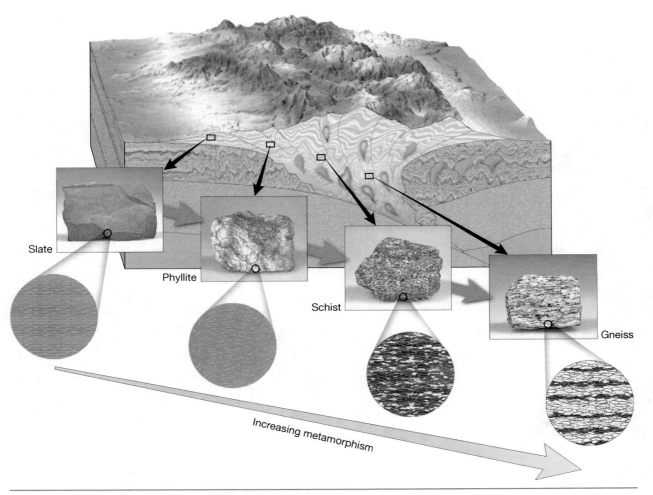

Figure 32 Idealized illustration showing the effect of increasing metamorphism in foliated metamorphic rocks. (Photos by E. J. Tarbuck)

Nonfoliated Metamorphic Rocks

Nonfoliated metamorphic rocks are most often identified by determining their mineral composition. The minerals that comprise them, most often calcite or quartz, are neither elongated nor sheet structured and therefore cannot be as easily aligned. Hence, no foliation develops during metamorphism.

24. Examine the nonfoliated metamorphic rocks supplied by your instructor to determine if any are composed of calcite or quartz. Hardness and the reaction to dilute hydrochloric acid often provide a clue.

CAUTION: Follow the directions of your instructor when using acid to test for calcite.

Using a Metamorphic Rock Identification Key

A metamorphic rock identification key is presented in Figure 33. To use the key, first determine a rock's texture, foliated or nonfoliated, and then proceed to further subdivisions to arrive at a name. The names of the medium or coarse foliated rocks are often modified with the mineral composition placed in front of the name (e.g., "mica schist").

25. Place each of the metamorphic rocks supplied by your instructor on a numbered piece of paper. Then complete the metamorphic rock identification chart, Figure 34, for each rock. Use the metamorphic rock identification key, Figure 33 to determine each specimen's name.

Rocks on the Internet

Associated with igneous rock, the most abundant rock on Earth, are often geologic hazards related to volcanic activity. Investigate this potentially destructive geologic process by completing the corresponding online activity on the *Applications & Investigations in Earth Science* website at http://prenhall.com/earthsciencelab

Texture	Grain Size	Rock Name	Comments	Parent Rock
Foliated	Very fine	Slate	Excellent rock cleavage, smooth dull surfaces	Shale, mudstone, or siltstone
Foliated	Fine	Phyllite	Breaks along wavy surfaces, glossy sheen	Slate
Foliated	Medium to Coarse	Schist	Micas dominate, scaly foliation	Phyllite
Foliated	Medium to Coarse	Gneiss	Compositional banding due to segregation of minerals	Schist, granite, or volcanic rocks
Nonfoliated	Medium to coarse	Marble	Interlocking calcite or dolomite grains	Limestone, dolostone
Nonfoliated	Medium to coarse	Quartzite	Fused quartz grains, massive, very hard	Quartz sandstone
Nonfoliated	Fine	Anthracite	Shiny black organic rock that may exhibit conchoidal fracture	Bituminous coal

Figure 33 Metamorphic rock identification key. Metamorphic rocks are divided into the two textual groups, foliated and nonfoliated. Foliated rocks are further subdivided based upon the size of the mineral grains.

Specimen Number	Foliated or Nonfoliated	Grain Size	Composition (if identifiable)	Rock Name

Figure 34   Metamorphic rock identification chart.

Notes and calculations.

Common Rocks

Date Due: _____

Name: _____

Date: _____

Class: _____

After you have finished this exercise, complete the following questions. You may have to refer to the exercise for assistance or to locate specific answers. Be prepared to submit this summary/report to your instructor at the designated time.

1. Write a brief definition of each of the three rock types.

   Igneous rocks: _____

   _____

   _____

   Sedimentary rocks: _____

   _____

   _____

   Metamorphic rocks: _____

   _____

   _____

2. What unique factor about the arrangement of mineral crystals occurs in many metamorphic rocks?

   _____

3. Describe the procedure you would follow to determine the name of a specific igneous rock.

   _____

   _____

   _____

4. Describe the basic difference between detrital and chemical sedimentary rocks.

   _____

   _____

5. List the *texture* and mineral *composition* of each of the following rocks.

	TEXTURE	MINERAL COMPOSITION
Granite:	_____	_____
Marble:	_____	_____
Sandstone:	_____	_____

6. What are two possible environments for the origin of the sedimentary rock sandstone?

   _____

   _____

   _____

7. Of the three rock types, which one is most likely to contain fossils? Explain the reason for your choice.

   _____

   _____

   _____

8. What factor determines the size of the crystals in igneous rocks?

   _____

9. What is a good chemical test to determine the primary mineral in limestone?

   _____

10. What factor(s) determine(s) the size of crystals in metamorphic rocks?

    _____

    _____

11. If the sedimentary rock limestone is subjected to metamorphism, what metamorphic rock will likely form?

    _____

12. With reference to the rock cycle, describe the processes and changes that an igneous rock will undergo as it is changed first to a sedimentary rock, which then becomes a metamorphic rock.

    _____

    _____

    _____

13. Select two igneous, two sedimentary, and two metamorphic rocks that you identified, and write a brief description of each.

    Rock type: _____

    Rock name: _____

    Description: _____

    _____

    Rock type: _____

    Rock name: _____

    Description: _____

    _____

    Rock type: _____

    Rock name: _____

    Description: _____

    _____

    _____

Rock type: _____

Rock name: _____

Description: _____

_____

_____

Rock type: _____

Rock name: _____

Description: _____

_____

_____

Rock type: _____

Rock name: _____

Description: _____

_____

_____

14. Referring to Figure 35, list each rock's name and write a brief description of each.

    A: _____

    _____

    _____

    B: _____

    _____

    _____

    C: _____

    _____

    _____

A.

B.

C.

Figure 35   Three rock specimens for use with question 14.

3

GEOLOGY OF THE CSUEB CAMPUS -- A PIECE OF ANCIENT OCEAN CRUST

By
Elwood R. Brooks
John Wakabayashi
Calvin Lee

The geology of the California State University, East Bay campus is complex and, perhaps surprising to you, poorly known. A geologic map of the campus should have been prepared when the campus was first established in the early 1960's, and the ridges and hills were scraped off clearly exposing the bedrock. Canyons were filled in with materials from the hilltops to produce the flat surfaces you see today covered by buildings, lawns and parking lots. As the buildings were constructed and the lawns planted, most of the rocks and structures exposed by the bulldozers were rendered inaccessible. Now we can see the rocks in only a few places where they are still exposed and in the undeveloped portions of the campus. Our present understanding of the CUSEB geology is based on identification of the exposed campus rocks and correlation of these rocks with similar rocks throughout the Bay Area (Figures 1, 2).

The rocks underlying the CSUEB campus preserve evidence of processes which occurred in the Pacific Ocean between 140 and 170 million years ago, during the Middle to Late Jurassic Period of the geologic time scale. They record processes related to the formation of *lithospheric plates* and the growth of continents.

To understand what the rocks on campus represent and how they formed, we must consider briefly the _plate tectonic theory_. The surface of the earth is made up of about a dozen lithospheric plates of crust and uppermost, solid and rigid mantle which makes up the uppermost 70 to 150 km of the Earth. The plates move exceedingly slowly (a few cm per year) with respect to one another, on a "plastic" layer in the mantle. The plates are either moving away from one another (diverging), moving toward one another (converging), or sliding past one another (as they do along the San Andreas fault across the Bay).

OCEAN CRUST, SEA-FLOOR SPREADING AND FORMATION OF OCEANIC PLATES

The whole process of plate divergence and the addition of new igneous rocks to the separating plate margins have been termed *sea-floor spreading*. As two plates at a *divergent plate margin* moved apart, magma (molten rock) generated in the mantle ascended to form a magma chamber. Gabbro crystallizes along the roof and sides of such magma chambers (Figure 3). Considerable magma rises along tension fractures produced as the plates diverge to form dikes which cut across older crust and to erupt on the sea floor as volcanic lava flows. Subsequently a layer of pelagic sediment, derived from tests (shells) of microscopic, floating marine organisms, builds up on top of the new sea floor. This assemblage of igneous rocks (gabbro, dikes, lava) plus sea-floor sediment is referred to as an *ophiolite* (Figure 3).

Once formed, the new oceanic crust moves away from the spreading ridge (where the processes described above occur) and may move toward an adjacent plate. If the two plates collide, most of the oceanic crust is consumed (goes down into the mantle or is subducted) under the colliding plate. Some of the oceanic crust may get *emplaced* ("scrapped-off" and attached to the overriding plate). The ophiolite emplaced onto the western edge of North America in the Late Jurassic is called the *Coast Range Ophiolite* for its wide distribution in the California Coast Ranges.

Most of the CSUEB campus has been built on *gabbro* of the Coast Range Ophiolite (Figures 1, 2). The *Leona Rhyolite*, exposed on the hills surrounding the campus, and *pillow basalt*, exposed in a downhill stream bed south of the Pioneer Heights student apartments, probably represents volcanic lava flows of the ophiolite. The campus gabbro, Leona Rhyolite and pillow basalt probably were strongly altered – even metamorphosed – possibly by circulation of heated sea water through fractures formed in them near the sea-floor spreading ridge axis. Bluish, banded (?) *chert* exposed in the downhill stream bed probably represents lithofied *pelagic* sediment deposited on the oceanic crust.

OCEANIC-CONTINENTAL COLLISION AND FORMATION OF AN ACCRETIONARY WEDGE AND FOREARC BASIN

The western edge of North America became a *convergent plate margin* 158-163 million years ago (Late Jurassic epoch). At this margin, the denser, oceanic plate is driven beneath the continental plate in a process called *subduction* (Figure 4). Subduction of some of the oceanic Coast Range ophiolite 158-163 million years ago resulted in its metamorphism at high temperature and pressure to a coarsely crystalline rock called amphibolite. The amphibolite occurs as very large blocks enclosed in shale; this odd mixture of metamorphic and sedimentary materials is referred to as a mélange, and is believed to be formed within an accretionary wedge above a subduction zone. This mélange formed the oldest component of a group of rock units designated as the Franciscan Complex or group. Subsequently, some of this "high-grade" amphibolite rose through overlying Coast Range ophiolite, probably along a narrow, steeply inclined shear zone. According to Platt (1986), continued underplating, or scrapping-off, of deeply-subducted, metamorphosed seafloor jacked up the metamorphosed rocks to near the earth's surface, and caused extension and normal faulting within the landward portion of the accretionary wedge (Figure 4). These metamorphic rocks, such as the amphibolite, were subsequently unroofed by erosion.

A thick sequence of sedimentary rocks, named the Great Valley sequence, was deposited upon the Coast Range ophiolite, in a forearc basin immediately behind the accretionary wedge of the Franciscan Complex. The Knoxville formation is the oldest unit of the Great Valley sequence, at between 145 and 150 million years old (Late Jurassic epoch);

the formation is believed to overlie the Leona Rhyolite. Where it is exposed on campus, the Knoxville formation consists largely of yellow-weathered, gray mudstone containing sandy limestone concretions. The mudstone is interbedded with sandstone exhibiting some grains that appear to have been derived by erosion of the underlying Leona Rhyolite.

MID-OCEAN RIDGE – CONTINENTAL COLLISION AND CHANGE FROM SUBDUCTION TO TRANSFORM MARGIN

Approximately 30 million years ago, the mid-ocean spreading center that was activated approximately 170 million years ago collided with the North American continent. The continental margin changed from a convergent margin to a strike-slip margin, represented by the San Andreas fault system; it is not a single fault trace, but a broad zone of faults extending as far as the east side of the Sierra Nevada mountains. Since approximately 30 million years ago, right-lateral strike-slip motion along the group of faults comprising the San Andreas fault system has slivered up and displaced northward large blocks of land along the western margin of North America by as much as 330 kilometers (205 miles).

Stop 1: Campus Gabbro
The campus gabbro is a grayish-green, visibly crystalline igneous rock (which was once molten and cooled at depth where large crystals form). "Fresh", unaltered gabbro consists largely of the minerals plagioclase feldspar and monoclinic pyroxene. But the campus gabbro has been strongly altered, so that the pyroxene crystals have been replaced by crystals of the mineral amphibole. The campus gabbro is approximately 163-169 million years old!

1. As you have done in the lab, describe the gabbro in terms of texture, color and minerals.

2. Can you identify individual minerals? Why or why not?

The campus gabbro, some of the least altered available, is exposed in small excavations along the east side of the sidewalk between the International Students/Temporary Support buildings and the University Union. It is foliated (crystals are in layers) in places, the darker minerals concentrated in parallel streaks, and it is highly fractured. More campus gabbro can be seen (and collected) in the large cut-slope to the east of the Pioneer Heights student apartments south of Harder Road.

Stop 2: Leona Rhyolite
The Leona Rhyolite a very finely crystalline rock consisting mostly of the minerals plagioclase feldspar (albite) and quartz. Microscopic examination of paper-thin slices of samples of the rhyolite reveals that it is not actually rhyolite, but a metamorphosed volcanic rock known as *keratophyre*. Originally thought to be a mere 5 million years old or less, the Leona Rhyolite is now known to be at least 99.2 million years old. This

radiometric age is from a sample of Alum Rock Rhyolite, collected near San Jose and thought to correlate with (be equivalent to) the Leona Rhyolite.

Across Harder Road, on the southwest side of the Pioneer Heights student apartments, a dirt road leaves the southeast end of the parking lot. Follow the dirt road to the PCB storage building and turn right onto another dirt road which will take you up the hill. This outcrop of Leona Rhyolite is typical in that it does not yield any secrets regarding its mode of formation; was it a lava flow or was it perhaps intruded into or just below the Knoxville mudstones? The variously oriented fractures which cut the outcrop are also typical.

1. Describe the rhyolite in terms of texture, color and minerals. Was this easy to do?

From the outcrop of Leona Rhyolite, with the hill on your left side, look down the valley towards a large, prominent building in the distance. Now look at your geologic map.

2. What type of geologic feature is located between the rhyolite and the building (be specific)?

3. What is the name of the building, and what type of work will be done to it?

Stop 3: "High-Grade" Amphibolite Block in Franciscan Complex Melange
Amphibolite occurs as very large blocks enclosed in shale; this odd mixture of sedimentary and metamorphic materials is referred to as *melange*. On campus, a 22-ft block of amphibolite is found on the southwest side of the Pioneer Heights student apartments; the amphibolite is in a dark gray mudstone matrix of the melange.

Some rather rare metamorphic minerals can be found in this block. The bluish cast seen in places is due to the presence of crossite, a blue amphibole. The silvery flakes are of phengitic muscovite mica and the pistachio green areas indicate concentrations of epidote. This forest-green veins of pumpellyite cut the block at one point, and white blades of lawsonite are found on fractures at another place.

1. Describe the rhyolite in terms of texture, color and minerals. Remember this is a metamorphic rock.

At Stop 3, look west toward the city of Hayward and San Francisco Bay.

2. Somewhere between where you are standing and the city of Hayward lies the Hayward fault. By looking at the landscape between where you are standing and the city of Hayward below, and studying your geologic map, where would you place the Hayward fault? (A) In the valley or low area between your location

and the next ridge, (B) On the next ridge, (C) On the other side of the next ridge, at the bottom.

3. Looking out along the edge of the Bay, there are some whitish- and orange-colored flat areas. What are these areas for?

4. Given enough time, what type of rock could be mined out of these areas?

Stop 4: Knoxville Formation Mudstone

On the campus, the Knoxville consists largely of yellow-weathered, dark gray (when fresh and unweathered) mudstone containing sandy limestone concretions (hard limy nodules). This assemblage of fine-grained, muddy, limy sedimentary rocks suggests deposition in a fairly deep sea, considerably removed from the continental margin. Continue down the dirt road past the steel gate. Upon rounding the hairpin turn, you will begin to encounter tiny yellow-weathered fragments of gray mudstone in the roadcuts on your left. These characterize the soils developed by weathering of the soft Knoxville Formation. Keep your eyes peeled for scarce, gray-brown chunks of sandy limestone which represents concretions encased in mudstone.

1. The mudstone fragments are typically in little mounds, surrounded by vegetation. Can you think of a reason why the fragments are mounded?

Stop 5: Knoxville Formation Sandstone

A sandstone outcrop with some limestone lenses can be found in the roadbed just around the next corner.

2. Noticed how easily both the sandstone and the mudstone break apart; they are relatively soft rocks. Look across at the surrounding hillsides. You can see steep-sided, bowl-shaped areas, with a flatter spot in the center where there is a change in color of the vegetation; these are landslide areas. The weak rocks of the Knoxville formation are prone to landslides.

Stop 6: Conglomerate in Leona Rhyolite

Walk back to Harder Road, then downhill to the intersection with West Loop Road. The top of the hill between the boxes of Greek Letters and the security booth contain conglomerate within the Leona Rhyolite. It is not at all clear what the conglomerate is doing in the Leona Rhyolite, but a possible interpretation is shown in Figure 2. Perhaps the conglomerate separates two lava flows (or pyroclastic flows) of Leona Rhyolite, having been deposited in the interval between emplacement of the flows. Alternatively, the Leona may be present as concordant sills intruded into the conglomerate.

REFERENCES

Platt, J.P., 1986, Dynamics of orogenic wedges and the uplift of high-pressure metamorphic rocks: Geological Society of America Bulletin, v. 97, p. 1037-1053.

GEOLOGIC MAP OF THE HAYWARD QUADRANGLE & CAL STATE EAST BAY

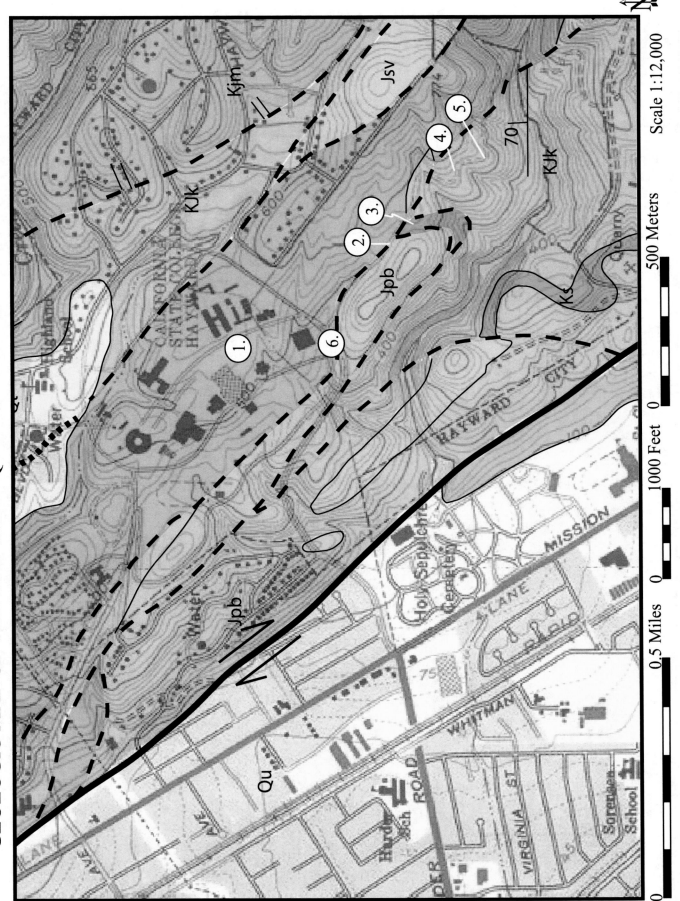

Scale 1:12,000

MAP EXPLANATION

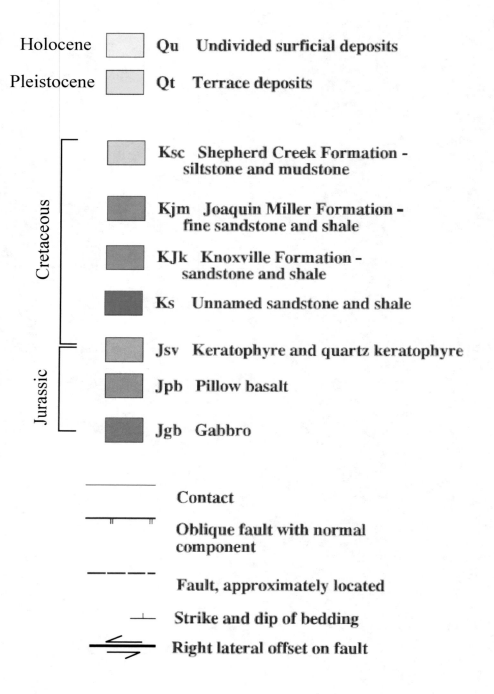

Holocene   Qu   Undivided surficial deposits

Pleistocene   Qt   Terrace deposits

Cretaceous

Ksc   Shepherd Creek Formation - siltstone and mudstone

Kjm   Joaquin Miller Formation - fine sandstone and shale

KJk   Knoxville Formation - sandstone and shale

Ks   Unnamed sandstone and shale

Jurassic

Jsv   Keratophyre and quartz keratophyre

Jpb   Pillow basalt

Jgb   Gabbro

———————   Contact

Oblique fault with normal component

— — — — —   Fault, approximately located

Strike and dip of bedding

Right lateral offset on fault

Data Set Citation Dataset Creator: R.W. Graymer, D.L. Jones, and E.E. Brabb
Dataset Title: Preliminary geologic map emphasizing bedrock formations in
Alameda County, California: A digital database
Dataset Series Name: USGS Open-File Report
Dataset Release Place: Menlo Park, CA, USA
Dataset Publisher: U.S. Geological Survey
Issue Identification: 96-252
Data Presentation Form: Map, text
Online Resource: http://pubs.usgs.gov/of/1996/of96-252/

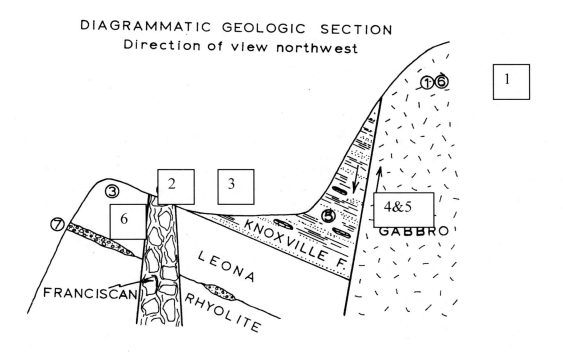

DIAGRAMMATIC GEOLOGIC SECTION
Direction of view northwest

Figure 2. Diagrammatic cross-section. Station numbers are keyed to the geologic map.

Structure of Ocean Crust

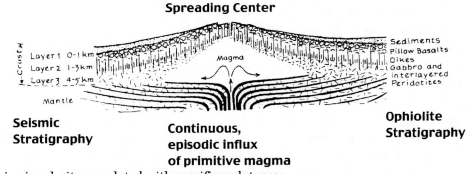

Seismic velocity correlated with specific rock types:

Layer 1   0-1 km thick,   Vp= 2.5 Km/s, sediments, pelagic ooze,
Layer 2   2 km thick   Vp= 4.5 km/s, pillow basalt, diabase
Layer 3   6-8 km thick   Vp= 6-7 km/s, gabbro, diorite

Rocks based on ophiolite model of oceanic crust and on Deep Sea Drilling Project results.

Figure 3. Stratigraphy of oceanic crust (from http://www.usu.edu/geo/shervais/ G4500_PDF/45Week5_MORB.pdf).

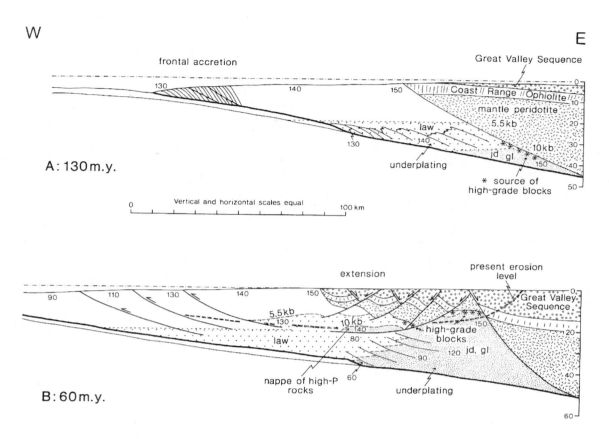

Figure 4.   Tectonic evolution of the Franciscan Complex, California (from Platt, 1986). A
Early Cretaceous. High-P/low-T metamorphism took place in sediment subducted benea
the leading edge of North America (represented by the Coast Range ophiolite and th
underlying mantle wedge). Amphibolite, eclogite, and high-grade blueschist formed
metamorphic sole beneath the peridotite; this provided the source for Franciscan high-grac
blocks.   B. Early Tertiary. Underplating and resultant extension have stretched the mant
wedge (now partly serpentinized) together with the overlying ophiolite and fore-arc bas
sediments (Great Valley Sequence). As a result, most of the contacts between ophiolite ar
Franciscan are low-angle normal faults. The high-P rocks have risen within reach
subsequent erosion and have been transported laterally over younger, lower-P rocks. Higl
grade rocks were dispersed by extensional faults.

4

MAPPING THE EARTH

Topographic Maps

Introduction

This laboratory is an introduction to the interpretation and use of topographic maps. Topographic maps differ from other maps because they introduce the third dimension of the Earth's surface, the elevation and configuration of the landscape. The principles and techniques introduced in this laboratory provide a foundation for later exercises.

Topographic maps are essential tools for many activities. Engineers use them to determine the routes for new highways, power lines, and pipelines, and to select sites for dams, airports, coastal facilities, and industrial and residential developments. Scientists and engineers use topographic maps as bases for other kinds of mapping and to delimit areas of potential natural hazards, such as floods and landslides. Topographic maps also have recreational uses for locating fishing and hunting areas, campsites, roads, and trails.

Exercise 1:   Location on Topographic Maps

Introduction

Location on a topographic map depends on understanding latitude and longitude, the Public Land Survey System, and map directions.

Latitude and Longitude

An international system for locating features on the surface of the Earth is a grid of east–west lines of **latitude** and north–south lines of **longitude** (Figure 1). This system uses the geographic north and south poles and the equator as location references. Distances are measured in fractions of a circle (degrees). Remember that all circles can be divided into 360°. A degree of latitude or longitude (or any degree of arc) can be divided into 60 minutes (60'), and each minute can be divided into 60 seconds (60").

The reference location for latitude is the **equator**, a circle defined by points halfway between the geographic north and south poles, dividing the Earth into the **Northern Hemisphere** and the **Southern Hemisphere** (Figure 1). Latitude indicates distances north and south of the equator. The measurement units are degrees, with the equator at 0° and the poles at 90°. The east–west lines of latitude are termed **parallels** because they are all parallel to one another.

Name _____

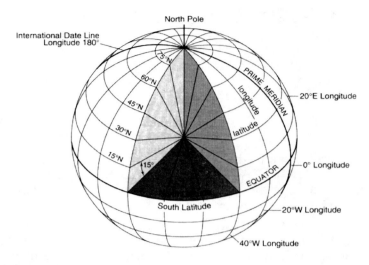

Figure 1. **The Earth's latitude and longitude.**

At the international Meridian Conference of 1884, the meridian passing through the Royal Astronomical Observatory in Greenwich, England, (near London) was chosen as the **prime meridian**. All longitudinal positions are measured from this reference. Longitude increases both east and west from 0° at the prime meridian to 180° at the **international date line** on the opposite side of the Earth. Unlike the lines of latitude, the meridians of longitude are neither parallel nor equally spaced except along a line of latitude (Figure 1). Because the meridians converge at the poles, the ground distance represented by a degree or minute of longitude varies.

Question Set 1:   Latitude and Longitude

Use the San Bernardino South, California, topographic map in the rear pocket to answer the following questions:

i. What is the latitude and longitude of each corner of the map?

Northwest Corner	Northeast Corner
Latitude	Latitude
Longitude	Longitude
Southwest Corner	**Southeast Corner**
Latitude	Latitude
Longitude	Longitude

Name _____

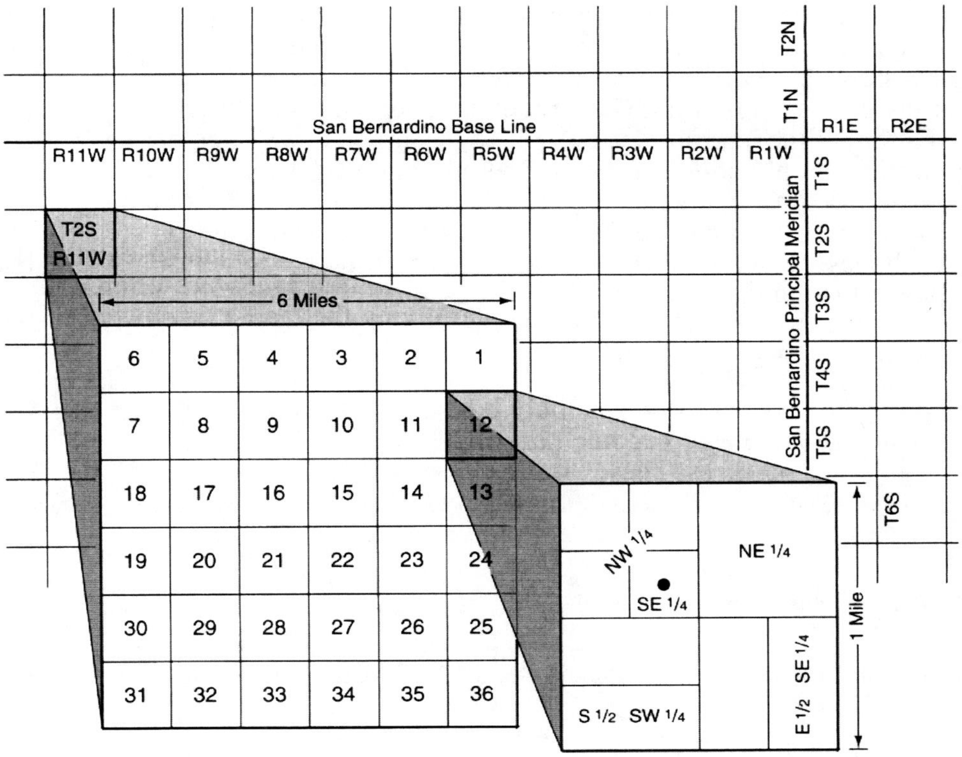

Figure 2.   **Explanatory figure for the use of base lines and principal meridians.**

The U.S. Public Land Survey System

In most of the United States, surveys of what were originally public lands provide another location reference system. This system is based on meridian reference lines running north–south called **principal meridians**, and east–west running lines called **base lines**. A principal meridian and a base line are shown in Figure 2. Topographic maps produced by the U.S. Geological Survey include latitude and longitude. In addition, the U.S. Public Land Survey System for location reference is also used, except in the original 13 states, Vermont, Maine, West Virginia (part of Virginia until 1863), Kentucky, Tennessee, parts of Texas and Ohio, and original Spanish land grants in California.

Starting from these surveyed reference lines the land is divided into **townships** that are 6 miles on a side. Townships are numbered with reference to the intersection of the principal meridian and base line (Figure 2). Whittier, California, for example, is located in the township that is in the second row of townships south and in the 11th column of *ranges* west of the San Bernardino base line and meridian. The notation used for this location is T2S, R11W, which would be read: township 2 south, range 11 west. Townships are further divided into 36 **sections**, each of which is 1 square mile (640 acres) in area (Figure 2). Numbering of the sections begins in the northeast corner with section 1 and then goes back and forth across each tier of sections, ending with section 36 in the southeast corner (Figure 2). More exact locations can be given by dividing the sections into smaller parts. Sections are usually divided first into **quarter sections** and referred to by the location of the quadrant, either northeast (NE), northwest (NW), southwest (SW), or southeast (SE). These quarter sections may be subdivided still further, into quarters or halves. When giving the location of something, the smallest division is given first. For instance, the dot in Figure 2 is in the SE 1/4 NW 1/4 Sec 12 T2S R11W (read as "the southeast quarter *of* the northwest quarter *of* Section 12 *in* Township 2 South, Range 11 West").

The rectangular land survey system has had a profound effect on land use in the United States. As you fly across the country, you can see that agricultural lands are often divided into neat squares, often containing a single kind of crop and giving the land a patchwork appearance. The squares are commonly quarter sections, a half mile on a side, or subdivisions of them. Road maps also show the rectangular pattern of the land survey system. Township lines are often marked by paved roads, and unpaved roads commonly bound sections. So important was the land survey system that references to it have become part of American speech. For example, a quarter of a quarter section contains 40 acres. These "forties" are the units often distinguishable from the air. A hundred years ago it was said that an honest person could raise a family with "forty acres and a mule," or that a farmer might spend a day "plowing the north forty."

Question Set 2: Public Land System

Use the San Bernardino South topographic map in the rear pocket to locate Section 11 in the extreme southeastern corner of the map.

i. In which township and range is section 11 located? _____

ii. Locate the water tank (WT) near the county line in Section 11. Give its location in the section to the nearest 40 acres.

Compass Directions

Because most topographic maps cover pieces of latitude and longitude, the edges of the maps are true north–south and east–west lines. The direction from one point to another can be determined with a **protractor**. However, this is *not* necessarily the compass direction between the points. The magnetic north pole, toward which compass needles point, is not the same place as the geographic north pole (the rotational axis of the Earth). The angular difference between true geographic north and magnetic north is the **magnetic declination**. Because declination varies from place to place and over time, a symbol and explanation is printed in the lower margin of most topographic maps. This symbol shows the magnetic declination at the center of the map at a particular time.

Within the conterminous United States, magnetic declinations vary from about 22° west in Maine to 24° east in Washington state (Figure 3). The magnetic declination must be considered if exact directions are needed and when navigating toward distant destinations. Sailors, geologists, and backcountry hikers all need to know the exact magnetic declination to use their compasses properly.

On magnetic declination diagrams from U.S. Geological Survey topographic maps, the star representative of Polaris, the north star, shows the direction of geographic north centered on the north rotational pole of the Earth. MN means magnetic north. The angle between these two lines is the magnetic declination. Because magnetic declination varies with time, the date at which the declination was measured is provided. GN is grid north, most commonly based on the Universal Transverse Mercator (UTM).

Name _____

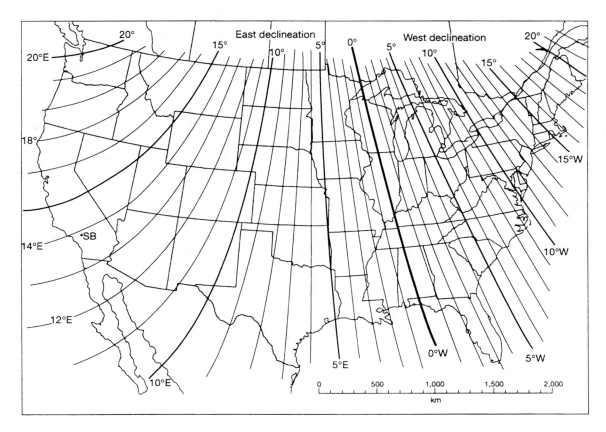

Figure 3.   **Map of magnetic declination in the United States for January 1, 1990.** *U.S. Geological Survey*

Question Set 3:   Magnetic Declinations

Use the San Bernardino South topographic map in the rear pocket to answer the following questions.

i. a.   What is the magnetic declination in this area?   _____

    b.   Why is this different in Figure 3?   _____

Referring to Figure 3:

ii. What is the magnetic declination of the southern tip of Florida?   _____

iii. What is the magnetic declination of the southern tip of Texas?   _____

iv. What is the magnetic declination of New York City?   _____

Exercise 2:   Working with Topographic Maps

Introduction

Like all other maps, topographic maps show the locations of things with respect to some references, but unlike other maps, they also show the configuration of the land itself. It is possible to look at a topographic map and get a good idea of the shape of the landscape. Colors used on topographic maps are given in Table 1. Symbols used on topographic maps are given on the inside of the front cover.

Table 1.   Colors of U.S. Geological Survey Topographic Maps

Topographic maps published in the United States use standard symbols and colors to depict natural and constructed features. A key to the symbols used on topographic maps published by the U.S. Geological Survey is given inside the front cover. The use of color follows a few general rules.

Blue—Not surprisingly, blue is used for water. Rivers, lakes, the oceans, waterfalls, glaciers, canals, and marshes are shown in blue.

Green—Green is, of course, the color used for vegetation. Green shadings and various patterns show different types of vegetation such as forests, orchards, vineyards, mangrove swamps, and scrub brush. Not all topographic maps include information on vegetation.

Brown—Contour lines and irregular surfaces are shown in brown. Index contours are printed in heavier brown lines than are regular contours. Supplementary contours, used to show detail in flat areas, are printed as dotted lines. Depressions are shown by *hachure* lines, contours with tick marks on them pointing into the depression. Natural or human-made surfaces that are highly irregular or changeable in shape are shown by brown-colored patterns. Such areas include mine dumps and tailings, sand dunes, beaches, lava flows, and levees.

Black—Most human-made features are shown in black. These include such items as individual structures, roads, wells, mines, wrecked ships, and bench marks.

Red—Red is also used for human-made features, especially survey lines, political boundaries, and major highways. A light red, actually pink, tint is used in developed areas where it would be difficult to show every building.

Purple—When topographic maps are revised on the basis of aerial photography, the changes, regardless of whether they are human-made or natural, are shown in purple.

Map Scale

The scale of a map is the relationship between a distance on a map and an actual distance on the Earth's surface. Map scales stated as ratios are **fractional scales** and are often expressed by a **representative fraction** or R.F. For example,

$$R.F.\ 1{:}24{,}000 = \frac{1}{24{,}000}$$

This scale means that one unit of distance on the map, regardless of what unit is used (inches, centimeters, or feet), represents a distance equal to 24,000 of the *same* units on the ground.

The U.S. Geological Survey, in cooperation with various state and federal agencies, publishes topographic maps of the United States at a variety of scales, called **quadrangles.** Plans have been made to cover all of the United States (except Alaska) with 7 1/2' quadrangles at a scale of 1:24,000. In addition, some maps are being published at a scale of 1:25,000 and completely in metric units. Complete 7 1/2'-quadrangle coverage of the United States will require 53,838 separate maps! Alaska will be covered by quadrangles at a scale of 1:63,360 (so that 1 inch on the map equals 1 mile on the ground).

The scale of a map is also shown graphically by graduated lines. On U.S. topographic maps, three **graphical scales** or bar scales are usually provided to show distances in miles, feet, and kilometers. If a map is reduced or enlarged in size, the fractional scale (e.g., 1:24,000) of the original map will not apply to a reduction or enlargement. A graphical scale, however, increases or decreases as the map is enlarged or reduced, and thus remains a valid scale. A **verbal scale** provides another explanation of the relationship between distance on a map and the ground distance. For example, a map at a scale of 1:24,000 could be described verbally as having a scale of "1 inch equals 2,000 feet."

Name _____

Contour Lines

Topographic maps depict the shape of the land's surface by using **contour lines**. A contour connects points that are at the same height above sea level. When you walk along a contour line, the shoreline of a lake for example, you stay at the same elevation, going neither uphill nor down. Contours are drawn at specified elevations. The vertical distance between contour lines is the **contour interval**. The difference in elevation between the highest and lowest points in an area, the total **relief**, and the scale of the map determine what contour interval is used. In areas of high relief (a large vertical distance between the highest and lowest elevations), a large contour interval (40 feet or more) is used so that the map will not be overcrowded with lines. Low relief areas commonly have a contour interval of 20 feet or less. In all cases, the contour interval is selected to show the maximum amount of detail with the minimum amount of clutter.

The spacing between contours on a map shows the slope of the land. The closer together contours are, the steeper the slope, and the farther apart they are, the gentler the slope. We generally assume that the ground surface slopes uniformly between contours. Although this is a reasonable assumption, it may not be true. The land between contours may be irregular, but as long as none of the "ups" or "downs" intersects another contour, the irregularities will not be shown. This is why more detail is shown when a smaller contour interval is used.

The contour interval of a topographic map will be printed somewhere on it, commonly below the graphical bar scales. **Index contours** have their elevation printed at various places along them and are shown as *thicker* lines than the other contours. **Intermediate contour** lines are shown between the index contours. They, like index contours, represent elevations that are multiples of the contour interval, but generally their elevations are not printed on the map.

In addition to contours, topographic maps also supply some other elevation data. Spot elevations are printed at various places on most maps, and carefully surveyed positions, known as **benchmarks**, are also shown.

Rules for Using Contour Lines

Remember that contour lines show the elevation of points and connect all the points that have the same elevation. As a result, there are some things contours cannot do.

1. *Contours of different elevations cannot cross each other.* Because all points on a single contour have the same elevation, contours crossing demand two different elevations.

2. *Contours do not split or join.* However, where the slope is extremely steep, vertical, or even overhanging, contours may crowd together so closely that they appear to merge and then divide again.

3. *Contours do not end except at the edges of a map or by closing on themselves.* Somewhere, every contour, including sea level, closes on itself.

Question Set 5:   Using Contour Lines

Use the San Bernardino South topographic map in the rear pocket to answer the following questions:

i. What is the contour interval used on this map? _____

ii. Locate the point with the highest and lowest elevations. These points will not be labeled, so you will need to think about the possibilities and search out the locations. Hints: The highest elevation is likely to be at the top of a ridge or hill. Where streams leave the map area is a good place to look for the lowest elevation. Mark the location of the highest and lowest elevations on the map. Note the elevations and briefly describe their locations below.

    a.   Highest elevation _____   b.   Lowest elevation_____

        Location _____   Location _____

iii. What is total relief in this area (the difference in elevation between the highest and lowest points)?

_____

Name _____

Slopes and Gradients

Slope is defined as the change in vertical distance divided by the horizontal distance. For example,

$$\text{Slope} = \frac{\text{vertical distance}}{\text{horizontal distance}} = \frac{80 \text{ ft}}{500 \text{ ft}} = 0.16 \text{ or } 16\%$$

Notice that the units of measurement (ft/ft) cancel each other out, so that slope has no dimensions.

The slope of a river, the **stream gradient**, is commonly given in units of feet per mile (ft/mi). Gradients are calculated by the following formula:

$$\text{Gradient} = \frac{\text{difference in elevation (ft)}}{\text{lenght of stream segment (mi)}} = \frac{40 \text{ ft}}{5.5 \text{ mi}} = 7.3\frac{\text{ft}}{\text{mi}}$$

The difference in elevation is determined from the contour elevation of the beginning and ending points. The length of the stream segment is measured from the map. A piece of string can be used to measure the distance along the irregular course of the river.

Question Set 6:   Santa Ana River Stream Gradient

Use the San Bernardino South topographic map in the rear pocket to determine the gradient of the Santa Ana River.

i. Locate the Tipppecanoe Avenue bridge over the Santa Ana River about a mile northeast of the Tri-City Airport in the east-central area of the map. Selecting the contour line just west of the bridge, what is the elevation of the river bed? _____ ft

ii. The river goes off the map in the southwestern corner of the map. Selecting the solid contour line just below the county line, what is the elevation of the river bed? _____ ft

iii. What is the elevation difference between the two points? _____ ft

iv. What is the distance in miles between the two points along the river? _____ mi

v. Calculate the stream gradient. _____ ft/mi

vi. What is the general direction of flow of the Santa Ana River? _____

Exercise 3:   Drawing Contours and Making Topographic Profiles

Drawing Contours

In the question set that follows you will construct a topographic map by drawing contours. Figure 4 shows the map base with the river system and a lake. Spot elevations (control points) are given at various locations, and part of the 600-foot index contour has been included to serve as a guide. You can start contouring anywhere on the map. The beginning point does not really matter, but the process you use in contouring does. Even the most practiced contourer does a lot of erasing.

Name _____

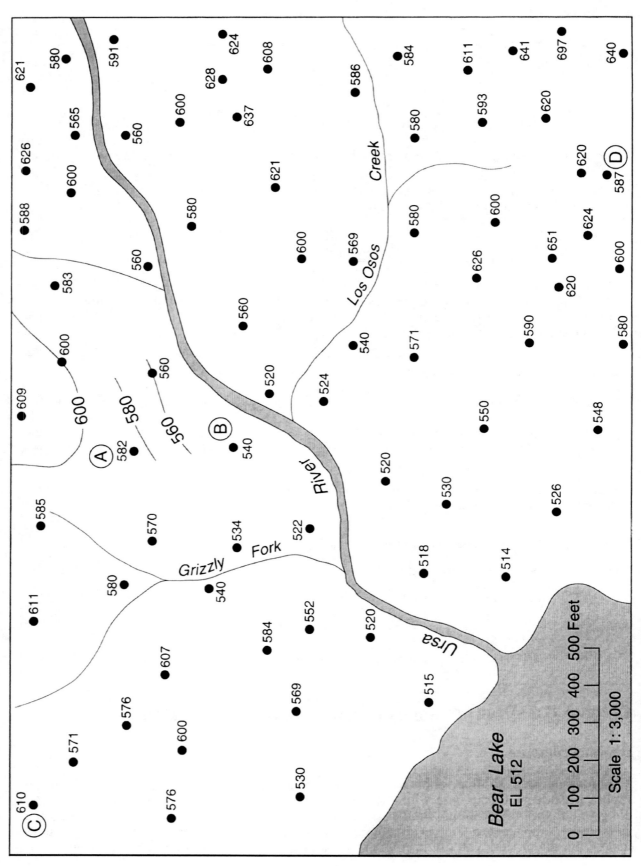

Figure 4. **Base of Bear Lake contour map.**

Name _____

Question Set 7:   Contouring the Bear Lake Map

Using the Bear Lake map (Figure 4), complete the contouring using a 20-foot contour interval. You may find it useful to consult the following:

In drawing contours, look at any pair of points noting the elevation represented by each. Take, for example, the points labeled A and B located near the center of Figure 4. Point A is at an elevation of 582 feet and point B is at 540 feet. Because point B has an elevation that is a multiple of the contour interval (20 feet) it will lie on a contour line (540 feet). However, point A at 582 feet will not be on a contour.

The 560-foot and 580-foot contours must pass somewhere between points A and B. We cannot know exactly where these two lines will pass between the points, so we must estimate their locations. We usually assume that the land slopes uniformly between two known elevations. Using this assumption, we will place the 580-foot contour near point A and the 560-foot contour about halfway between the two points. These two contours can now be extended by the same process, inspecting each pair of points along the path of the contour to estimate its location.

Checking each pair of spot elevations will prevent the most common mistake in contouring—trying to "force" a contour between two points where there is no evidence for it. For example, based on the available data, the 600-foot contour cannot pass between points A and B. Both points are below this elevation and there are no data to suggest that the land reaches 600 feet any place between the two points.

Drawing this contour map and interpreting the ones in the other exercises will be easier if you remember the following facts about how contours portray the landscape.

1. Contours end either at the edge of the map or by closing on themselves.
2. A series of closed concentric contours indicate a hill or mountain.
3. Concentric hachured contours depict a closed depression.
4. Contours form V's where they cross rivers. The point of the V is directed upstream (uphill).

Drawing Topographic Profiles

By combining the map locations of features and contour data, **topographic profiles** of the land's surface may be constructed. Such profiles are valuable as a base for geological cross sections. The line selected, along which the topographic profile will be made, must be laid out on the map. This line can actually be drawn on the map, or if this is not appropriate, penciled dots can be made at the two ends of the line. These points define the line of profile (Figure 5a).

To construct the profile, mark the vertical scale of the cross section on both ends of a piece of graph paper large enough to extend the length of your section line (Figure 5b). Crease the upper edge of the graph paper along one of the horizontal lines and position the paper along the profile line (Figure 5b). Wherever a contour crosses the line of section, project a line *straight down* to the horizontal line representing the elevation of the contour and make a pencil dot at that point. Where the topography is steep and contours are closely spaced, marking only the index contours will provide enough control to produce a good topographic profile. The vertical lines serve as a guide in projecting the lines downward. Draw a smooth curve through the points to complete the profile (Figure 5c). Note that the profile has title, scales, vertical exaggeration, and directions.

Using the same scale for both the horizontal and vertical axes of the graphed cross section will produce an unexaggerated profile. The approximate slope of the surface may be measured directly from these undistorted profiles with a protractor. Sometimes, however, topographic profiles will need to have different scales on the horizontal and vertical axes. For example, if the topography is gentle, an unexaggerated profile may be a nearly featureless line. To show the detail in a surface, the vertical scale of the profile is increased to exaggerate the topography. Vertical exaggeration is described next.

Name _____

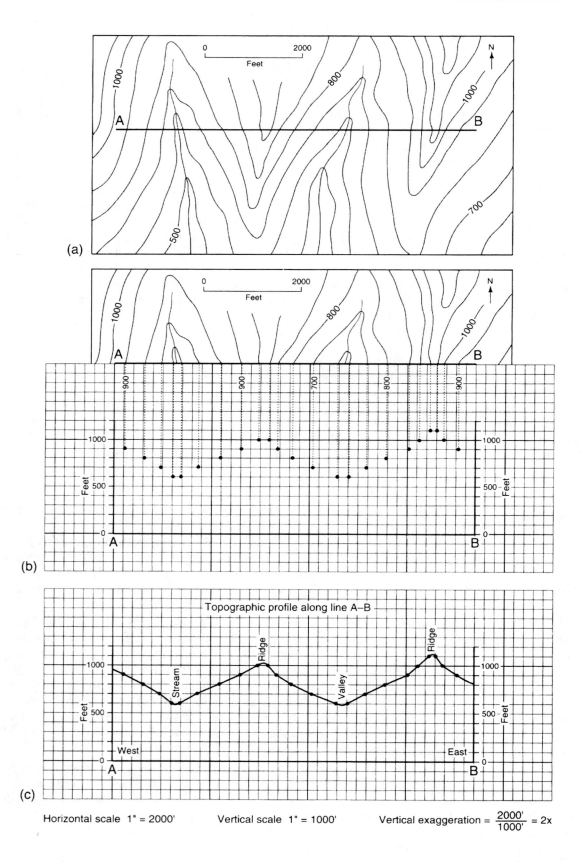

(a)

(b)

(c)

Horizontal scale 1" = 2000'   Vertical scale 1" = 1000'   Vertical exaggeration = $\dfrac{2000'}{1000'}$ = 2x

Figure 5. **Illustration of procedure for construction of topographic profiles.**

Name _____

Vertical Exaggeration

Vertical exaggeration (V.E.) is used to add detail to a profile. If the total relief along a profile is small compared to the profile length, vertical exaggeration is needed. This occurs when a cross section covers a long distance or when the total relief is small. In general, profiles should be drawn with the smallest exaggeration necessary to bring out the required detail in the landscape. The vertical exaggeration of a profile can be calculated with the formula:

$$\text{V.E.} = \frac{\text{denominator of horizontal fractional scale}}{\text{denominator of vertical fractional scale}}$$

The following example shows how to use this formula. The horizontal scale of a profile is 1:24,000. If the vertical scale is 1 inch = 100 feet, this is a fractional scale of 1:1,200 (there are 1,200 inches in 100 feet). In the case of the example, the vertical exaggeration is found by this formula, which uses *fractional* scales only:

$$\text{V.E.} = \frac{24,000}{1,200} = 20$$

This formula can also be used with verbal scales *if both the horizontal and vertical scales are expressed in the same units.* In the preceding example, the vertical scale of the profile is 1 inch = 100 feet. The horizontal scale is 1:24,000, which is the same as a verbal scale of 1 inch = 2,000 feet (there are 24,000 inches in 2,000 feet). We can compute the vertical exaggeration by dividing the horizontal scale by the vertical scale. When we do this the units of feet in the numerator and denominator will cancel out.

$$\text{V.E.} = \frac{2,000}{100} = 20$$

Notice that the same value for the vertical exaggeration (20×, sometimes noted as 20:1) is obtained by both methods.

The formula can be used to determine the vertical scale necessary to produce a certain amount of exaggeration. For example, if you want to draw a profile with a vertical exaggeration of 5x from a topographic map with a scale of 1:24,000 (1 inch = 2,000 feet), the required vertical scale can be determined by the following:

$$\text{V.E.} = 5 = \frac{2,000 \text{ ft}}{x}$$

or

$$x = \frac{2,000 \text{ ft}}{5} = 400 \text{ ft}$$

This means that to produce a profile with a vertical exaggeration of 5×, you should use a vertical scale of 1 inch = 400 feet.

Name _____

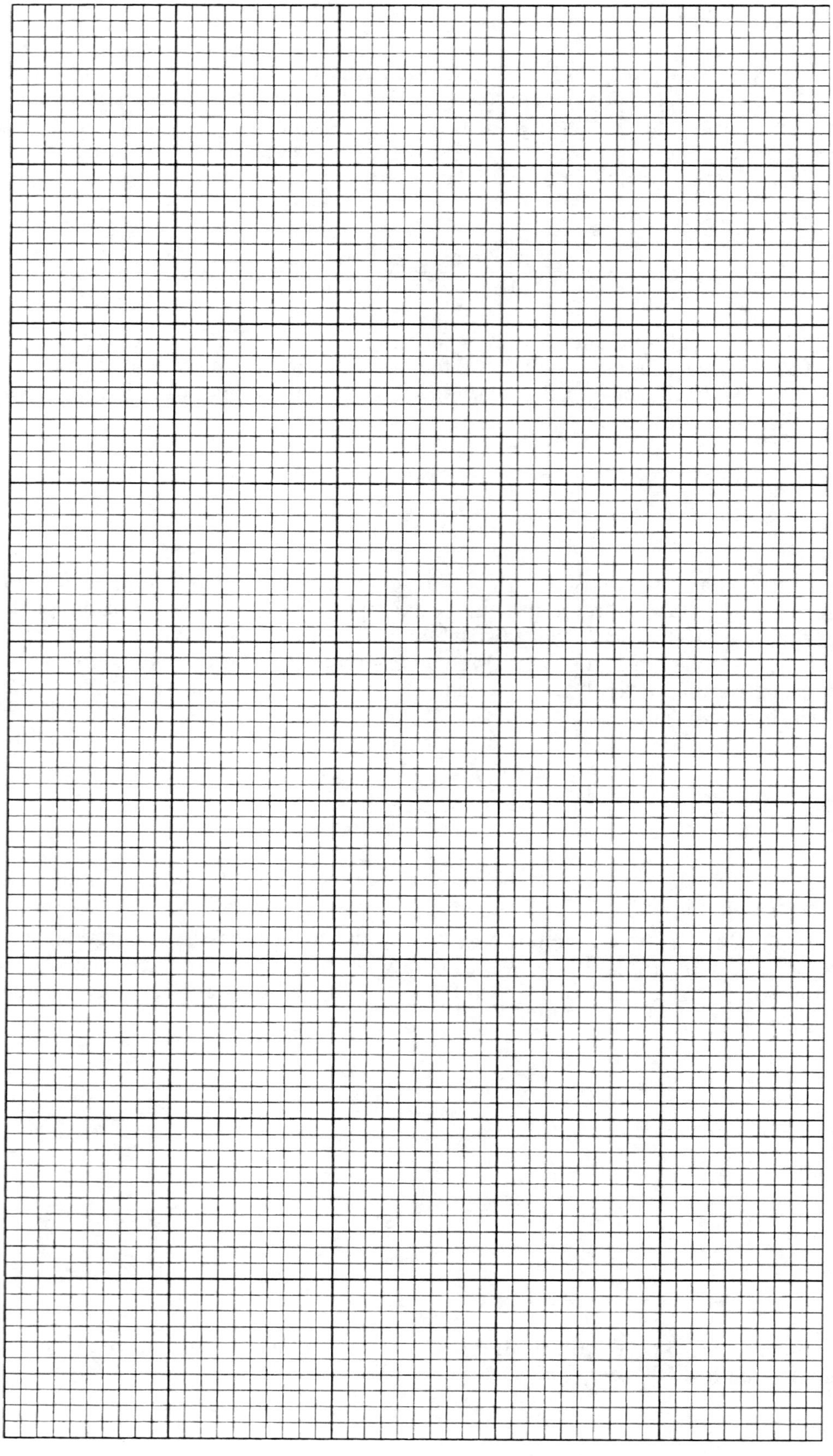

Figure 6.   **Topographic profile of Bear Lake map.**

Name _____

Question Set 8:   Drawing a Topographical Profile

i.   Draw a topographical profile from Point C to Point D on the Bear Lake map (Figure 4) using the graph paper provided (Figure 6). The vertical scale of the profile should be 1 inch = 50 feet and the horizontal scale of the map is given as 1:3,000.

ii. What is the fractional scale of the vertical scale? _____

iii. What is the vertical exaggeration of the profile? _____

iv. If you wanted to draw a profile with an exaggeration of 10×, what would the vertical scale need to be?

_____

v.   What is the vertical scale in feet per inch with no vertical exaggeration? 1 in = _____ ft

vi. On the topographic profile you have drawn, replot the profile with no vertical exaggeration and compare the results.

Exercise 4:   Using Topographic Maps: A Road Rally

Introduction

This question set is a simulated road rally. Instead of actually driving according to the directions, you are to follow the route on the San Bernardino South, California, topographic map in the rear pocket.

The rally route becomes more complex and the directions become less explicit as you go along. If you get lost, ask your instructor to get you back on the route. Asking for this kind of assistance may cost you penalty points, so try to stay on course.

Your instructor will give you the rules for the rally. Make sure that you understand them before you begin. Follow the directions carefully and answer the questions as they occur. Unless you are instructed otherwise, trace your travel on the map in *pencil.*

We will use this map in a later exercise.

Question Set 9:   San Bernardino Road Rally

i.   Start at the intersection of Columbia Avenue and Main Street, located near the southwest corner of the map. Note that Main Street becomes Riverside Avenue north of the Santa Ana River. Check to make sure you are at the correct beginning point.

   a.   **Label the starting point with the letter S and circle it.**

   In what county are you located?

   b.   What kind of structure is the large building located southeast of this intersection?

Name _____

Question Set 9 (continued):   San Bernardino Road Rally

---

ii.   Start northward along Main Street.

    a.   Are you going uphill or downhill?

    b.   What are the dashed brown lines you are crossing?

    c.   About 1.1 mi north of the starting point you will cross the Santa Ana River. Why is this "river" shown in brown instead of blue?

---

iii.   Turn right onto Agua Mansa Road. **This is Check Point 1. Label it and circle the number.**

    a.   About 0.75 mi along Agua Mansa (near the word "Mansa") an area north of the road is shown with a purple pattern. What does the purple color signify?

    b.   What kind of land surface is indicated by the pattern?

---

iv.   Follow Agua Mansa Road until you reach the first *paved* road and then turn to the southeast onto this road. Follow the paved road as it bends to the left and proceed to 8th Street. Turn right on 8th Street. **Label the 8th Street intersection as Check Point 2.** Proceed southward.

    a.   The road is crossed by four dashed-and-dotted lines. What are these lines?

    b.   What is the approximate latitude and longitude of this location?

    c.   What is the name of the hills to the west of 8th Street?

---

v.   Turn east across the railroad on Palm Avenue, then south on Mt. Vernon Avenue. **Label the De Barry–Mt. Vernon intersection as Check Point 3.**

    a.   What is the large building located near the intersection of De Barry and Mt. Vernon?

---

vi.   Continue along Mt. Vernon Avenue to Spring Street.

    a.   For what is the land between Center Street and Spring Street used?

---

vii.   Turn east onto Spring Street and then left at the first unnamed unimproved road. Stop here for a moment to answer the following questions. **Label this location as Check Point 4.**

    a.   In which section, township, and range are you now located?

    b.   Have you been traveling uphill or downhill?

    c.   How could you tell the distance between the intersection of Spring Street and Mr. Vernon Avenue and your current location without measuring it?

Name _____

viii. The most physically strenuous portion of the rally starts here. Unload your mountain bike from the rack and ride east along the unpaved road until it ends.

a. Your immediate objective is to reach another paved road which ends at the center of section 10 (east of your current location). Select your route so that you will not be forced to go up and down a hill. In other words you should plot a course that will allow you to progress steadily toward your objective without wasting effort. Plot the route on your map.

b. What is the approximate elevation of the end of the road at the center of section 10?_____ft

c. Follow the unpaved road eastward until it intersects another unpaved road and make a left turn. In what compass direction are you travelling now? _____

d. When this road crosses a small stream, leave the road and follow the stream down valley until you cross the county line. This line is the boundary between which two counties? _____and
_____ counties

e. Just north of the county line, a trail forks off to the left, uphill toward Blue Mountain. Take this trail, but you had better downshift first. It's a steep climb. A little more than half way up the trail it crosses a saddle between two small streams, one flowing northward and one to the south. What is the elevation of this saddle? _____ft

f. What is the difference in elevation between your current location and the summit of Blue Mountain?

Approximate elevation of Blue Mountain summit _____ft

Approximate elevation of current location_____ft

Approximate difference in elevation _____ft

g. Continue up the trail to its end and the Highgrove bench mark. With reasonably good binoculars you should be able to see your car from this point. What is the straight-line distance to your car? _____ft

h. What is the approximate difference in elevation between Highgrove and your car?

Approximate elevation of Highgrove benchmark _____ft

Approximate elevation of car _____ft

Approximate difference in elevation _____ft

j. What is the approximate gradient of the slope between Highgrove benchmark and the unpaved road that lies due south at the southern base of Blue Mountain?

Approximate elevation of Highgrove benchmark _____ft

Approximate elevation of unpaved road _____ft

Approximate difference in elevation _____ft

Distance between them _____mi

Gradient of the slope _____ft/mi

k. What are your chances of getting down this slope without killing yourself?

You're on your own now. Get back to your car the best way you can and **return to Check Point 4.**

Name _____

Question Set 9 (continued):   San Bernardino Road Rally

---

ix. From **Check Point 4** proceed northward along the unimproved road to its intersection with Palm Avenue. Turn left and then take the *first two* available right turns. **Label the *second* right turn as Check Point 5.**

   a. What is the name of the road on which you are now traveling? _____

---

x.   Proceed along this road to its intersection with Waterman Avenue. Turn north onto Waterman and proceed.

   a. What is the elevation at the first railroad crossing you reach? _____

---

xi. *After* your cross the railroad track, turn right, left, and right at the first opportunities. After making these turns drive about 0.5 mile, then stop for a moment.

   a. What is the name of the university located about 0.7 mile south of your present position?

xii. Continue in the direction you were traveling. Turn north onto the last available road before you leave the map. **Label this intersection as Check Point 6.**

   a. The road you were on would have carried you off from the San Bernardino South quadrangle and onto another map. What is the title of the map covering the area you would have entered?

---

xiii. Follow the road you have just entered until it ends at a T-intersection. Turn west, then take the first available right. Proceed straight ahead over the Santa Ana River bridge until you cross the 1,060-foot contour line twice. Make the first available left turn *after* you cross this contour the *second* time. **Label this intersection as Check Point 7.**

   a. What is the road distance in feet between Check Points 6 and 7?   _____ft

   b. What is the name of the large military base located just north of this turn?

   c. What elevation is represented by the first *index contour line* you cross after making the left turn?

---

xiv. Continue along this road, passing beneath the freeway (interstate highway). Turn south at bench mark (BM) 1064. Make the third left turn available and stop. **Label this point with an E for the end of the rally.**

   a. What is the name of the college campus on which you are located?

5

Google Earth Exercise

Name: _____

Getting Started

1. First, select a computer that has a mouse with a scroll wheel. Turn it on.

Orienting yourself to GE

2. When GE loads, you should see a picture like this. Zoom in to the US using the mouse wheel or clicking on the vertical zoom bar

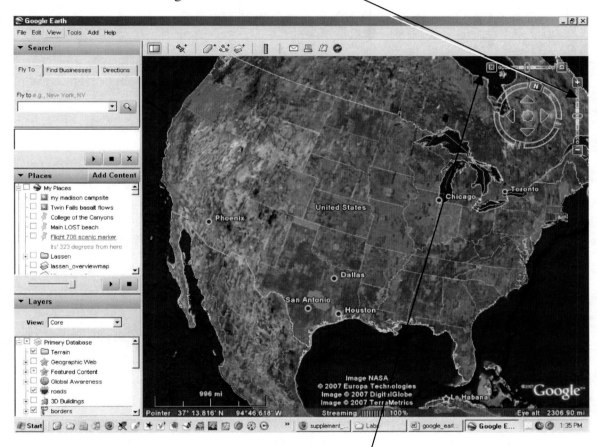

3. Now pan the image down using the horizontal slider. This changes the angle of viewing and is useful for seeing the shape of mountains.

4. You want to clean up the image by getting rid of the borders. How do you do that? Unclick "borders" to remove the yellow lines.

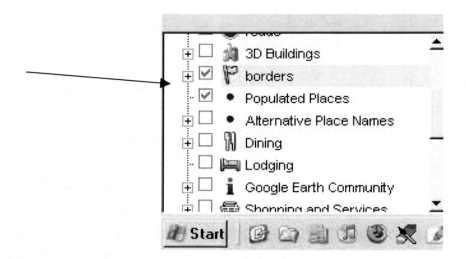

5. Now rotate the image by dragging the "N" on the north bar in the upper right corner.

6. To set the image back so that north is straight up, double-click the "N"
7. To remove the panning, double-click the "X" to the upper left.
8. Note that wherever you move your cursor, a longitude and latitude are displayed on the bottom as well as a scale.

Ok, now you're set to start working in GE!

San Diego & Environs

Let's check out some sites in San Diego. In the "fly to" bar on the upper left, type in "San Diego Airport." GE will find the airport and zoom in on it. Are there any planes taking off or landing?

9. If it looks like this airport is a little too close to houses, it is. In fact, in 1978, there was a terrible crash, PSA 182. Go to http://en.wikipedia.org/wiki/PSA_Flight_182 and from the information in this article, find the neighborhood in San Diego where the plane went down. Make sure to turn on "roads" under layers.

PSA jet approx longitude/latitude_____

10. Let's now go to the waterfront of San Diego. Zoom in and pan along the shoreline until you see a large ship with its sails fully up, even though it's docked on the side. This is part of the San Diego Maritime Museum.

    What is the length of this ship? _____

Finding Campus
11. When GE loads, you should see the image of the Earth.
12. Use the mouse's scroll wheel to zoom in to find our campus.
13. Judging by the recent construction, about how old are these satellite photos? _____
14. Identify the long/lat as close as possible to this room. _____
15. Select the "ruler" icon on the top bar or go to Tools/Ruler.
16. Measure one side of the our building in meters._____
17. Measure another side in feet. _____
18. Remember where you parked. Find that approximate spot and measure the distance you'll have to walk to your car tonight. _____

Local Geology
19. Launch a browser and go to the website:
    http://geomaps.wr.usgs.gov/sfgeo/geologic/downloads.html

20. Click on "Alameda County." This may take a while to load. The file (a native GE .kmz file) may load up in GE or may save to your desktop, depending on your browser's settings. If it saves to the desktop, click on it to load it into GE.
21. Once this loads, you should see the campus in the midst of a purple color. Dim the color by adjusting the transparency of the geology layer. Do this by sliding this tab:

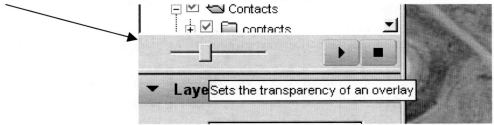

22. Now go the "Places" on the left and click in the box next to "Units Labels." This will turn on the geologic labels for the units on this map.
23. The unit under campus is _____
24. But what is this stuff? Now you'll need to go to another web site,
    http://geomaps.wr.usgs.gov/sfgeo/geologic/shell/mapkey.html
25. What kind of material is this?
26. What does the J stand for? _____-

27. Now go to the "Geologic Units" and click the button on the left, turning off all these units.

28. Click the "+" sign, expanding the geologic units. Click on only the unit we're sitting on.
29. Zoom out using the mouse wheel. You may want to turn off the Unit Labels for clarity.
30. Approximately what percentage of the area is of the same material as campus? _____

31. Now find out what kind of material your house sits on. Type in your address, or something close to it, in the "Fly to" box in the upper left corner. GE will zoom to your location.
32. My house sits on _____.
33. Click-off the geology.

Tectonics
1. Go to http://earthquake.usgs.gov/regional/nca/virtualtour/
2. Click on "global geologic setting."
3. Click on "tectonic plates of the world."
4. When the dialogue box opens, chose to save the .kmz file on the desktop.

5. How many plates are there in this map? _____

6. What are the 3 types of plate boundaries? _____

7. Find the Galapagos Islands. What type of plate boundary do they sit near? _____

8. Find Japan. What type of plate boundary does it sit on? _____

9. Go to Places and under this file, Earth's Tectonic Plates, expand the "+" signs until you see "Plate boundaries." Now you can turn on/off specific types of boundaries.

10. Turn off every plate boundary type except "divergent." Where are these boundaries most often encountered? _____

11. Turn off every plate boundary type except "convergent." Where are these boundaries most often encountered? _____

12. Turn on divergent and convergent. Identify two areas of the world where these two plate boundary types do not meet up. _____ _____

13. Now turn on "transform" and "diffuse" and see how the two area you identified meet. _____ _____

14. The 2004 Indonesian Tsunami began close to the city of Banda Aceh. Describe the tectonic situation where the earthquake originated:

     _____

15. Go to http://www.gearthhacks.com/dlcat84/Asian-Tsunami---December-2004.htm and download the .kmz file for "Gleeburk"
     It's hard to grasp the scale of this devastation … what can you use to orient yourself?

     _____

     Using the ruler tool, find the length of beach this photo covers. _____-

16. Turn off the tectonic plates .kmz file in the Places sidebar.
17. Go back to http://earthquake.usgs.gov/regional/nca/virtualtour/global.php and click on "Real Time Earthquakes."
18. Download and open the .kmz of the past 7 days of earthquake activity around the world.
19. Make sure the plate boundaries are turned on when this file opens.

20. What's the magnitude of the earthquake that has occurred closest to this classroom?

     _____

21. Zoom out and observe the entire planet. Which areas of the world have clusters of earthquakes? _____

22. Where is the farthest point away from quakes on the planet? I mean, if you really wanted to avoid one, where would you go? _____

23. How fast are the Himalayas converging with Eurasia? (in mm/year) _____
24. How fast is the Pacific Plate converging with Japan? (in mm/year) _____

25. How fast is the Juan de Fuca plate converging with Oregon and Washington? (in mm/year) _____--

26. Where is the fastest rate of plate movement on the planet?

     _____

27. Many people in LA don't worry about earthquakes. How far away (in km) is downtown LA from the nearest approach of the San Andreas fault? Use the measuring tool in GE.   _____

28. "Go the Plate Boundary Ruptures." Unclick everything else. Bring up the file.
29. Describe how these 4 rupture events in California compare in terms of length. Which of them do you think might be the most devastating if it were to happen again today?

     _____.

6

Geologic Structures, Maps, and Block Diagrams

·CONTRIBUTING AUTHORS·

Michael J. Hozik • *Stockton State College*

William R. Parrott, Jr. • *Stockton State College*

Raymond W. Talkington • *Stockton State College*

OBJECTIVES

A. Be able to identify common kinds of geologic structures in three dimensional block diagrams and know the symbols used to represent them on geologic maps.

B. Be able to construct geologic cross sections from geologic maps and interpret them.

C. Be able to read and interpret geologic maps.

MATERIALS

Pencil, eraser, laboratory notebook, ruler, set of colored pencils, scissors, Models 1–6 (located at the end of this chapter), and a geologic map (provided by your instructor, or obtained as noted by your instructor).

INTRODUCTION

Structural geology is the study of how *geologic units* (bodies of rock or sediment) are arranged when first formed and how they are deformed afterward. When a body of rock or sediment is subjected to severe *stress* (directed pressure), then it may eventually *strain* (undergo deformation, such as a change in shape). Therefore, deformed formations are geologic units that have adjusted to a severe stress. Much of the study of structural geology involves deciphering stress and strain relationships.

Generally, geologists can see how bodies of rock or sediment are positioned where they *crop out* (stick out of the ground as an outcrop) at Earth's surface (Figure 1A). Geologists record this outcrop data on flat (two-dimensional) **geologic maps** using different colors and symbols to represent the different units of rock or sediment and their positions (Figures 1B, 2, 3). They apply information from geologic maps to infer the three-dimensional arrangement of the units. The structural geology of an area can be described and interpreted from this three-dimensional arrangement, viewed as a conceptual model in your mind, or as a physical model. You will interpret as many as six different (physical) cardboard models of structural geology in this laboratory.

PART A: STRUCTURAL GEOLOGY

Three representations of Earth are commonly used by structural geologists. These are the geologic map, cross section, and block diagram:

- **Geologic map**—shows the distribution of rocks at Earth's surface. The rocks commonly are divided into mappable rock units that can be recognized and traced across the map area. This division is made on the basis of color, texture, or composition.

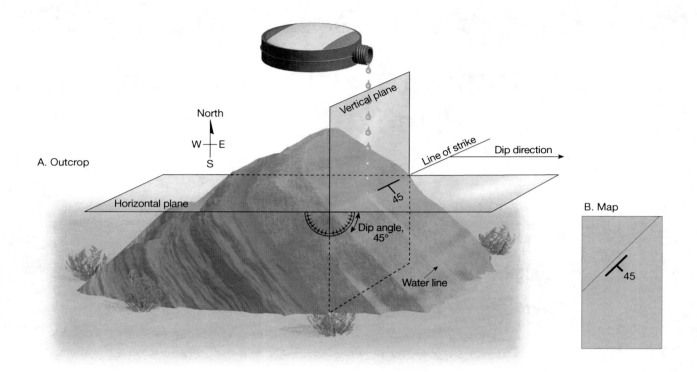

FIGURE 1   Strike and dip of a rock layer as directly observed in nature **(A)** and as represented on a geologic map **(B)**. *Strike* is the direction of a line formed by the intersection of the surface of an inclined (tilted) rock layer and a horizontal plane. *Dip* is the maximum angle of inclination (tilting) of the rock layer, always measured perpendicular to the line of strike (looking straight down on it, in map view) and in the direction that the rock layer tilts down into the ground. Water poured onto a dipping rock layer drains along the angle of dip. The **"T"** and **45** together form the standard strike-and-dip symbol. The long top of the **"T"** is the line of strike, the short upright of the **"T"** shows the dip direction, and **"45"** is the dip angle in degrees.

Such mappable rock units are called **formations.** They may be subdivided into **members** comprised of **beds** (individual layers of rock or sediment). The boundaries between geologic units are **contacts,** which form lines on geologic maps. A geologic map also shows the topography of the land surface with contour lines, so it is both a geologic *and* topographic map.

- **Geologic cross section**—a drawing of a vertical slice through Earth, with the material in front of it removed: a cutaway view. It shows the arrangement of formations and their contacts. A good cross section also shows the topography of the land surface, like a topographic profile.

- **Block diagram**—a combination of the geologic map and cross section. It looks like a solid block, with a geologic map on top and a geologic cross section on each of its visible sides (e.g., Figure 4). Each block diagram is a small three-dimensional model of a portion of Earth's crust.

FIGURE 2   Geologic maps with strike and dip symbols indicating the attitude of rock layers. Note that strike and dip can be expressed in quadrant or azimuth form. When expressing strike and dip directions as azimuth bearings, they should be expressed as three digits in order to distinguish them from two-digit dip angles. Note also that a line of strike can be expressed as a bearing in either direction. For example **(A),** a line of strike with a quadrant bearing of North 45° West also has a bearing of South 45° East. A line of strike with an azimuth bearing of 335° also has a bearing of 155° (i.e., 180° less than 335°).

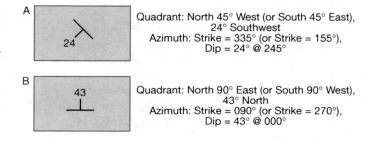

A   Quadrant: North 45° West (or South 45° East), 24° Southwest
Azimuth: Strike = 335° (or Strike = 155°), Dip = 24° @ 245°

B   Quadrant: North 90° East (or South 90° West), 43° North
Azimuth: Strike = 090° (or Strike = 270°), Dip = 43° @ 000°

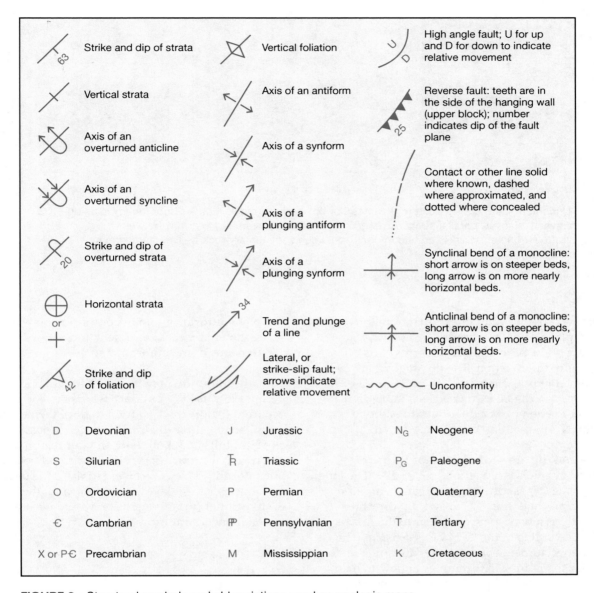

FIGURE 3   Structural symbols and abbreviations used on geologic maps.

Measuring the Attitude of Rock Units

Attitude is the orientation of a rock unit or surface. Geologists have devised a system for measuring and describing attitude to understand three-dimensional relationships of formations and geologic structures. Strike and dip serve this purpose (see Figure 1):

- **Strike**—the *compass bearing* (direction) of a line formed by the intersection of a horizontal plane (such as the surface of a lake) and an inclined layer (bed, stratum) of rock, fault, fracture, or other surface (Figure 1). If strike is expressed in

degrees east or west of true north or true south, it is called a *quadrant bearing*. Strike can also be expressed as a three-digit *azimuth bearing* in degrees between 000 and 360. In azimuth form, north is 000° (or 360°), east is 090°, south is 180°, and west is 270°.

- **Dip**—the *angle* between a horizontal plane and the inclined (tilted) stratum, fault, or fracture. As you can see in Figure 1, a thin stream of water poured onto an inclined surface always runs downhill along the **dip direction,** which is always perpendicular to the line (bearing) of strike. The

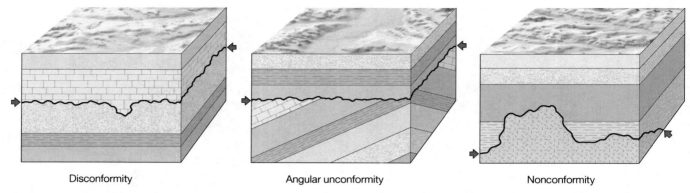

| Disconformity | Angular unconformity | Nonconformity |

FIGURE 4   Unconformities. Arrows point to the unconformity surface (black line). A *disconformity* is an unconformity between relatively *parallel* strata. An *angular unconformity* is an unconformity between *nonparallel* strata. A *nonconformity* is an unconformity between sedimentary rock/sediment and igneous or metamorphic rock.

inclination of the water line, down from the horizontal plane, is the **dip angle.**

Dip is always expressed in terms of its dip angle and dip direction. The dip angle is always expressed in two digits (e.g., 45° in Figure 1). The dip direction can be expressed as a three-digit azimuth direction or as a quadrant direction (e.g., North, Northeast, East).

Strike and dip are shown on maps by use of "T"-shaped symbols (see Figures 1, 2, and 3). The long line (top of the "T") shows strike direction, and the short line (upright of the "T") shows dip direction. Note that dip is always perpendicular to the line of strike. The short line of the "T" points *downdip*. The accompanying numerals indicate the dip angle in degrees. Refer to Figure 2 for examples of how to read and express strike and dip in quadrant or azimuth form. Also note that special symbols are used for horizontal strata (rock layers) and vertical strata (Figure 3).

Unconformities

Structural geologists must locate, observe, and interpret many different structures. Fundamentally, these include unconformities, faults, and folds. There are three common types of *unconformities* (see Figure 4):

- **Disconformity**—an unconformity between relatively *parallel* strata.

- **Angular unconformity**—an unconformity between *nonparallel* strata.

- **Nonconformity**—an unconformity between sedimentary rock/sediment and *non-sedimentary* (igneous or metamorphic) rock.

Any unconformity may be a very irregular surface, because it is usually a surface where erosion has occurred (before it was buried to form the unconformity). For example, bedrock surfaces exposed on the slopes of hills and mountains in your region are part of a regional surface of erosion that could become an unconformity. If sea level were to rise and cover your region with a fresh layer of mud or sand, then the uneven regional surface of erosion would become a regional unconformity.

Faults

Faults in rock units are breaks along which movement has occurred. Faults form when brittle rocks experience three kinds of severe stress: *tension* (pulling apart or lengthening), *compression* (pushing together, compacting, and shortening), and *shear* (smearing or tearing). The three kinds of stress force the rocks to fault in distinctive ways (Figure 5).

Normal faults, reverse faults, and *thrust faults* all involve vertical motions of rocks. These faults are named by noting the *sense of motion* of the top surface of the fault (top block) relative to the bottom surface (bottom block), regardless of which one actually has moved. The top surface of the fault is called the **hanging wall** and is the base of the **hanging wall** (top) **block** of rock. The bottom surface of the fault is called the **footwall** and forms the top of the **footwall block.** The headwall block sits on top of the footwall block.

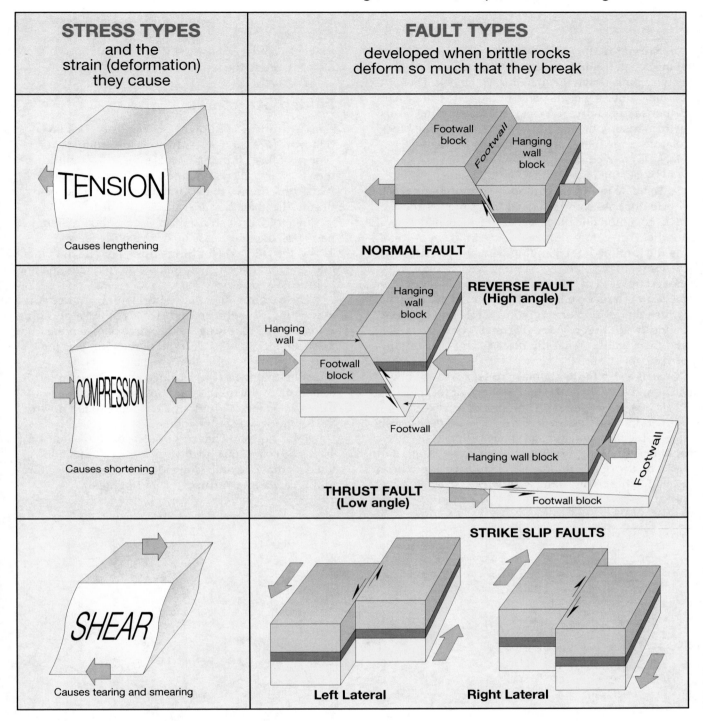

STRESS TYPES and the strain (deformation) they cause	FAULT TYPES developed when brittle rocks deform so much that they break

FIGURE 5 Three types of stress and strain and the fault types they produce.

Normal faults are caused by tension (rock lengthening). As tensional stress pulls the rocks apart, gravity pulls down the hanging wall block. Therefore, normal faulting gets its name because it is a normal response to gravity. You can recognize normal faults by recognizing the motion of the hanging wall block relative to the footwall block. If the hanging wall block has moved downward in relation to the footwall block, then the fault is a normal fault.

Reverse faults are caused by compression (rock shortening). As compressional stress pushes the rocks together, one block of rock gets pushed atop another. You can recognize reverse faults by recognizing the motion of the hanging wall block relative to the footwall block. If the hanging wall block has moved upward in relation to the footwall block, then the fault is a reverse fault. **Thrust faults** are reverse faults that develop at a very low angle and may be very difficult to recognize (Figure 5). Reverse faults and thrust faults generally place older strata on top of younger strata.

Strike slip faults (**lateral faults**) are caused by shear and involve horizontal motions of rocks (Figure 5). If you stand on one side of a strike slip fault and look across it, then the rocks on the opposite side of the fault will appear to have slipped to the right or left. Along a *right-lateral (strike slip) fault*, the rocks on the opposite side of the fault appear to have moved to the right. Along a *left-lateral (strike slip) fault*, the rocks on the opposite side of the fault appear to have moved to the left.

Folded Structures

Folds are upward or downward bends of rock layers (Figures 6, 7, 8, and 9). **Antiforms** are "upfolds" or "convex folds." If the *oldest* rocks are in the middle, then they are called **anticlines. Synforms** are "downfolds" or "concave folds." If the *youngest* rocks are in the middle, then they are called **synclines.**

In a fold, each stratum is bent around an imaginary axis, like the crease in a piece of folded paper. This is the **fold axis** (or **hinge line**). For all strata in a fold, the fold axes lie within the **axial plane** of the fold (Figures 6 and 7).

The fold axis may not be horizontal, but rather it may plunge into the ground. This is called a **plunging fold** (Figure 7B). **Plunge** is the angle between the fold axis and horizontal. The **trend** of the plunge is the bearing (compass direction), measured in the direction that the axis is inclined downward. You can also think of the trend of a plunging fold as the direction a marble would roll if it were rolled down the plunging axis of the fold.

Folds normally have two sides, or **limbs,** one on each side of the axial plane (see Figure 7). If a fold is tilted so that one limb is upside down, then the entire fold is called an **overturned fold** (Figure 8).

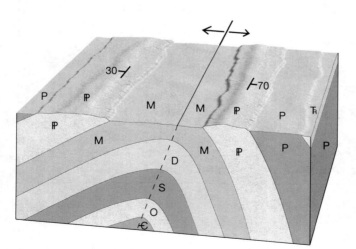

A. ANTICLINE (asymmetrical): oldest rocks (€) occur in the center of the fold

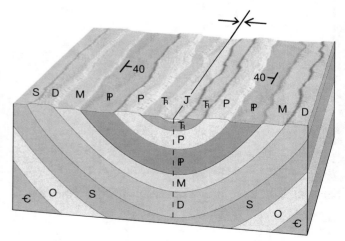

B. SYNCLINE (symmetrical): youngest rocks (J) occur in the center of the fold

FIGURE 6 Folds—the two common types. Letters on rock layers indicate their relative ages on the geologic time scale (Figure 3). Note that solid lines (dashed where underground) are used to show the position of the axial planes of the folds. Note the symbols for axis of an anticline and axis of a syncline in Figure 3. Also note the orientation of symbols for strike and dip in relation to the attitude (orientation) of rock layers (strata).

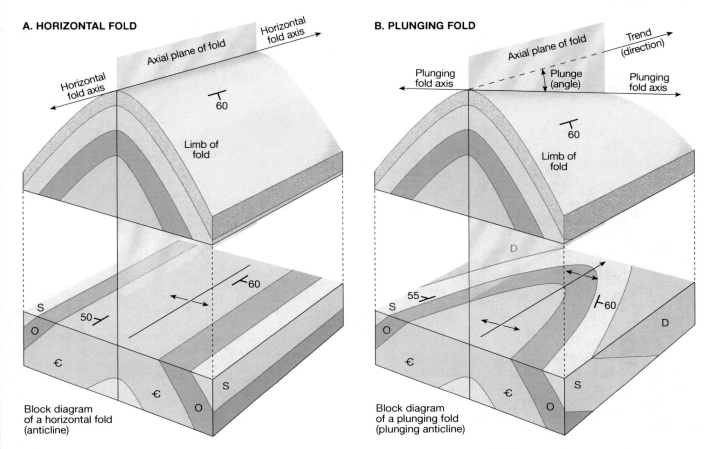

A. HORIZONTAL FOLD

Axial plane of fold

Horizontal fold axis

Horizontal fold axis

Limb of fold

60

S
O
€
50
60
€
S
€
O

Block diagram of a horizontal fold (anticline)

B. PLUNGING FOLD

Axial plane of fold

Trend (direction)

Plunging fold axis

Plunge (angle)

Plunging fold axis

60

Limb of fold

D

S
O
€
55
60
D
€
S
€
O

Block diagram of a plunging fold (plunging anticline)

FIGURE 7 Fold terminology and block diagrams. **A.** Simple horizontal fold (anticline). **B.** More complex plunging fold (plunging anticline). Note that the fold axis plunges into Earth, but the *trend* is the compass direction (bearing) on the surface. Also note the orientation of rock layers, symbols for strike and dip, and symbols for the fold axes in the block diagrams.

Monoclines have two axial planes that separate two nearly horizontal limbs from a single, more steeply inclined limb (Figure 9).

Domes and **basins** (Figure 10) are large, somewhat circular structures formed when strata are warped upward, like an upside-down bowl (dome) or downward, like a bowl (basin). Strata are oldest at the center of a dome, and youngest at the center of a basin.

Block Diagrams

Six block diagrams (Models 1–6) are provided at the back of this chapter. Carefully remove them from the book and cut off the torn edges, so you can fold them into blocks. To fold them, follow the procedure in Figure 11. *Be sure that you have cut out and folded your cardboard models before you proceed to the items below.*

You will also need to understand and apply the symbols for geologic structures from Figure 3 and follow the set of simple rules for interpreting geologic maps on the tops of the block diagrams.

Model 1

This model shows Devonian (green), Mississippian (brown), Pennsylvanian (yellow), and Permian (salmon) formations striking due north and dipping 25° to the west. Cambrian (tan) and Ordovician (gray) formations strike due north and are vertical (dip angle = 90°). Provided are a complete geologic map (the top of the diagram) and three of the four vertical cross sections (the south, east, and west sides of the block diagram).

OVERTURNED ANTICLINE

MONOCLINE

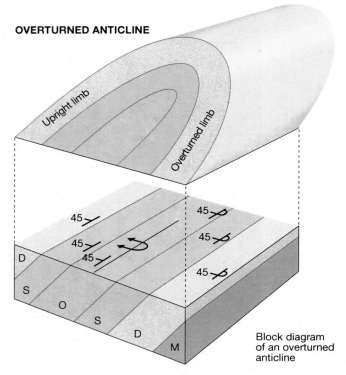

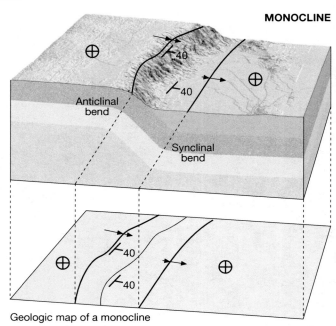

Block diagram
of an overturned
anticline

Geologic map of a monocline

FIGURE 8 Overturned fold. Note that one limb of the fold
has been turned under the other, so it is overturned (upside
down). Also note the symbols used for strike and dip of
strata (rock layers), strike and dip of overturned strata, and
axis of an overturned anticline in the block diagram and
Figure 3.

FIGURE 9 Monocline. Not all folds have two limbs. The
monocline is a fold inclined in only one direction. A monocline has two axial planes (shown as dashed lines in bends)
that separate two nearly horizontal limbs from a more
steeply inclined limb. Note the symbols used to indicate
horizontal strata (rock layers) and the axes of a monocline
in the block diagram and Figure 3.

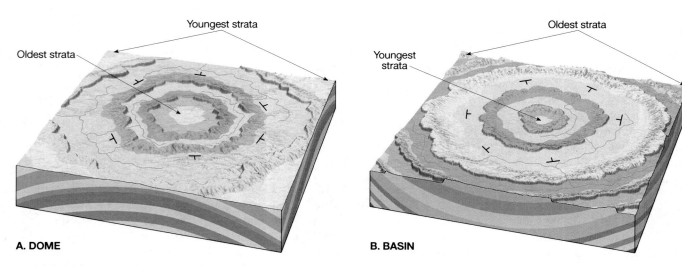

FIGURE 10 Dome and basin. Both of these structures are bowl-shaped in three dimensions and appear
as relatively circular "bull's eye" patterns on maps. **A.** A *dome* is convex (bowed upward, like an upside-
down bowl) and has the oldest strata in its center. Rocks dip away from the center of the dome (note strike-
dip symbols). **B.** A *basin* is concave (bowed downward; bowl shaped) and has the youngest strata in its
center. Rocks dip toward the center of the basin (note strike-dip symbols).

FORMING THE STRUCTURE MODELS

1. Lay the paper with the model on it face down in front of you. Orient the long dimension of the paper up and down, as if you were going to read a normal typewritten page.

2. Carefully curl back one side until you can see the solid black line that runs all the way from the top to the bottom of the page. Crease the paper exactly along that line.

3. Now repeat this process for the other side of the paper.

4. Unfold the two sides, and curl back the top until you see the solid black line that runs across the page. Crease the paper exactly along that line.

5. Now repeat this process for the bottom of the paper.

6. To make a block, you still need to do something about the extra material where the corners are. In each corner there is a dashed line. Start at one corner and push that line toward the inside of the block. Fold the sides down so that they match, and crease the flap you folded in. Your crease should be approximately along the dashed line. Do the same thing with the other three corners.

7. If the block is folded correctly, the top will be flat and the strata will match on the map (top) and on the cross sections (sides).

8. The block will not really stay together without tape, but do not tape it. You will find that it is easier to draw on the block if you can unfold it and lay it out flat.

9. Write your name on the blank inside of the block so that your instructor can identify your work when you hand it in.

FIGURE 11 Directions for forming the structure models.

Questions

1. Finalize Model 1 as follows. First construct the vertical cross section on the north side of the block so it shows the formations and their attitudes (dips). On the map, draw a strike and dip symbol on the Mississippian sandstone that dips 25° to the west and on the Ordovician gray shale that is vertical (see Figure 3 for the strike and dip symbol for a vertical bed). Also draw in the symbol for an unconformity (Figure 3) at the contact between the Ordovician gray shale and the Devonian and Mississippian formations plus everywhere else that the unconformity occurs in the north and south cross sections of the diagram.

2. Complete the following questions:

   a. Note that both the yellow Pennsylvanian sandstone and Ordovician gray shale formations have the same thickness, but the yellow sandstone makes a much wider band on the geologic map (top of block). Why?

   b. What kind of unconformity is present in this block diagram, and how can you tell?

   c. Explain the sequence of events that led to the relationships that now exist among the formations in this block diagram.

Model 2

This model is slightly more complicated than the previous one. The geologic map is complete, but only two of the cross sections are available.

Questions

3. Finalize Model 2 as follows. First, complete the north and east sides of the block. Notice that the rock units define a fold. This fold is an antiform, because the strata are convex upward. It is nonplunging, because its axis is horizontal. (Refer back to Figure 7 for the differences between plunging and nonplunging folds if you are uncertain about this.) On the geologic map, draw strike and dip symbols to indicate the attitudes of formation **E** (gray formation) at points **I, II, III,** and **IV.** Also draw the proper symbol on the map (top of model) along the axis of the fold (refer to Figure 3).

4. How do the strikes at all four locations compare with each other?

5. How does the dip direction at points **I** and **II** compare with the dip direction at points **III** and **IV?** *In your answer, include the dip direction at all four points.*

Model 3

This model has a complete geologic map. However, only one side and part of another are complete.

Questions

6. Finalize Model 3 as follows. Complete the remaining two-and-a-half sides of this model, using as guides the geologic map on top of the block and the one-and-a-half completed sides. On the map, draw strike and dip symbols showing the orientation of formation **C** at points **I, II, III,** and **IV**. Also draw the proper symbol along the axis of the fold (refer to Figure 3).

7. How do the strikes of all four locations compare with each other?

8. How does the dip direction (of formation **C**) at points **I** and **II** compare with the dip direction at points **III** and **IV**? *Include the dip direction at all four points in your answer.*

9. Is this fold plunging or nonplunging? Is it an antiform or a synform?

10. On the basis of this example, how much variation is there in the strike at all points in a nonplunging fold?

Model 4

This model shows a plunging antiform and an unconformity. The antiform plunges to the north, following the general rule that *anticlines plunge in the direction in which the fold closes* (refer to rules, Figure 12).

Questions

11. Finalize Model 4 as follows. Complete the north and east sides of the block. Draw strike and dip symbols on the map at points **I, II, III, IV,** and **V**. Draw the proper symbol on the map along the axis of the fold, including its direction of plunge. Also draw the proper symbol on the geologic map to indicate the orientation of beds in formation **J**.

12. How do the directions of strike and dip differ from those in Model 3?

13. What type of unconformity is at the base of formation **J**?

A SET OF SIMPLE RULES FOR INTERPRETING GEOLOGIC MAPS

1. Anticlines have their oldest beds in the center.
2. Synclines have their youngest beds in the center.
3. Anticlines plunge toward the nose (closed end) of the structure.
4. Synclines plunge toward the open end of the structure.
5. Contacts between horizontal beds "V" upstream and are parallel to topographic contour lines.
6. Contacts of horizontal beds, or of beds that have a dip lower than stream gradient, "V" upstream.
7. Contacts of beds that have a dip greater than stream gradient "V" downstream if they are dipping downstream.
8. Contacts of beds that have a dip greater than stream gradient will "V" upstream if they are dipping upstream.
9. Vertical beds do not "V" or migrate with erosion.
10. The upthrown blocks of faults tend to be eroded more than downthrown blocks.
11. Contacts migrate downdip upon erosion.
12. True dip angles can only be seen in cross section if the cross section is perpendicular to the fault or to the strike of the beds.

FIGURE 12 Simple rules used by geologists to interpret geologic maps.

Model 5

This model shows a plunging synform. Two of the sides are complete and two remain incomplete.

Questions

14. Finalize Model 5 as follows. Complete the north and east sides of the diagram. Draw strike and dip symbols on the map at points **I, II, III, IV,** and **V** to show the orientation of layer **G**. *Synforms plunge in the direction in which the fold opens* (refer to rules, Figure 11). Draw the proper symbol along the axis of the fold to indicate its location and direction of plunge.

15. In which direction does this synform plunge?

Model 6

This model shows a fault that strikes due west and dips 45° to the north. Three sides of the diagram are complete, but the east side is incomplete.

Questions

16. Finalize Model 6 as follows. At point **I**, draw a strike and dip symbol showing the *orientation of the fault*. On the west edge of the block, draw arrows parallel to the fault, indicating relative motion. Label the hanging wall and the footwall. Complete the east side of the block. Draw arrows parallel to the fault, indicating relative motion. Now look at the geologic map and at points **II** and **III**. Write **U** on the side that went up and **D** on the side that went down. At points **IV** and **V**, draw strike and dip symbols for formation **B**.

17. Is the fault in this model a normal fault or a reverse fault? Why?

18. On the geologic map, what happens to the contact between units **A** and **B** where it crosses the fault?

19. There is a general rule that, as erosion of the land proceeds, *contacts migrate downdip*. Is this true in this example? Explain.

20. Could the same offset along this fault have been produced by strike-slip motion?

PART B: BLOCK DIAGRAMS, GEOLOGIC CROSS SECTIONS, AND GEOLOGIC MAPS

Illustrated block diagrams and geologic maps are provided for you to develop your skills of identifying, describing, and interpreting geologic structures. You will need to understand and apply the symbols from Figure 3 and follow the set of simple rules for interpreting geologic maps (Figure 12). Refer back to Figures 4–10 as needed.

Questions

21. Complete each block diagram in Figure 13 as directed. On the line provided, indicate what kind of geologic structure is represented in the diagram.

22. Complete the geologic cross section in Figure 14 (you will need pencil, scratch paper, ruler, and protractor; colored pencils are optional). Place the edge of a piece of scratch paper along line X – Y and mark it to record the exact width of each colored formation. Transfer this information to the topographic surface line in the geologic cross section. Use a protractor to extend the colored formations with known dips into the subsurface of the geologic cross section (lightly in pencil). Draw in the remaining colored formations parallel to the ones with known dips, and smooth the contacts to form the geologic structure(s) beneath the surface. Finally, project the geologic structure up above the topographic surface line to show how the geologic structure(s) existed there before being eroded.

    a. Label your geologic cross section to indicate the kind(s) of geologic structure(s) revealed by your work. Then add the appropriate symbols from Figure 3 to the geologic map in order to show the axes of the folds revealed in your geologic cross section.

    b. Add half-arrows to the fault near the center of the geologic map to show the relative motions of its two sides. Exactly what kind of fault is it (Refer to Figure 5)?

23. Complete the geologic cross section in Figure 15 (you will need pencil, scratch paper, ruler, and protractor; colored pencils are optional). Place the edge of a piece of scratch paper along line X – Y and mark it to record the exact width of each colored formation. Transfer this information to the topographic surface line in the geologic cross section. Use a protractor to extend the colored formations with known dips into the subsurface of the geologic cross section (lightly in pencil). Draw in the remaining colored formations parallel to the ones with known dips, and smooth the contacts to form the geologic structure(s) beneath the surface. Finally, project the geologic structure up above the topographic surface line to show how the geologic structure(s) existed there before being eroded.

    a. What kind of geologic structure is present, and how do you think it formed?

    b. Modify the geologic map by adding the appropriate symbols from Figure 3 to show the - position of the structure on the map the best you can.

24. Refer to the geologic maps in Figure 16. Do the following for each of these maps.

    a. Make a list of the ages of rocks present in the map, from oldest at the bottom of the list to youngest at the top of the list. Indicate in your list, and on the map, where there are unconformities (gaps or missing intervals of rock in the sequence), if any.

    b. Make a list of other geologic structures that you can identify on the map, then describe where each structure is located.

    c. Write a paragraph or outline of the general geologic history of the region (i.e., describe when the rock layers formed and how they were deformed or eroded).

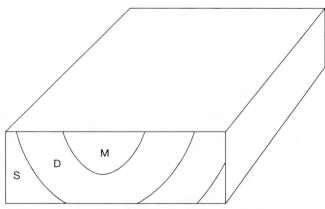

A. Complete top and side. Add appropriate symbols from Figure 3. What geologic structure is present?

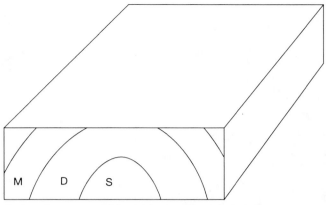

B. Complete top and side. Add appropriate symbols from Figure 3. What geologic structure is present?

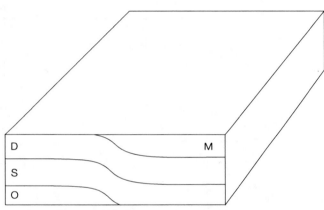

C. Complete top and side. Add appropriate symbols from Figure 3. What geologic structure is present?

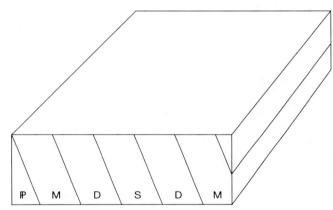

D. Complete top of diagram. Add appropriate symbols from Figure 3. What geologic structure is present?

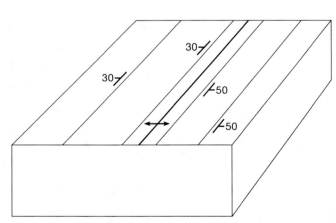

E. Complete the sides of the diagram. What geologic structure is present?

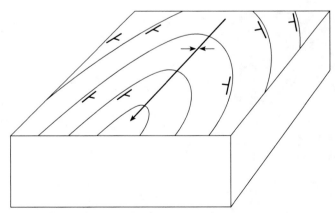

F. Complete the sides of the diagram. What geologic structure is present?

FIGURE 13   Block diagrams to complete (Question 21).

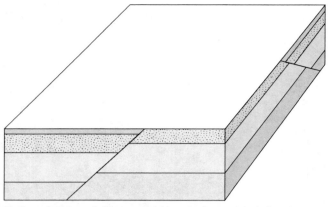

G. Complete top of diagram. Add appropriate symbols from Figure 3. What geologic structure is present?

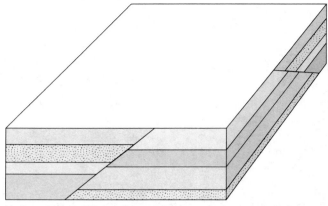

H. Complete top of the diagram. Add appropriate symbols from Figure 3. What geologic structure is present?

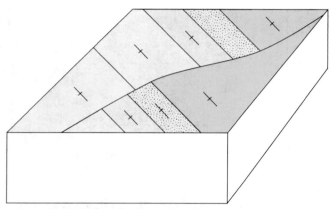

I. Complete the sides of the diagram. Add half-arrows. What geologic structure is present?

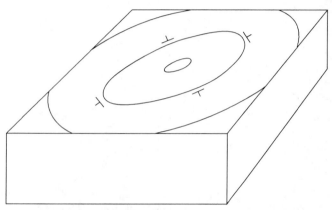

J. Complete the sides of the diagram. What geologic structure is present?

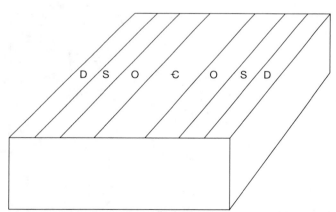

K. Complete sides of the diagram. Add appropriate symbols from Figure 3. What geologic structure is present?

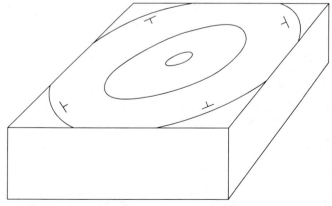

L. Complete the sides of the diagram. What geologic structure is present?

FIGURE 13 (CONTINUED)   Block diagrams to complete (Question 21).

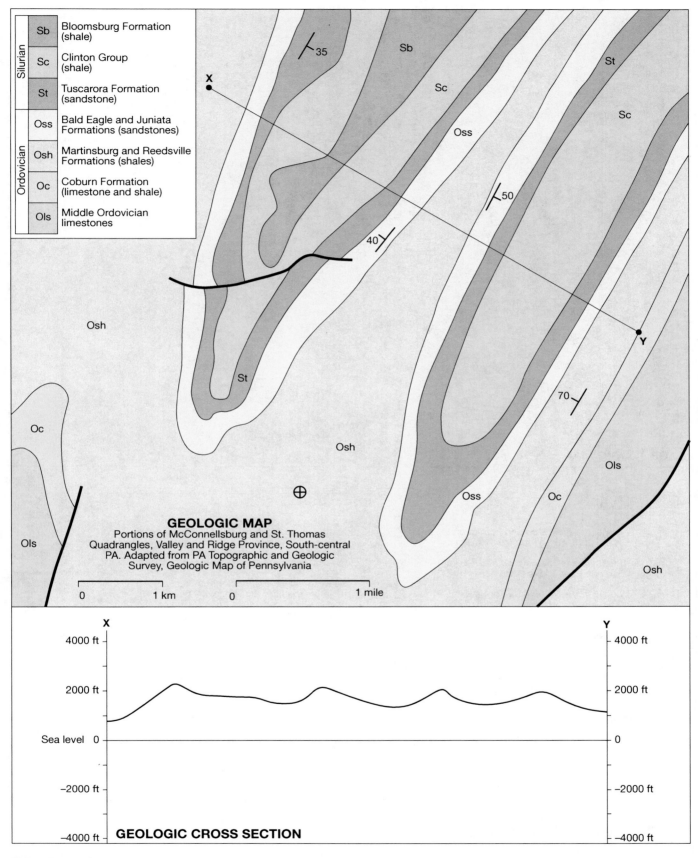

GEOLOGIC MAP

Portions of McConnellsburg and St. Thomas Quadrangles, Valley and Ridge Province, South-central PA. Adapted from PA Topographic and Geologic Survey, Geologic Map of Pennsylvania

Silurian		
Sb	Bloomsburg Formation (shale)	
Sc	Clinton Group (shale)	
St	Tuscarora Formation (sandstone)	

Ordovician		
Oss	Bald Eagle and Juniata Formations (sandstones)	
Osh	Martinsburg and Reedsville Formations (shales)	
Oc	Coburn Formation (limestone and shale)	
Ols	Middle Ordovician limestones	

GEOLOGIC CROSS SECTION

FIGURE 14   Geologic map and cross section to complete (Question 22).

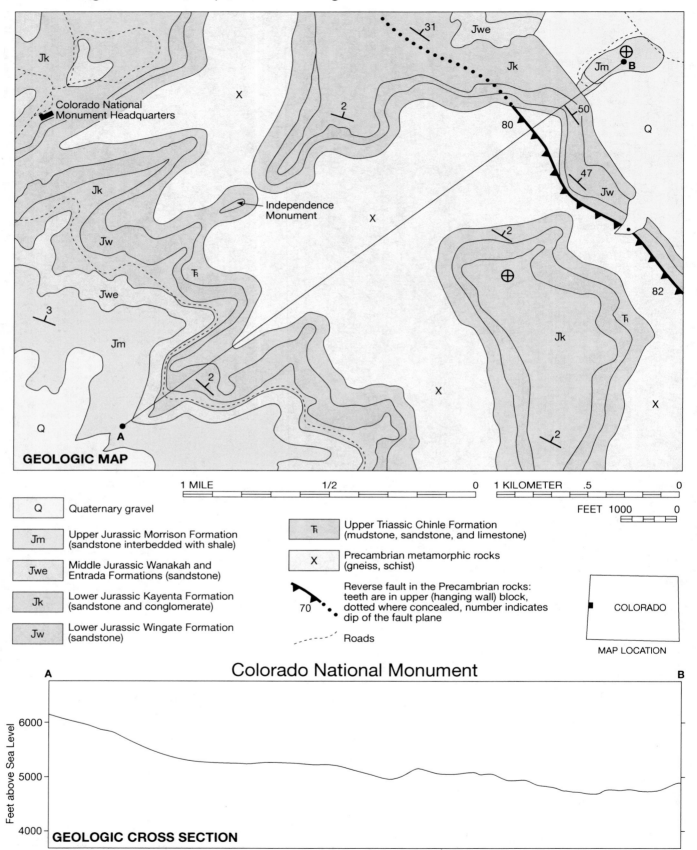

GEOLOGIC MAP

Q	Quaternary gravel
Jm	Upper Jurassic Morrison Formation (sandstone interbedded with shale)
Jwe	Middle Jurassic Wanakah and Entrada Formations (sandstone)
Jk	Lower Jurassic Kayenta Formation (sandstone and conglomerate)
Jw	Lower Jurassic Wingate Formation (sandstone)

ᴦ̵	Upper Triassic Chinle Formation (mudstone, sandstone, and limestone)
X	Precambrian metamorphic rocks (gneiss, schist)
70 ▲▲▲····	Reverse fault in the Precambrian rocks: teeth are in upper (hanging wall) block, dotted where concealed, number indicates dip of the fault plane
------	Roads

COLORADO

MAP LOCATION

Colorado National Monument

GEOLOGIC CROSS SECTION

A   B

Feet above Sea Level

6000

5000

4000

FIGURE 15   Geologic map and cross section to complete (Question 23). Map data adapted from USGS Geologic Investigations Series I-2740 by Robert B. Scott *et al.*

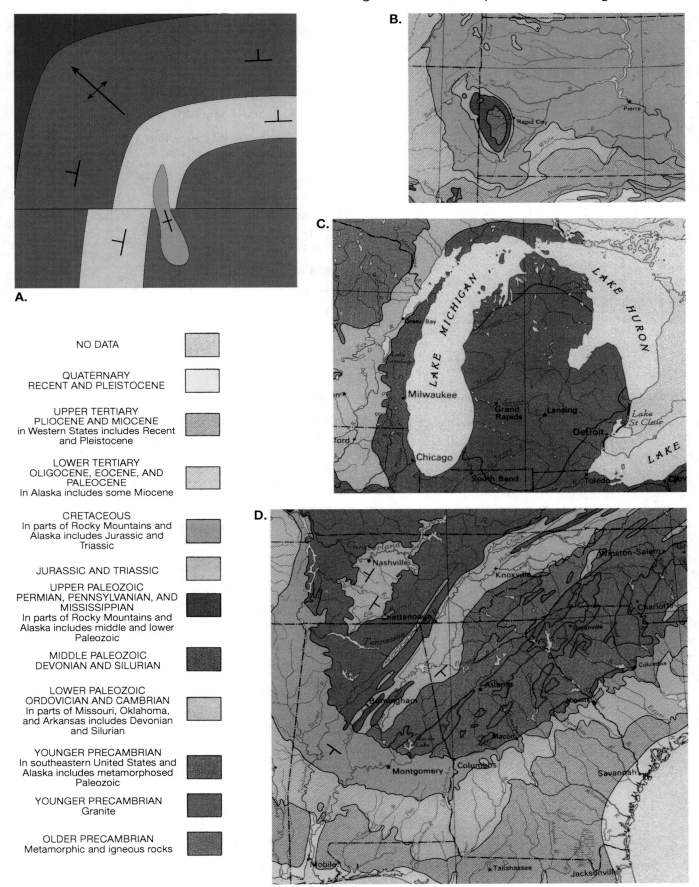

FIGURE 16   Geologic maps for analysis and interpretation (Question 24).

PART C: ANALYSIS OF A GEOLOGIC MAP

Refer to the geologic map provided by your instructor. Otherwise, obtain a geologic map as directed to do so by your instructor. (*Do not mark the map with any dark lines or pen marks!*)

Questions

25. What geographic area (quadrangle or other geographic division) does this geologic map represent?

26. What is the general topography of the area? *Use elevations, if available, and describe orientations of hills and valleys.*

27. What is the name and age of the oldest formation represented on the map?

28. What is the name and age of the youngest formation represented on the map?

29. Make three list headings: igneous formations, sedimentary formations, and metamorphic formations. Under each heading, list the names of the formations that are the indicated type of rock. If there are no formations of one rock type, then write *none* under the heading.

30. What unconformities (see Figure 4) have developed, or are currently developing, in the sequence of formations of this area? Describe where they

occur and how much time/rock is missing at each unconformity.

31. What formations form the hilltops? Why?

32. What formations form the valleys? Why?

33. Where are modern sediments accumulating, and what symbol(s) is/are used to map them?

34. How does the geology of the map area influence:
    a. the topography?
    b. the location of streams or other bodies of water?
    c. the location of natural vegetation, orchards, farms, and ranches?
    d. the location of communities?
    e. the location of quarries or mines, if any?

35. List and describe any folds, domes, basins, or significant faults in the map area.

36. List, describe, and give the ages of any igneous intrusions in the map area.

37. Write a one- or two-page summary of the geologic history of this region. Start with the oldest formation and events and end with the present time. Mention all of the formations by name and how they developed (sedimentary, igneous, or metamorphic processes). Mention when any formations were eroded or deformed into geologic structures (unconformities, folds, domes, basins, faults). Also describe the kinds of stresses that may have caused the structures to develop.

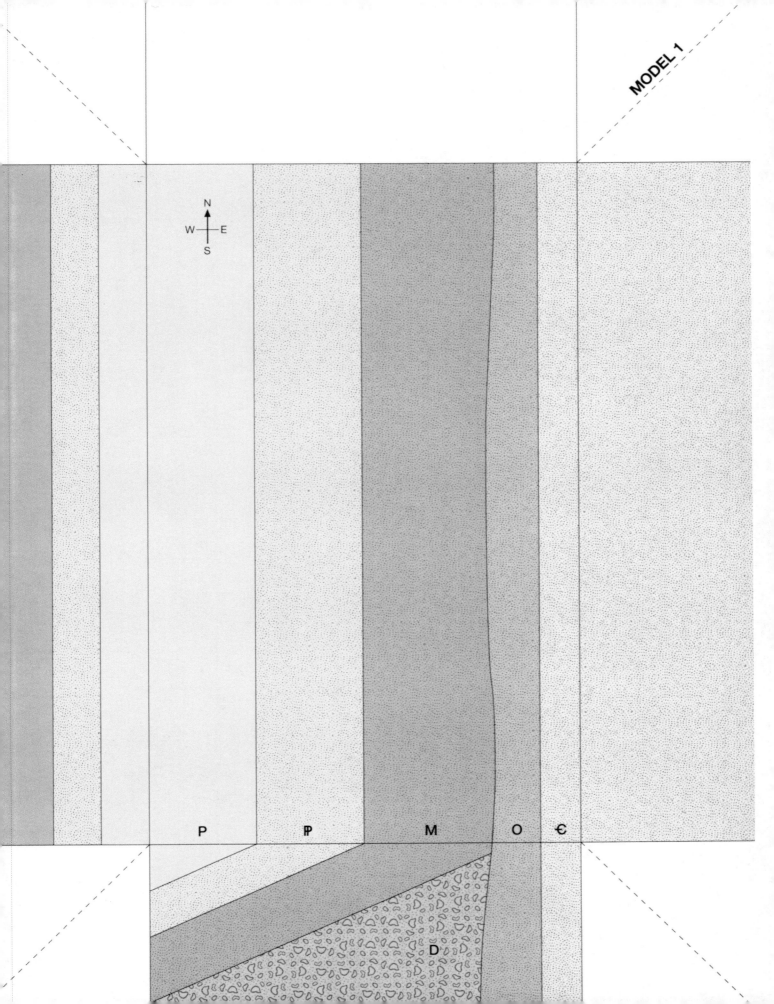

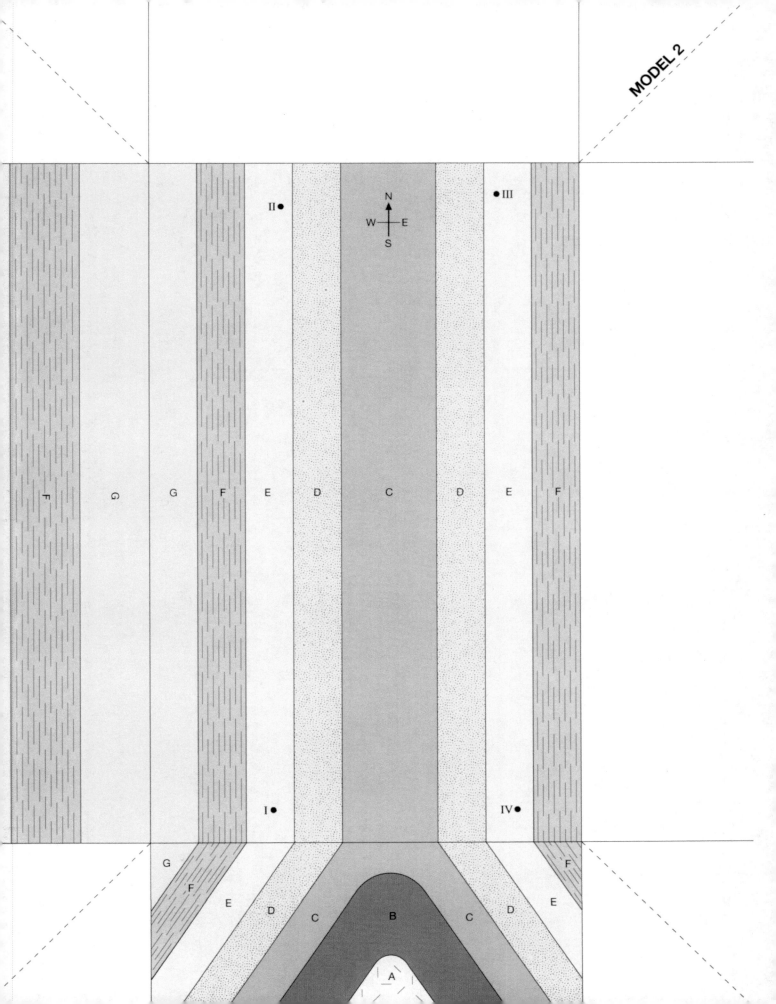

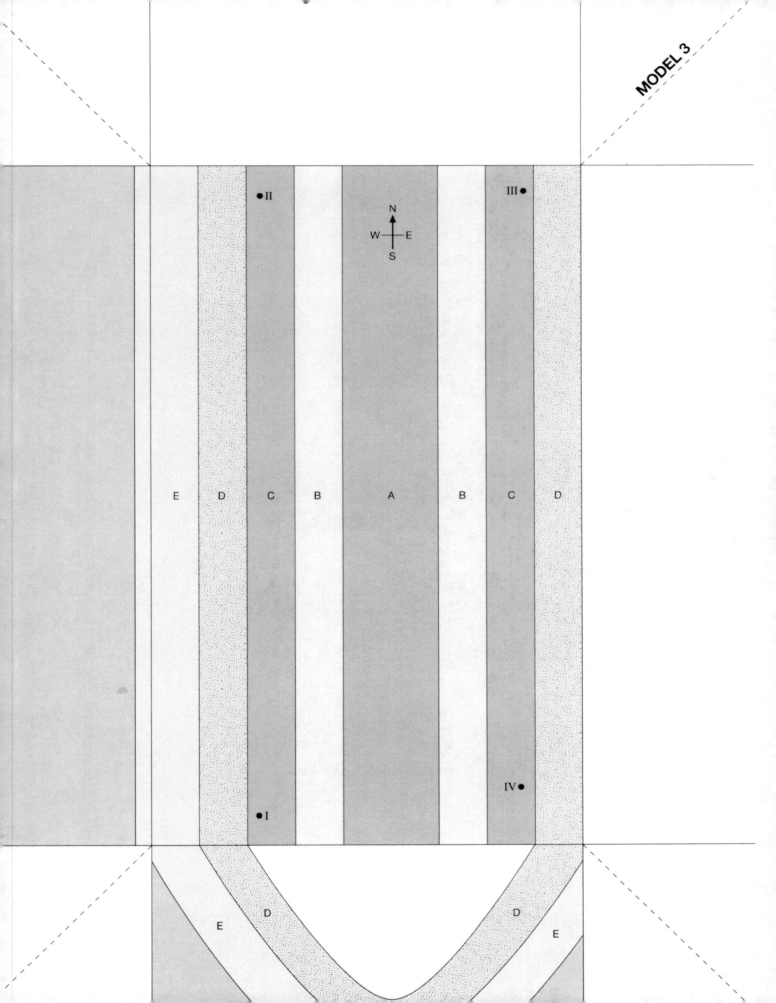

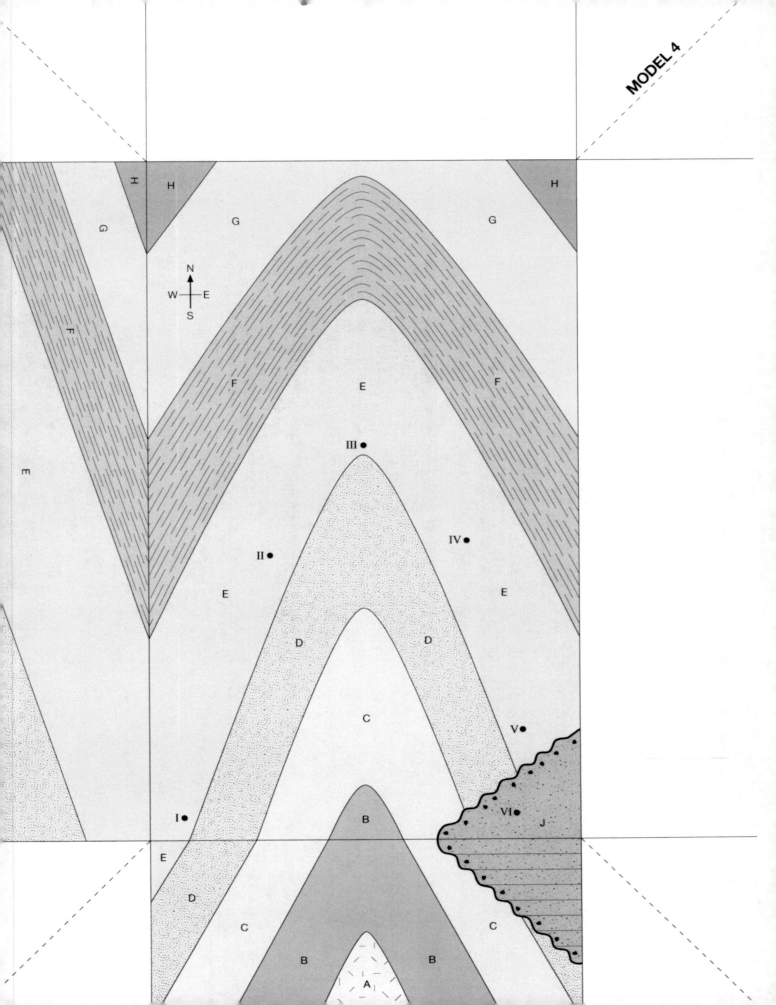

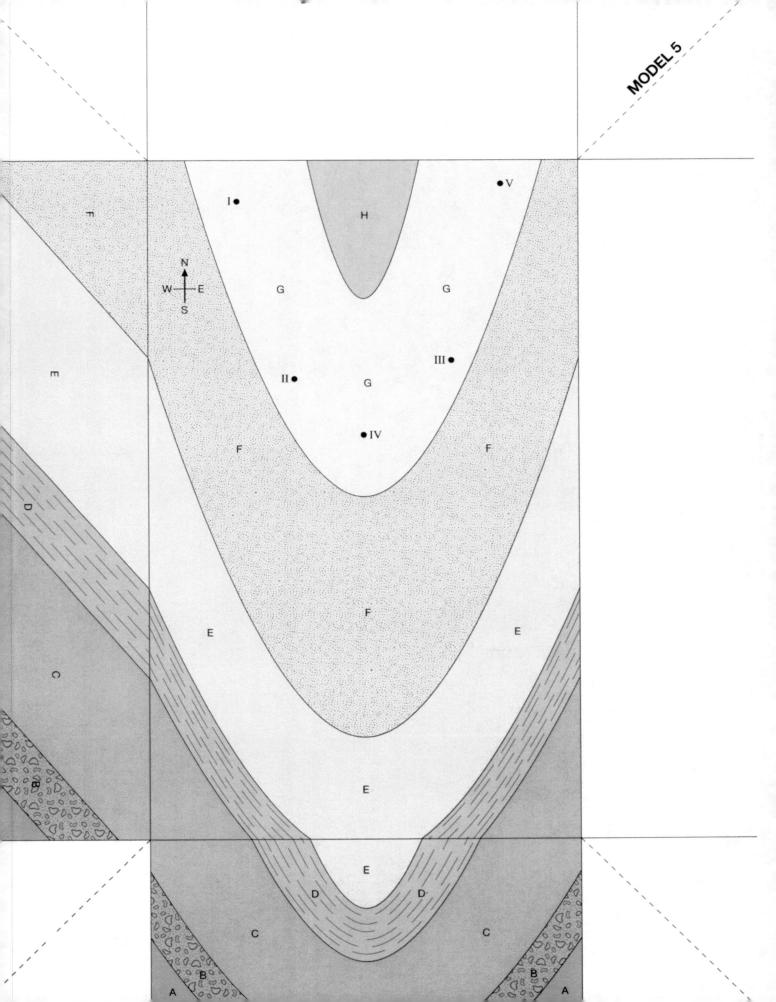

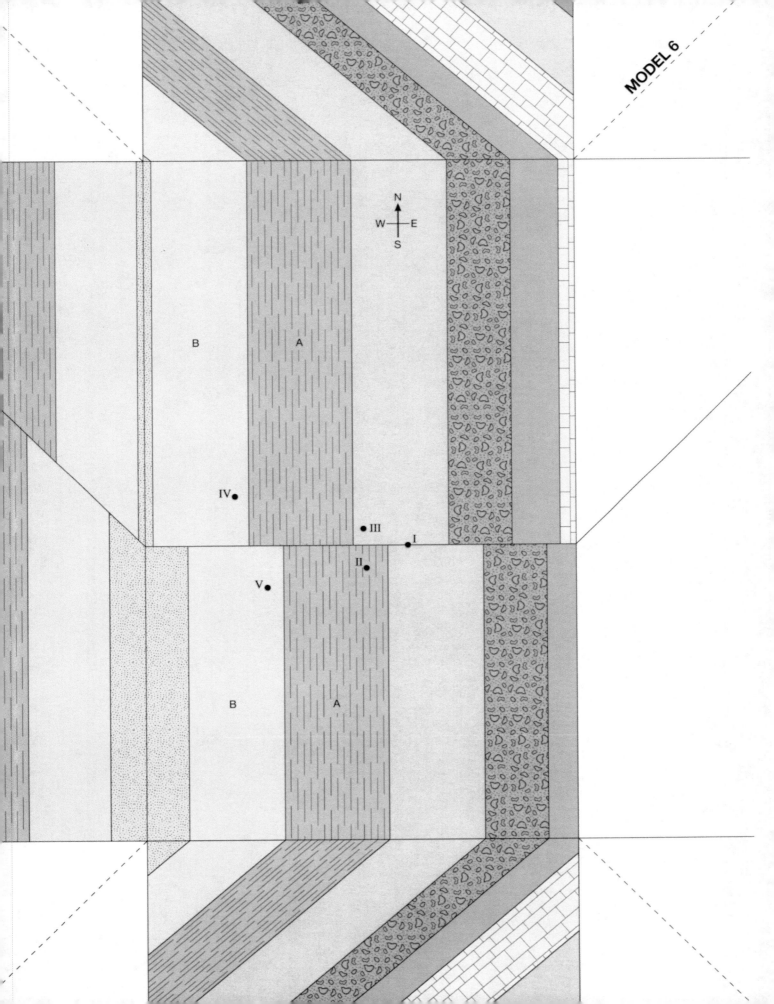

MODEL 6

7

Earthquake Epicenters, Intensities, Risks, Faults, Nonstructural Hazards and Preparation

Earthquake Epicenters, Intensities, Risks, Faults, Nonstructural Hazards and Preparation

INTRODUCTION

Zachary Grey, writing in 1750, said "An earthquake is a vehement shake or agitation of some considerable place or part of the Earth, from natural causes, attended with a huge noise, like thunder; and frequently with an eruption of water, fire, smoke or wind. They are looked upon to be the greatest and most formidable phenomena of nature." Although our present understanding of earthquakes is much more refined, they are still considered to be formidable phenomena. An earthquake is the ground shaking caused by elastic waves propagating in the Earth generated by a sudden release of stored strain energy. The sudden release of stored strain energy is the result of an abrupt slip of rock masses along a break in the Earth called a *fault*. Most fault slip occurs below the Earth's surface without leaving any surface evidence. The place where this slippage occurs is known as the *hypocenter* or *focus* of the earthquake, and the point on the surface vertically above the focus is the *epicenter*.

In this exercise we review earthquake wave types, locate an earthquake epicenter, determine earthquake intensities, assess seismic risk, examine fault types, and study fault zone characteristics.

Earthquake Waves

The energy released at the focus of an earthquake sets up several types of vibrations or waves that are transmitted through the Earth in all directions. Some waves travel through the Earth to the surface and are known as body waves. Others travel along the Earth's surface and are known as surface waves (Figure 1).

One type of body wave is a compressional wave in which the particles of rock vibrate back and forth in the direction of wave travel; the motion is similar to that of sound waves that alternately compress and dilate the medium—solid, liquid, or gas—through which they travel. Compressional waves are also called longitudinal or *primary* waves (P waves); the latter name is given because these waves appear first on seismograms (Figure 2) that record earthquake waves. Another type of wave is the shear or transverse wave, in which the particles vibrate at right angles to the direction of wave progress, in the same manner as a wave moving along a stretched string that is plucked. Because these waves are the second waves to appear on the seismogram, they are called *secondary* waves (S waves).

After the body waves, another class of seismic waves, the surface waves, arrive. They have frequencies of less than 1 cycle per second and often approximate the natural frequency of vibration in tall buildings. Surface waves in general decrease in amplitude more slowly than body waves. The surface waves consist of *Love* waves (horizontal lateral vibrations perpendicular to direction of transmission; they travel forwards but shake sideways) and *Rayleigh* waves (rotational displacement of particles to produce a wavy or undulating surface; they travel up and down in small circles).

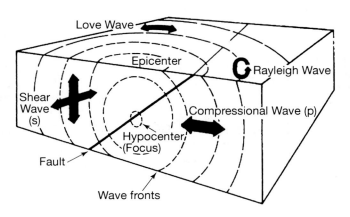

FIGURE 1   Diagram of directions of vibrations of body (P and S) and surface (Love and Rayleigh) waves (Hays, 1981).

PART A. EPICENTER, INTENSITY, AND SEISMIC RISK

Epicenter (Part A1)

After an earthquake, seismologists are faced with the task of finding when and where the shaking began. They do this by examining the *seismograms* from several seismograph stations. Because the P and S waves travel at different rates, the difference in arrival times varies from station to station depending on the distance from the source.

The average travel times of P and S waves compiled from many earthquake records are used to make travel-time graphs and tables showing the time required for waves to travel various distances from a hypocenter. These records show that P waves travel more rapidly than S waves. Therefore, travel-time curves will show P and S waves as separate curves. Surface waves travel at about 90 percent of the velocity of S waves because the surface waves are traveling through lower velocity materials located at the Earth's surface.

If arrival times are available from several seismograph stations, the distances given by the travel-time curves may be used to determine the earthquake's location. The distance provides the radius of a circle about the seismograph station. The *epicenter* is located somewhere on that circle. With at least three stations, the location of the epicenter may be determined as the point where the three circles intersect.

We can also arrive at the distance to the epicenter by using simple subtraction and a proportional relationship. Because of their different velocities, there is a time lag between arrival of the first P and first S wave at a seismograph station. The time lag (time of S minus time of P) can be determined from seismograms. This time lag can be used to compute the distance to the epicenter, provided the average velocity of each wave type is known. In the first part of the exercise, we will use seismograms from four different stations to locate the epicenter and time of an earthquake.

QUESTIONS (PART A1)

Epicenter

1. In Figure 2, use the time scale to determine the lag in arrival time between the P and S waves at four stations: St. Louis, Missouri (SLM); Bloomington, Indiana (BLO); Minneapolis, Minnesota (MNM); and Bowling Green, Ohio (BGO). The first major impulse on the left in the seismogram indicates the arrival of the first P wave at the station, the second impulse, the arrival of the first S wave. The lag time, T, is given by the difference between S and P times. Enter the lag time value for each station below:

SLM: __21__ sec	BLO: __31__ sec
MNM: __81.5__ sec	BGO: __59__ sec

2. To determine the distance from the earthquake to each seismograph station we must first determine the time lag between P and S wave arrivals at a given distance from an earthquake, say 100 km, knowing the average velocities of the P and S waves. If the average velocity of the P wave is 6.1 km/sec and the average velocity of the S wave is 4.1 km/sec, what is the time required for each wave to travel 100 km? (It may help to think of this problem like a very fast driving trip: if you want to go 100 km, and you drive at a rate of 6.1 km/sec, how long, in seconds, will it take you to get to your destination?)

P waves (6.1 km/sec) travel 100 km in __16.39__ seconds.

S waves (4.1 km/sec) travel 100 km in __24.39__ seconds.

Thus the time lag between the arrival of P and S waves at a distance 100 km from the hypocenter (T_{100}) is __8__ seconds.

3. Remembering that for longer distances there is a proportionally longer lag time, we can construct a simple equation to calculate the unknown distance x to each station:

$$\frac{x}{T_x} = \frac{100 \text{km}}{T_{100}} \qquad x = 12.5\,T_x$$

where x = unknown distance in km; Tx = lag time for distance x; T_{100} = lag time at 100 km

Since values for Tx are known from Question 1 and the value of T_{100} is known from Question 2, the equation can be solved for x for each station. More than one station is needed to determine the epicenter since the information from one station can only give the distance to the earthquake and not the direction. The minimum number of stations needed to locate an epicenter is three.

Using the data from Figure 2 and the equation above, determine the distance to the earthquake epicenter from each station and enter below.

SLM: __262.5__	km
MNM: __1019__	km
BLO: __387.5__	km
BGO: __737.5__	km

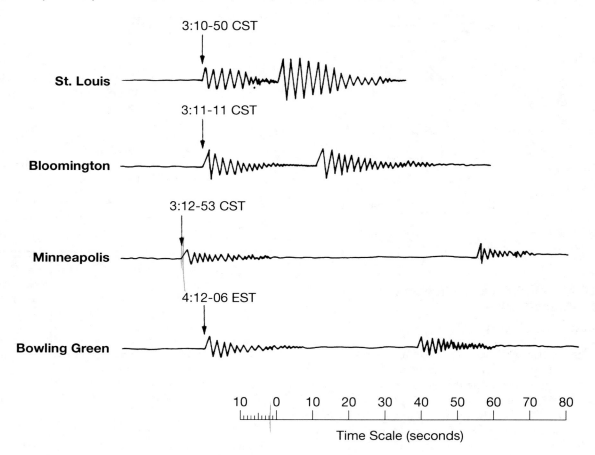

FIGURE 2   Partial seismograms for an earthquake. The P wave arrived at the St. Louis seismograph at 10 minutes and 50 seconds after 3:00 P.M. CST. The second disturbance on the seismogram represents the arrival of the S waves.

4. a. The epicenter of the earthquake can be pinpointed by drawing compass arcs from three of the stations with radii corresponding to the distances calculated in Question 3. The intersection of these radii marks the epicenter. Do this in Figure 3.

b. Where is the epicenter? (Give location within a state.)

Missouri - Arkansas - Tennesse border

c. Label it on the map (Figure 3).

d. At what time did the earthquake occur? (Refer to Figure 2.)

SLO - 3:10:50 - 262.5km/6.1km/sec = 3:10:07

BLO - 3:11::11 - 387.5/6.1 = 3:10:7.5

MNM = 3:12:53 - 173/6.1 = 3:10:5

BLO : 3:10:5

Intensity (Part A2)

The *intensity* of an earthquake at a site is based on the observations of individuals during and after the earthquake. It represents the severity of the shaking, as perceived by those who experienced it. It is also based on observations of damage to structures, movement of furniture, and changes in the Earth's surface as a result of geologic processes during the earthquake. The Modified Mercalli Intensity Scale is commonly used to quantify intensity descriptions. It ranges from I to XII (Table 1).

An *isoseismal* map shows the distribution of seismic intensities associated with an earthquake. The greatest impact of an earthquake is usually in the epicentral region, with lower intensities occurring in nearly concentric zones outward from this region. The quality of construction and variation of geologic conditions affect the distribution of intensity.

Seismic risk maps have been based on the distribution and intensities of past earthquakes or on the probability of future earthquake occurrences (of a given ground motion in a given time period). In this exercise the first type of map is adequate for our examination of seismic risk in middle North America; however, maps based on the probabilistic approach may be needed in other investigations. The latter maps do not express intensity. Rather, they show probability of occurrence of ground shaking that has a 10 percent probability of being exceeded in 50 years.

Note that we also use the term *magnitude* to describe an earthquake. The magnitude of an earthquake is a measure of the amplitude of an earthquake wave on a seismograph (Bolt, 1988). The Richter magnitude scale is a commonly used standardized system of amplitude measurement, and allows for comparison of different

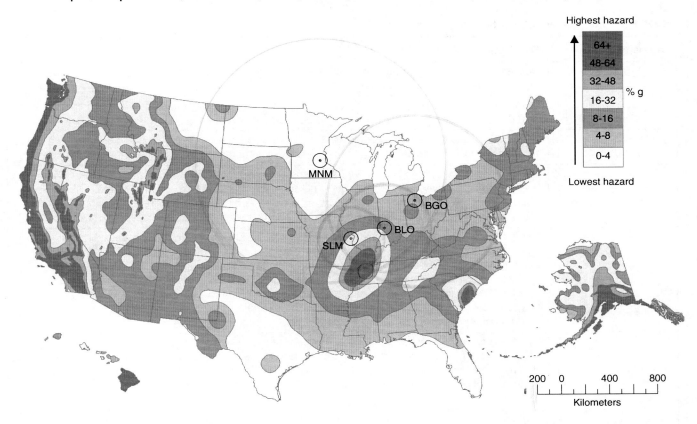

FIGURE 3 Seismic acceleration, expressed as a percent of gravity, that can be expected during a 50 year period. Higher numbers indicate greater potential for shaking (From Peterson and others, 2008).

earthquakes around the world. The Richter scale is a logarithmic scale, which means that each increase in number, for example from M5 to M6, represents a 10-fold increase in amplitude (and about a 30-fold increase in actual energy released by the earthquake).

QUESTIONS (PART A2)

1. Following are some historical descriptions of earthquakes (a–d). Such statements, made to scientists or reporters or recorded in diaries or on survey forms distributed by government agencies, allow scientists to determine the intensity of an earthquake. Using the Modified Mercalli Intensity Scale (Table 1), assign each of the quakes an intensity number. Pick the lowest number exhibiting the characteristics given. The first quotation describes the observations of an eyewitness to a California earthquake around 1913. The second, third, and part of the fourth descriptions are from data gathered by the U.S. Coast and Geodetic Survey after the Daly City, California, earthquake of 1957 (Richter magnitude 5.3).

a. "There was a keen frost, and when we reached the water-hole a thin film of ice was seen upon the water. I dismounted and led my horse by the bridle, and walked to the edge of the water. Just as I reached it, the ground seemed to be violently swayed from east to west. The water splashed up to my knees; the trees whipped about and limbs fell on and all around me. I was affected by a fearful nausea, my horse snorted and in terror struggled violently to get away from me, but I hung to him, having as great a fear as he had himself. The lake commenced to roar like the ocean in a

storm, and, staggering and bewildered, I vaulted into the saddle and my terrified horse started, as eager as I was to get out of the vicinity." (Eisman, 1972)

Intensity: _VIII_

b. "The shock seemed to be a sort of gentle swaying back and forth, causing hanging fixtures to swing, but doing no damage." (Iacopi, 1971)

Intensity: _II_

c. "The earthquake was very intense . . . a heavy oak china cabinet and massive table moved 2 to 3 inches away from original positions; kitchen stove moved 2 inches; furnace in basement moved two inches off base and water heater tilted off base." (Iacopi, 1971)

Intensity: _IV_

TABLE 1 Modified Mercalli Intensity Scale of 1931.

Intensity	Description of Effects
I	Not felt by people, except under especially favorable circumstances. Sometimes birds and animals are disturbed. Trees, structures, liquids, and bodies of water may sway gently, and doors may swing slowly.
II	Felt indoors by a few people, especially on upper floors of multistory buildings. Birds and animals are disturbed, and trees, structures, liquids, and bodies of water may sway. Hanging objects may swing.
III	Felt indoors, usually as a rapid vibration that may not be recognized as an earthquake at first, similar to that of a light truck passing nearby. Movements may be appreciable on upper levels of tall structures.
IV	Felt indoors by many, outdoors by few. Awakens a few individuals. Characterized by vibration like that due to passing of heavy or heavily loaded trucks, a heavy body striking building, or the falling of heavy objects inside. Dishes, windows, and doors rattle. Walls and house frames creak. Hanging objects often swing. Liquids in open vessels are disturbed slightly. Stationary automobiles rock noticeably.
V	Felt indoors by practically everyone, outdoors by most people. Awakens many or most sleepers. Frightens a few people; some persons run outdoors. Buildings tremble throughout. Dishes and glassware break to some extent. Windows crack in some cases, but not generally. Vases and small or unstable objects overturn in many instances. Hanging objects and doors swing generally. Pictures knock against walls, or swing out of place. Pendulum clocks stop, or run fast or slow. Doors and shutters open or close abruptly. Small objects move, and furnishings may shift to a slight extent. Small amounts of liquids spill from well-filled containers.
VI	Felt by everyone, indoors and outdoors. Awakens all sleepers. Frightens many people; there is general excitement, and some persons run outdoors. Persons move unsteadily. Trees and bushes shake slightly to moderately. Liquids are set in strong motion. Plaster cracks or falls in small amounts. Many dishes and glasses, and a few windows, break. Books and pictures fall. Furniture may overturn or heavy furnishings move.
VII	Frightens everyone. There is general alarm, and everyone runs outdoors. People find it difficult to stand. Persons driving cars notice shaking. Trees and bushes shake moderately to strongly. Waves form on ponds, lakes, and streams. Suspended objects quiver. Damage is negligible in buildings of good design and construction; slight to moderate in well-built ordinary buildings; considerable in poorly built or badly designed buildings. Plaster and some stucco fall. Many windows and some furniture break. Loosened brickwork and tiles shake down. Weak chimneys break at the roofline. Cornices fall from towers and high buildings. Bricks and stones are dislodged. Heavy furniture overturns.
VIII	There is general fright, and alarm approaches panic. Persons driving cars are disturbed. Trees shake strongly, and branches and trunks break off. Sand and mud erupt in small amounts. Flow of springs and wells is changed. Damage slight in brick structures built especially to withstand earthquakes; considerable in ordinary substantial buildings, with some partial collapse; heavy in some wooden houses, with some tumbling down. Walls fall. Solid stone walls crack and break seriously. Chimneys twist and fall. Very heavy furniture moves conspicuously or overturns.
IX	There is general panic. Ground cracks conspicuously. Damage is considerable in masonry structures built especially to withstand earthquakes; great in other masonry buildings, with some collapsing in large part. Some wood frame houses built especially to withstand earthquakes are thrown out of plumb, others are shifted wholly off foundations. Reservoirs are seriously damaged, and underground pipes sometimes break.
X	Most masonry and frame structures and their foundations are destroyed. Ground, especially where loose and wet, cracks up to widths of several inches. Landsliding is considerable from riverbanks and steep coasts. Sand and mud shift horizontally on beaches and flat land. Water level changes in wells. Water is thrown on banks of canals, lakes, rivers, etc. Dams, dikes, and embankments are seriously damaged. Well-built wooden structures and bridges are severely damaged, and some collapse. Railroad rails bend slightly. Pipelines tear apart or are crushed endwise. Open cracks in cement pavements and asphalt road surfaces.
XI	Few if any masonry structures remain standing. Broad fissures, earth slumps, and land slips develop in soft wet ground. Water charged with sand and mud is ejected in large amounts. Sea waves of significant magnitude may develop. Damage is severe to wood frame structures, especially near shock centers, great to dams, dikes, and embankments, even at long distances. Supporting piers or pillars of large, well-built bridges are wrecked. Railroad rails bend greatly and some thrust endwise. Pipelines are put out of service.

TABLE 1 Modified Mercalli Intensity Scale of 1931.   (Continued)

Intensity	Description of Effects
XII	Damage is nearly total. Practically all works of construction are damaged greatly or destroyed. Disturbances in the ground are great and varied, and numerous shearing cracks develop. Landslides, rockfalls, and slumps in riverbanks are numerous and extensive. Large rock masses are wrenched loose and torn off. Fault slips develop in firm rock, and horizontal and vertical offset displacements are notable. Water channels, both surface and underground, are disturbed and modified greatly. Lakes are dammed, new waterfalls are produced, rivers are deflected, etc. Surface waves are seen on ground surfaces. Lines of sight and level are distorted. Objects are thrown upward into the air.

(Modified from Cluff and Bolt, 1969, p. 9)

d. "It was as if giant hands took the house and shook it . . . the pea soup jumped out of the pot and the grandfather clock was silenced." (modified from Iacopi, 1971)

Intensity: V

2. Not all earthquakes occur in areas where high levels of risk have been identified. On July 27, 1980, an earthquake of Richter magnitude 5.1 shook Kentucky, Ohio, and adjacent states. The earthquake epicenter was determined to be at latitude 38.2° N, longitude 83.9° W, near Sharpsburg, Kentucky (approximately 30 miles southwest of the Ohio River town of Maysville, Kentucky). It had a focal depth of 13 km. Damage to structures along the Ohio River in Maysville, Kentucky, and in the Ohio communities of Aberdeen, Manchester, Ripley, and West Union, consisted of chimneys being knocked down, cracks in plaster and concrete blocks, and merchandise being toppled from store shelves. In Cincinnati a cornice reportedly fell from city hall.

a. Based on the reported damage, what was the intensity of this earthquake along the Ohio River?

b. Locate the earthquake epicenter with an X on Figure 3.

Isoseismal Maps (Part AB)

Large earthquakes have the potential for significant damage. This damage varies with the geologic nature of the earthquake and the rocks between the focus and the site, types and properties of the materials at a site, and the nature of the buildings. In this part of the exercise we use data from 1949 and 1965 earthquakes in western Washington to construct isoseismal maps.

QUESTIONS (PART A3)

1. The intensity of an earthquake is a measure of the impact of seismic shaking on the ground, structures, and people. It is described on a scale of I to XII (in Roman numerals), where I

is only rarely felt and XII is total destruction. Use the Modified Mercalli Intensity Scale (Table 1) and the descriptions of site damage for the April 13, 1949, earthquake (Table 2) to determine the intensity at each site. Record the intensity and the primary evidence used in determining the intensity for each site, beside the names of the sites in Table 3. Several intensities, with evidence, are given.

2. Place the intensity values from Table 3 on the map of Washington (Figure 4). Then draw boundaries between these intensities to produce an isoseismal map.

3. What was the maximum intensity from the 1949 earthquake?

4. Where does the epicenter for the 1949 earthquake appear to have been?

5. What observation in Table 2 was the most interesting or surprising to you? Why?

6. Using intensity numbers from the April 29, 1965, western Washington earthquake shown in Table 4, enter the intensity values on the map of Washington (Figure 5).

7. Draw the approximate boundaries of the intensity zones as determined by the values you entered for each locality. Part of one boundary is given for you in Figure 5.

TABLE 2 Impact of the 1949 Earthquake in Western Washington at Various Sites.

Aberdeen	One death. Scores of chimneys tumbled at roof level. Broken dishes and windows.
Bellingham	Hanging objects swung. Swaying of buildings. Pendulum clocks stopped or ran fast or slow.
Bremerton	One death. Considerable falls of plaster. Elevator counterweights pulled out of guides. Swaying of buildings. Trees shaken moderately to strongly.
Buckley	Part of high school building fell. Most chimneys in town toppled at roofline. Cracked plaster and ground.
Centralia	One death; 10 persons hospitalized. Very heavy damage. Collapse of building walls and many chimneys. Water mains broken; Water and sand spouted from ground. Violent swaying of buildings and trees. Many objects moved, including pianos. Objects fell from shelves. Pendulums swinging east–west stopped. Many persons panic-stricken. Four miles southwest of town, water spouted 18 in. high in middle of field, leaving a very fine sand formation around each hole (1–3 in. in diameter). Gas or air boiling up through river.
Cle Elum	Pendulum clocks stopped. Small objects and furnishings shifted. Trees and bushes shaken moderately.
Eatonville	Chimneys toppled. Plaster fell in large pieces in schoolhouse. People had difficulty in maintaining balance.
Hyak	Few windows broke. Trees and bushes shaken moderately. Furnishings shifted.
Longview	Two minor injuries. Gable of community church fell. Water main broke, beams cracked in school. Extensive but scattered damage to business buildings, industrial properties, and residences. Considerable damage to irrigation ditches. Landslides on cuts along highway. Objects fell in all directions. Some heavy furniture overturned. Glass figurine on mantle thrown 12 ft.
Olympia	Two deaths; many persons injured. Conspicuous cracks in ground and damage in masonry structures. Capitol buildings damaged. Nearly all large buildings had cracked or fallen walls and plaster. Two large smokestacks and many chimneys fell. Streets damaged extensively; many water and gas mains broken. Portion of a sandy spit in Puget Sound disappeared during the earthquake.
Port Townsend	Pendulum clocks facing northeast stopped. Hanging objects swung. Slight damage in poorly built buildings. Subterranean sounds heard. Bells rang in a small church.
Puyallup	Many injured. High school stage collapsed. Nearly every house chimney toppled at roof line. Several houses were jarred off foundations. Minor landslides blocked roads. Water mains broke. Multiple-story brick buildings most severely damaged. Some basement floors raised several feet, driving supports through floor above. Plaster badly damaged. Water spouted in fields, bringing up sand.
Randle	Twisting and falling of chimneys; about one-fourth of all chimneys fell. Damage considerable. Water spilled from containers and tanks. Plaster and walls fell; dishes and windows broke. Lights went out.
Satsop	Cracked ground. Pendulum clocks stopped. Trees and bushes shaken strongly. Furnishings overturned.
Seattle	One death; many seriously injured with scores reporting shock, bruises, and cuts. Many houses on filled ground demolished; many old buildings on soft ground damaged considerably. Collapse of top of one radio tower and one wooden water tank with damage to many tanks on weak buildings. Many chimneys toppled. Heavy damage to docks (fractures in decayed pilings). Several bridges damaged; many water mains in soft ground broken. Telephone and power service interrupted. Large cracks in filled ground; some cracking of pavement. Water spouted 6 ft or more from ground cracks. At the federal office building, bookcases thrown face down. Very heavy furniture overturned. Plaster badly cracked and broken with pieces 1–3 ft square thrown from walls. Pictures on north–south walls canted; those on east–west walls—little cant. Some doors did not fit after shock. Many old brick buildings partially destroyed.
Snoqualmie	Most damage confined to brick chimneys, windows, and plaster. Overturned vases and floor lamps. Coffee shaken out of cups. Rockslides on Mt. Si. Trees and bushes shaken strongly.
Tacoma	One death. Many buildings damaged and parts fell. Many chimneys toppled. Several houses slid into Puget Sound. One smokestack fell. One 23-ton cable saddle was thrown from the top of tower at Tacoma Narrows Bridge, causing considerable loss. Railroad bridges thrown out of line. Tremendous rockslide, a half-mile section of a 300-ft cliff, into Puget Sound. Considerable damage to brick; plaster, windows, walls, and ground cracked.

(Modified from Murphy and Ulrich, 1951)

TABLE 3 Intensities from the April 13, 1949, Earthquake

Location (symbol)	Intensity	Primary Evidence for 1949 Earthquake
Aberdeen (Ab)		
Bellingham (Be)		
Bremerton (Br)		
Buckley (Bu)	VIII	Walls and chimneys fall; cracked ground
Centralia (Ce)	VIII–IX	Sand and mud eruption: pipes break; damage considerable
Cle Elum (Cl)		
Eatonville (Ea)	VII	Plaster falls in large pieces; difficulty maintaining balance
Hyak (Hy)	VI	Trees/bushes shake moderately; few windows break
Longview (Lo)	IX	
Olympia (Ol)		
Port Townsend (Po)		
Puyallup (Pu)		
Randle (Ra)	VIII	Twisted and fallen chimneys; walls fall
Satsop (Sa)		
Seattle (Se)		
Snoqualmie (Sn)	VII	Damaged chimneys/windows; trees/bushes shaken strongly
Tacoma (Ta)		

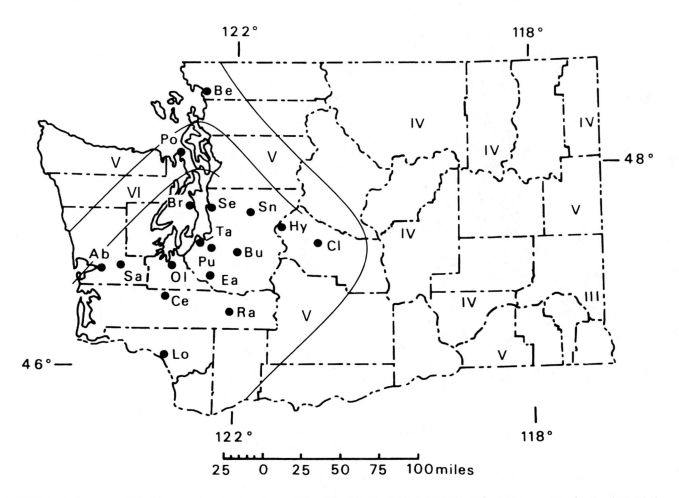

FIGURE 4 Index map of Washington showing locations of the sites listed in Table 3. Modified Mercalli Intensities for April 13, 1949, earthquake are given for eastern Washington. Some boundaries of intensity zones shown. Completed map is an isoseismal map.

TABLE 4 Locations and Intensity Data for the April 29, 1965, Western Washington Earthquake

Location	Intensity	Location	Intensity
Aberdeen (Ab)	V	Longview (Lo)	V
Arlington (Ar)	VI	Olympia (Ol)	VI
Bellingham (Be)	V	Port Angeles (Pa)	V
Bremerton (Br)	VI	Port Townsend (Po)	V
Buckley (Bu)	VI	Puyallup (Pu)	VII
Centralia (Ce)	VI	Randle (Ra)	V
Cle Elum (Cl)	V	Satsop (Sa)	VI
Concrete (Cc)	VI	Seattle (Se)	VII
Eatonville (Ea)	VI	Snoqualmie (Sn)	VII
Forks (Fo)	IV	Tacoma (Ta)	VII
Hyak (Hy)	VI	Vancouver (Va)	V

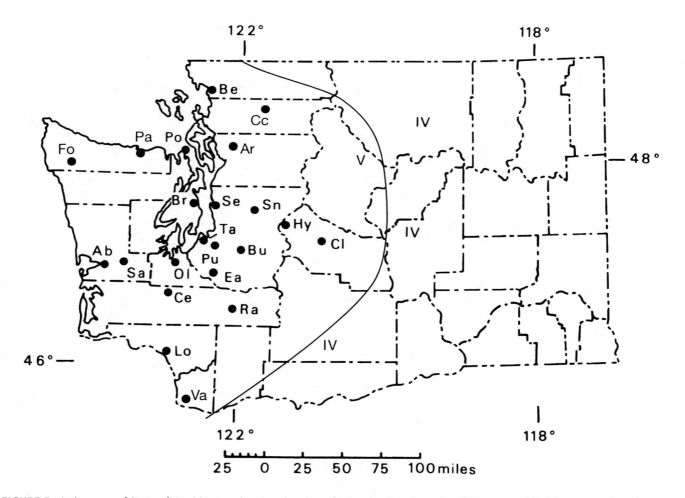

FIGURE 5   Index map of State of Washington showing the sites of intensity data from the 1965 western Washington earthquake.

8. a. What was the maximum intensity for the 1965 earthquake?

b. Where does the epicenter for the 1965 earthquake appear to have been?

9. On the Web you will find additional information on these two earthquakes (and others) at http://earthquake.usgs.gov/eqcenter/dyfi.php. Complete the following blanks for these two western Washington earthquakes.

a.   **1949 Earthquake**   **1965 Earthquake**

Date

Maximum Intensity

Name (Earthquake)

Magnitude

Number of Reports

b. You might still be curious about earthquake intensities. Below write a question for your TA or instructor about some aspect of the exercise that you don't understand.

Note: If you experience an earthquake you can report what you saw/felt during the earthquake and what damage you noted. It is useful to write your account of the event as soon as you are safe and can make notes. Then use those notes when completing the form at http://pasadena.wr.usgs.gov/shake/pnw/html/unknown_form.html.

Earthquake Shaking Hazard Maps (Part A4)

National maps of earthquake shaking hazards provide information that helps to save lives and property by providing data for building codes. Buildings designed to withstand severe shaking are less likely to injure occupants. These hazard maps are also used by insurance companies, FEMA (for support of earthquake preparedness), EPA (for landfill design), and engineers (for landslide potential).

The map shows the hazard by zones (or in some maps contour peak values) of the levels of horizontal shaking. The higher the number the stronger is the shaking. The number is % g or percent of acceleration due to gravity (in this case as horizontal acceleration). Acceleration is chosen, because building codes prescribe how much horizontal force a building should be able to withstand during an earthquake. 10% g is the approximate threshold for damage to older (pre-1965) structures. Additional information on these maps is available from Frankel et al. (1997) and from the USGS (Fact Sheet 183-96).

Figure 3 is a ground-shaking hazard map that shows a 10 percent probability of exceeding a given value in a 50-year period (Peterson and others, 2008). That is, over the next 50 years there is a 1 in 10 chance that the acceleration given for any area will be exceeded. Use information in Figure 3 to help answer the following questions.

QUESTIONS (PART A4)

1. Which areas of the country have the lowest hazard from earthquake shaking (where 4% g, or less, peak acceleration is expected)?

2. If damage to older (pre-1965) structures can be expected with horizontal accelerations of 10% g or more, which areas of your home state are:
   a. at some risk?

   b. at greatest risk?

   c. what is your home state?

3. What three or four regions of the country have the highest accelerations?

4. What geologic processes, other than shaking and fault displacement, could produce a hazard in an earthquake? List two.

5. The geologic material on which a building rests plays a role in the type of shaking that occurs during an earthquake. Weak materials amplify the shaking. Which of the following foundation materials would most likely result in less shaking and a safer building? (circle one)

artificial fill, poorly consolidated sediments, marine clays, unweathered bedrock

6. If the Internet is available, now or after class, determine and list (places and magnitudes) where the largest two earthquakes have occurred in the last 2 weeks. Also list what processes, other than shaking, contributed to the loss of structures and life. A possible source to begin the search is: http://earthquake.usgs.gov/recenteqs/

7. The Mississippi Valley is indicated as a high-risk area because of earthquake activity that is associated with stress within the continental lithospheric plate. Consider the types of plate margins in the plate tectonics model to answer the following questions. (See a geology text for basic details on plate margins.)

   a. What is the tectonic explanation for the major shaking hazard in southern California?

   b. What is the tectonic explanation for the major shaking hazard around Seattle?

PART B. FAULTS AND FAULT DETECTION

Earthquakes are related to movements along fault zones. Diagrams of several types of faults are shown in Figure 6. If necessary, the review questions in this portion of the exercise may be answered with the aid of a standard introductory geology textbook.

   Fault zones can be recognized on aerial photographs, satellite and LIDAR images, geologic maps, and topographic maps, as well as by field observations. Features that might indicate a fault zone area are (1) scarps (cliff or break in slope) formed by horizontal or vertical movement; (2) steep mountain fronts; (3) offset streams and ridges; (4) sag ponds and lakes; (5) lineaments of vegetation; (6) valleys in fault zones; (7) changes in rock type, structure, moisture, and vegetation and (8) faceted spurs. These features are shown in Figure 7, which depicts a strike-slip fault (largely horizontal displacement). Normal faults also can have distinct features, which are illustrated in Figure 8.

QUESTIONS (PART B)

Fault Diagrams

1. The freshly exposed cliff of bedrock or regolith along a fault line is known as a fault _____.

2. Following an earthquake, the horizontal distance between two utility poles on opposite sides of a fault trace (not a strike-slip fault) had increased. Are the regolith (soils) and bedrock in this area in a region of compression (squeezing together) or tension (pulling apart)? Explain your reasoning.

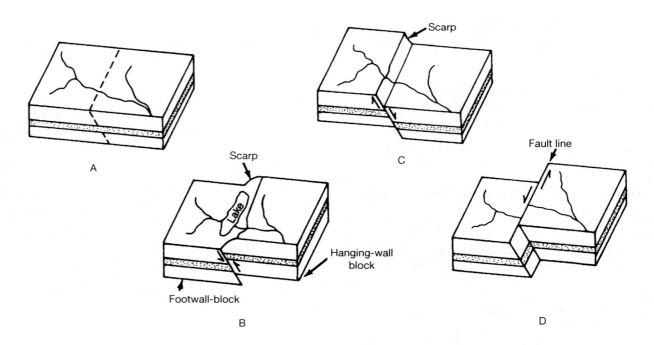

FIGURE 6 Types of fault movement: (a) block before movement; (b) reverse fault, or thrust fault, in which the hanging-wall block has moved up relative to the footwall block; (c) normal fault, in which the hanging-wall block has moved down relative to the footwall block; (d) strike-slip fault, in which the blocks on either side of the fault have moved sideways past each other. Arrows indicate relative motion of the blocks.

(Modified in part from McKenzie, Pettyjohn, and Utgard, 1975)

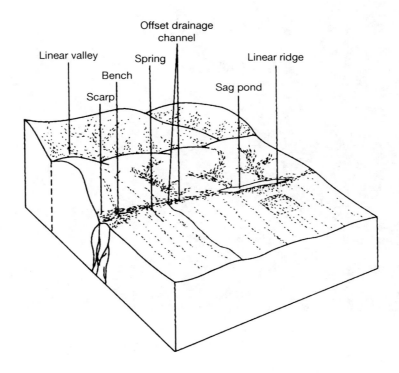

FIGURE 7   Distinctive landforms and drainage patterns aligned along a strike-slip fault are visible evidence that fault movement is recent enough to have interrupted the more gradual processes of erosion and deposition.

(Brown and Kockelman, 1983)

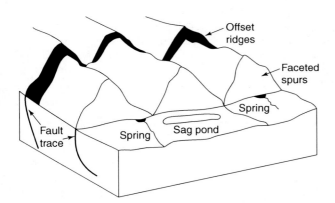

FIGURE 8   Typical geologic features found associated with a normal fault in mountainous terrain.

3. Sketch two utility poles on Figure 6a, placing one on each side of the fault. Use fault diagrams Figure 6b and c, and determine if the relative motion of the fault blocks in Question 2 indicates that it is a normal fault or reverse fault. Explain your reasoning.

San Andreas Fault

Study Figure 9, which is a photo of the San Andreas Fault, and then answer the questions below. It will help to review Figure 7.

4. What geological features can be used to identify the location of the fault? Outline the fault zone in Figure 9.

5. Does the fault zone consist of a single fracture or several parallel fractures? What is your evidence?

6. In addition to faults, what other natural or human-made features can create straight lines in topography? Are any of these features present in this photograph?

7. Indicate the direction of movement along the fault by drawing arrows on either side of the fault in Figure 9.

FIGURE 9   Aerial photograph of the San Andreas Fault in the Carrizo Plain at Wallace Creek, California. The fault runs horizontally across the middle of the photograph; the horizontal white line in the lower part of the photograph is a road. Agricultural features on the photo include fences and crop harvest patterns (Wallace, 1990).

Refer to Map: Satellite Image of the San Francisco Bay Area. The yellow dots on this image are earthquake epicenters. Use this figure to answer the following questions.

8. Which features of strike-slip faults shown of Figure 7 can be seen easily on the satellite image? Why are some features easier than other features to see on the image?

9. How do the locations of earthquake epicenters help you determine geographic features that are related to faults?

10. Mark on the Map: Satellite Image of the San Francisco Bay Area, or on a tracing, the several major faults in this area.

Study the radar image of southern California in Figure 10. This image was made from an airplane that bounced radar waves off the earth. The radar is able to penetrate vegetation and clouds, so the image is very clear. The surface of the land is shown as if the sun lighted it, with bright slopes facing the sun and dark areas of shadow. Of course, in a radar image it is not sunlight but is the location of the airplane sending out the radar that creates the bright and shadow areas.

Different geologic and land use patterns are distinctive on the image. Areas with large shadows indicate high topography (mountains). Linear alignments of valleys, rivers, lakes, or mountains may indicate a fault zone. Flat, dark areas may be lakes, reservoirs, or the ocean. Mottled gray patterns, with very small rectangles, are urban areas, broken into blocks and dissected by rivers and freeways. Larger rectangular patterns can represent agricultural fields. Rivers often have winding patterns through mountain, agricultural, and urban areas.

11. What evidence of faults do you see on the radar image?

12. Draw on the image all the fault traces you can find.

13. Use the Web, or material provided by the instructor, to label faults including the Elsinore and San Andreas on Figure 10.

14. Find and label an example of the following: agriculture pattern (A), urban region (U), major highway (H), lake (L), and river (R).

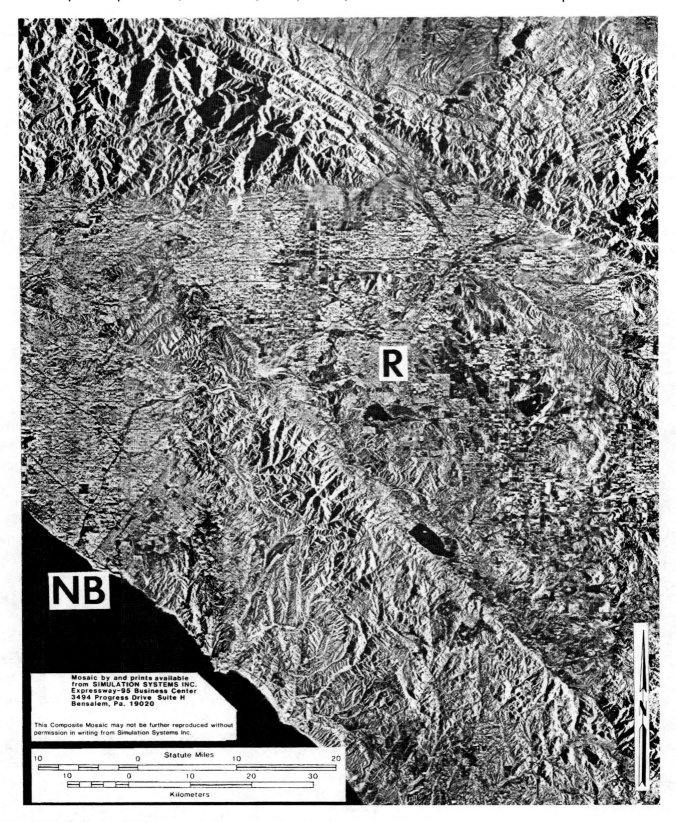

FIGURE 10   Radar image of southern California. R = Riverside, NB = Newport Beach.

(Courtesy of and copyrighted by Simulation Systems, Inc.)

Wasatch Fault

15. Study Map: Draper, Utah, and mark on the map the location of the Wasatch Fault along the mountain front. (Hint: Refer to Figure 8 for features found along normal faults, and begin your identification at Beaver Ponds Springs.)

Photograph: Little Cottonwood Canyon, Salt Lake City, Utah is a color stereo photograph of this area. Locate Beaver Ponds Springs on the photograph, and extend the fault based on topographic features.

Faults can also be seen on color oblique photographs. Use Figure 11 and identify on it the fault scarp and extend trace of the fault both north and south.

16. Using information on normal faults from Figures 6, 7, and 8, review the Salt Lake City photographs and Map: Draper, Utah, and describe the location and appearance of at least one of each of the following features of a normal fault:

spring

sag pond

fault scarp

faceted spur

FIGURE 11   Salt Lake City oblique photo, Little Cottonwood Canyon. North to left. (U.S. Department of Agriculture, Soil Conservation Service, Salt Lake City, UT).

17. In the San Andreas Fault example (questions 4 and 5 above), lateral stream offset was an important clue to movement along the fault. Follow the traces of streams in Map: Draper, Utah as they flow west from the mountains to the valley. Is there any offset of streams where they cross the fault(s)? Why or why not?

18. Can you tell from Map: Draper, Utah which side of the fault has moved up and which side has moved down? Describe your evidence. What additional kinds of information might be helpful in determining the movement along the fault?

Faults in Forests (Bainbridge Island, Washington)

Urban areas and thick forests are two environments in which it can be difficult to locate active or potentially active faults. In urban areas, faults may only be exposed in excavations for construction, or detectable if there is offset of roads or structures. In forested areas, virtual deforestation provided by LIDAR can allow the identification of faults. The example below is from such a forested area.

19. Look at the aerial photograph in Figure 12. Identify on this figure any linear zones you see that might be faults, being careful to avoid roads and property lines that are marked by cut forests.

20. Figure 13 is a LIDAR image of the same area, processed to remove the forest from the image. Mark on this figure any traces of faults that you see. Compare the trace of the fault with the drawings in Figures 7 and 8. What are the surface features that you see along the fault? What kind of fault movement and offset is most likely here? (Circle One) Normal, Reverse, Strike slip?

PART C. RECOGNITION OF NONSTRUCTURAL HAZARDS

This exercise looks at the recognition of nonstructural earthquake hazards and approaches the question, how safe are we in our daily lives? Recognition of nonstructural hazards, however, is something that everyone should know to be able to lead safer lives in earthquake country.

The structure of a building consists of those parts that help it stand up and withstand the forces of weight, wind, and earthquakes that may impact it. Everything else in a building is nonstructural. Structural failure can cause partial or total collapse of a building and injury or death to occupants and those

near a building. Nonstructural hazards can be caused by things the occupants of a building do, such as hanging plants or positioning bookshelves, or they may arise from the failure of the integral components of buildings such as water pipes, ventilation systems, and electrical systems. Nonstructural hazards may also be external, such as decorative trim that can fall off a building (Figure 14) or glass that can break out of windows. In summary, nonstructural hazards include building furniture, utility systems, and internal and external trim and decoration. The behavior of these items in an earthquake can cause damage, destruction, and injury, even if the building remains standing during and after an earthquake.

According to the U.S. Geological Survey, falling objects and toppling materials present the greatest hazards in earthquakes. Falling objects account for about two-thirds of the casualties from earthquakes. Also, replacement of these materials and loss of building use can be very expensive.

In this exercise you will draw a careful sketch of a room (or other indoor site) and complete a checklist to identify and comment on the hazards you find.

QUESTIONS (PART C)

1. Select a site that you frequently use. Make a sketch of this room on the graph paper provided in Figure 15. The choice of site is up to you. It could be a dorm room, a bedroom at home, a place where you work, a place where you study, or some other room or facility. You may do a map view or an elevation, but there is no need to do both. Identify and label the nonstructural hazards that you find. Include a scale on your drawing.

2. The list in Table 5 identifies some of the nonstructural hazards that you may encounter in your search. This list is not intended to be comprehensive; there are undoubtedly some missing hazards. Space is left at the bottom of the list for you to add other hazards that you discover.

Identify the room and building in the table title. Then identify all hazards in the room that you select. In the space provided, make brief comments about the specific nature of each hazard and your vulnerability (such as "Textbooks in environmental geology may fall off shelf and hit me"). Remember, in analyzing earthquake hazards you need to imagine what would happen to the objects around you if they were suddenly launched horizontally.

PART D. EARTHQUAKE PREPARATION AND HAZARD REDUCTION

This exercise explores specific coping techniques to reduce earthquake hazards and improve safety during and after an earthquake. Consider situations in which electric power and water supplies are not available; ATMs, credit cards and other sources of money are not

FIGURE 12   Aerial photograph of a portion of Bainbridge Island, WA. (USGS)

functioning; and the only transportation is by foot or bicycle. By imagining the conditions in a disaster, seeking information from various sources on preparation and coping, and preparing for the disaster, you and your family, friends, and coworkers or students can minimize losses. And remember, many of the preparations for an earthquake can be transferred to other types of natural and human-induced disasters. Even if you do not live in an earthquake hazard area, an earthquake could occur when you are traveling. It makes sense to understand the nature of disasters and to prepare for them.

Use a separate sheet of paper for answers to Questions 1 and 2.

1. Assume that you have three different amounts to spend on earthquake preparation for you or your family: $25, $100, and $200. Develop specific earthquake safety strategies for each amount. Explain what you would buy, how you would store

it, and how you would cope with safety and survival issues in and after an earthquake. Are there simple lifestyle changes before the earthquake that would also help you? You may find it helpful to use your textbook or other sources from a library to do research on earthquake hazard reduction.

2. Imagine that an earthquake occurs while you are in a class. What would you want from your educational institution immediately? What would you want over the next few days? How soon would you want to be back in class? Develop a separate list of items that you believe your educational institution should be ready to provide or situations that it should be prepared to deal with after an earthquake. Divide your list into two sections, with the first section itemizing needs during the first 72 hours, and the second section listing longer-term considerations. Who do you contact at your school to determine which preparations on your list have been made and which are still needed?

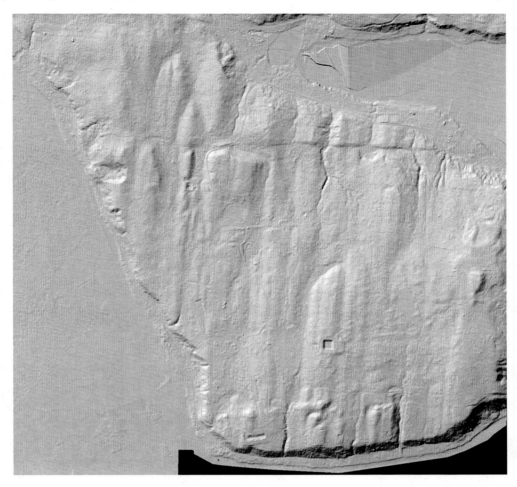

FIGURE 13   LIDAR image of part of Bainbridge Island, WA. (Image courtesy of Puget Sound Lidar Consortium)

FIGURE 14   The statue of Louis Aggasiz at Stanford University after the 1906 earthquake illustrates what can happen when large unsecured objects fall.

(W.C. Mendenhall, USGS).

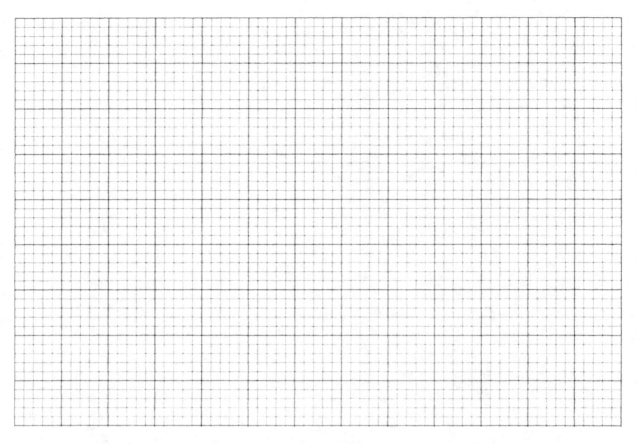

FIGURE 15 Sketch of _____ (your caption)

TABLE 5 List of Possible Hazards in _____.

Type of Hazard	Nature and Effect of Hazard	Possible Methods to Reduce Hazard
Windows: may implode in large pieces; consider proximity to furniture, especially beds		
Bookcases: may topple if not secured		
Books: may fall out of bookshelves		
Furniture: may slide across room; if tall and narrow, such as files, may tip over		
Cabinets: doors may open and contents may fall out if unsecured		
Storage items on desks, shelves, or other surfaces: may fly or fall if unsecured; special hazards if toxic or flammable		
Fixtures: heavy objects may fall if unsecured or poorly secured		
Hanging objects: if unsecured, plants, pictures, mirrors may fall		
Lights: can swing, shatter, and fall		
Exits: consider conditions that would block room exits, such as toppled furniture		
Lifelines: problems in room if adjacent to lifelines, such as water pipes, break		
Other items:		

Bibliography

Algermissen, S. T., 1969, *Seismic risk studies in the United States*. Fourth World Conference on Earthquake Engineering: Santiago, Chile, v. 1, no. 26.

Algermissen, S. T., and Perkins, D. M., 1976, *A probabilistic estimate of maximum acceleration in rock in the contiguous United States*: U.S.G.S. Open File Report 76–416, 45 p.

Algermissen, S. T., Perkins, D. M., Thenhaus, P. C., Hanson, S. L., and Bender, B. L., 1982, *Probablistic estimates of maximum acceleration and velocity in rock in the contiguous United States*, U.S. Geological Survey Open-File Report 82-1033, 99 p.

Berthke, P. R., and Beatley, T., 1992, *Planning for earthquakes, risk, politics and policy*: Baltimore, MD, Johns Hopkins University Press, 210 p.

Bolt, B. A., 2003, *Earthquakes*: New York, W. H. Freeman and Company, 320 p.

Brown, R. D., and Kockelman, W. J., 1983, *Geologic principles for prudent land use—A decision maker's guide for the San Francisco Bay region*: U.S.G.S. Professional Paper 946, 97 p.

Coburn, A., and Spence, R., 1992, *Earthquake protection*: New York, Wiley, 355 p.

Cluff, L. S., and Bolt, B. A., 1969, Earthquakes and their effects on planning and development. In *Urban environmental geology in the San Francisco Bay region*: ed. E. A. Danehy. Sacramento, CA, Special Publication of the San Francisco Section of the Association of Engineering Geologists, p. 25–64.

Earthquake Engineering Research Institute, 1996, *Scenario for a magnitude 7.0 earthquake on the Hayward Fault*: Pub. HF-96, Oakland, CA, 109 p.

Eisman, D. B., 1972, Dust from antelope: *California Geology*, v. 25, no. 8, p. 171–73. Originally printed in *Historic fact and fancies*, (1913?), California Federated Women's Clubs.

Executive Office of the President, Office of Science and Technology, 1970, *Report of the task force on earthquake hazard reduction*: Washington, D.C., U.S. Government Printing Office, 54 p.

Frankel, Arthur, Mueller, Charles, Barnhard, Theodore, Perkins, David, Leyendecker, E.V., Dickman, Nancy, Hanson, Stanley, and Hopper, Margaret, 1997, Seismic-hazard maps for the conterminous United States, U.S. Geological Survey Open-File Report 97-131-F.

Grey, Z., 1750, *A chronological and historical account of the most memorable earthquakes that have happened in the world, from the beginning of the Christian period to the present year 1750*: Cambridge, UK, J. Bentham.

Hanks, T. C., 1985, *National earthquake hazard reduction program - Scientific status*: U.S.G.S. Bulletin 1659, 40 p.

Hays, W. W., 1980, *Procedures for estimating earthquake ground motions*: U.S. Geological Survey Professional Paper 1114, 77 p.

Hays, W. W., 1981, Hazards from earthquakes. In *Facing geologic and hydrologic hazards*, ed. W. W. Hays. U.S.G.S. Professional Paper 1240-B, 108 p.

Hays, W. W., and Gori, P. L., eds., 1986, *Earthquake hazards in the Puget Sound, Washington, area*. Workshop presented at Conference XXXIII: U.S. Geological Survey Open-File Report 86-253, 238 p. plus appendices.

Hopper, M. G., Langer, C. J., Spence, W. J., Rogers, A. M., and Algermissen, S. T., 1975, *A study of earthquake losses in the Puget Sound, Washington, area*: U.S. Geological Survey Open-File Report 75-375, 298 p.

Iacopi, R., 1971, *Earthquake country* (3rd ed.): Menlo Park, CA, Lane Books, 160 p.

Keller, E. A., 2000, *Environmental geology* (8th ed.): Upper Saddle River, NJ, Prentice Hall, 562 p.

Keller, E. A., and Pinter, N., 1996, *Active tectonics*: Upper Saddle River, NJ, Prentice-Hall, 338 p.

McKenzie, G. D., Pettyjohn, W. A., and Utgard, R. O., 1975, *Investigations in environmental geoscience*: Minneapolis, Burgess, 180 p.

Murphy, L. M. and Ulrich, F. P., 1951, *United States earthquakes 1949*, U.S. Department of Commerce, Coast and Geodetic Survey Serial 748, p. 20–28. Reprinted in Thorsen, G. W., comp., 1986, *The Puget lowland earthquakes of 1949 and 1965*: Washington Division of Geology and Earth Resources Information Circular 81, p. 25–34.

Nichols, D. R. and Buchanan-Banks, J. M., 1974, *Seismic hazards and land-use planning*: U.S.G.S. Circular 690, 33 p.

Peterson, M. D,. Frankel, A. D., Harmsen, S. C., Mueller, C. S., Haller, K. M., Wheeler, R. L., Wesson, R. L., Seng, Y., Boyd, O. S., Perkins, D. M., Luco, N., Field, E. H., Wills, C. J., and Rukstales, K. S., 2008, Documentation for the 2008 Update of the United States National Seismic Hazard Maps: U.S. Geological Survey Open-File Report 2008–1128, 120 p.

Reiter, L., 1991, *Earthquake hazard analysis*: New York, Columbia University Press, 254 p.

Reitherman, R., 1985, *Reducing the risks of nonstructural earthquake damage: A practical guide*: Federal Emergency Management Agency, Earthquake Hazards Reduction Series 1, 87 p.

Rogers, A. M., Walsh, T. J., Kockleman, W. J., and Priest, G. K., 1998, Assessing earthquake hazards and reducing risk in the Pacific Northwest, Volume 2: USGS Professional Paper 1560. Available on line http//pubs.usgs.gov/prof/p1560/p1560po.pdf

Solomon, B. J., Storey, N., Wong, I., Silva, W., Gregor, N., Wright, D., and McDonald, G., 2004, Earthquake-hazards scenario for a M7 earthquake on the Salt Lake City segment of the Wasatch fault zone, Utah, CD-ROM, ISBN 1-55791-704-3.

The Federal Emergency Management Agency offers a series of brochures on earthquake preparation. Two that may be particularly helpful are FEMA 113, Family earthquake safety home hazard hunt and drill, and FEMA 46, Earthquake safety checklist.

Wallace, R. E., 1974, *Goals, strategy, and tasks of the earthquake hazard reduction program*: U.S.G.S. Circular 701, 26 p.

Wallace, R. E., ed., 1990, *The San Andreas fault system*: U.S.G.S. Professional Paper 1515, 283 p.

Weaver, C. S., and Smith, S. W., 1983, Regional tectonic and earthquake hazard implications of a crustal fault zone in southwestern Washington: *Journal of Geophysical Research*, v. 88, no. B12, p. 10371–83.

Wong, I., Silva, W., Olig, S., Thomas, P., Wright, D., Ashland, F., Gregor, N., Pechmann, J., Dober, M., Christenson, G., and Gerth, R., Earthquake scenario and probabilistic ground shaking maps for the Salt Lake City, Utah, metropolitan area, CD-ROM, ISBN 1-55791-666-7.

Yanev, P., 1991, *Peace of mind in earthquake country*: San Francisco, Chronicle Books, 218 p.

Yanev, P. I., 1991, *Peace of mind in earthquake country*: San Francisco, Chronicle Books, 218 p.

Yeats, R. S., 2004, *Living with earthquakes in the Pacific Northwest*: Corvallis, Oregon State University Press, 390 p.

Map: Satellite Image of the San Francisco Bay Area

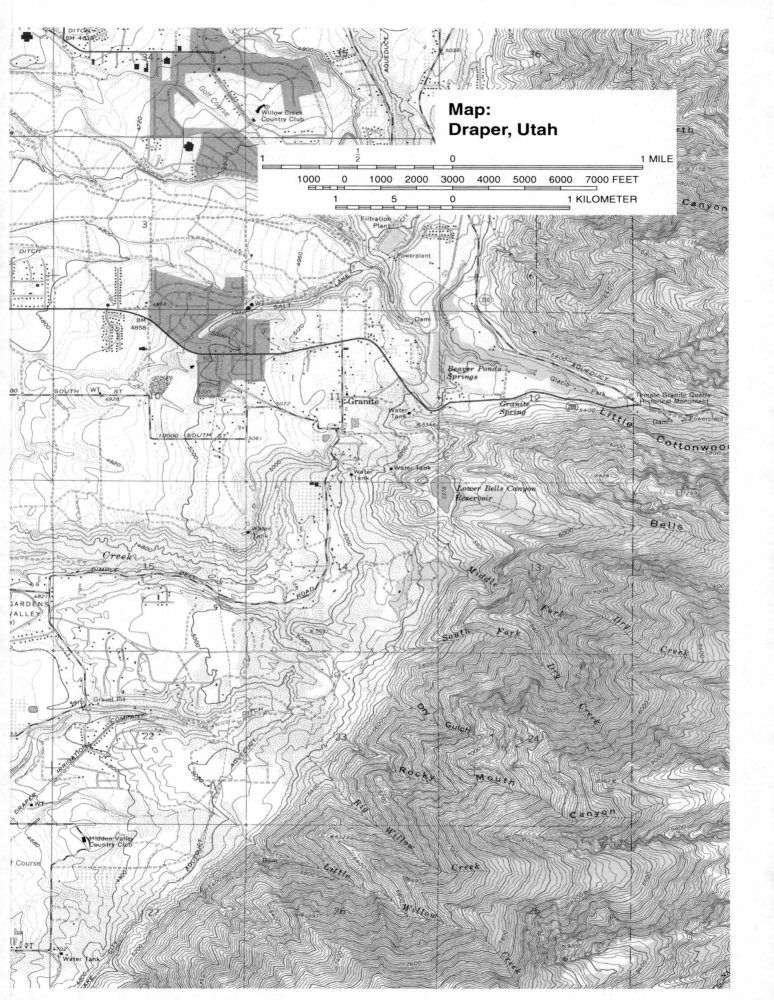

Map:
Draper, Utah

Map:
Little Cottonwood Canyon
Salt Lake City, Utah

Hayward Fault

Name _____

Stop 1: Spring Dr., Hayward

What are two lines of evidence for the fault trace here?

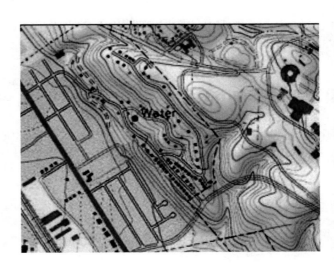

Why do springs tend to occur at faults?

Stop 2: Central St., Hayward

What type of faulting can you see in the old quarry? How is this faulting related to the Hayward – transform fault?

Check out the house at 932 Central. What's wrong with the garage?

What's wrong with the brick wall at the house to the west of 932?

Stop 3: Palisade St., Hayward

What is the direction of movement indicated by the offset features?

Use string to make a straight line where the curb is now curved, and measure the deviation using a ruler or meter stick. How much offset has occurred here? (in mm) _____

What is the purpose of the nearby instrument pole?

Stop 4: The Hayward Plunge

What's the direction of offset in the old wall? Measure the offset in millimeters. _____

If the old wall dates from the Works Public Administration (Depression Era, say 1934), then what is the rate of offset? _____mm/year

Measure the amount of offset in the playground wall (in mm) _____

If the wall was constructed in 1974, what is the rate of movement on the Hayward fault based on the playground wall offset? _____mm/year

Stop 5: Rose & Prospect Sts., Hayward

What features here are related to displacement on the Hayward Fault? Why is the topographic relief associated with the fault zone so much less than that observed near campus?

How much offset has occurred since the marker line was drawn in April 2006? (in mm) _____ offset rate _____
Compare the three rates of offset you calculated.

1971   **1974**   **1979**   **1987**   **1993**

Stop 6: Downtown Hayward

Look up, look down, look in the windows of the abandoned City Hall, and find at least five features that tell you you're in the vicinity of an active, transform fault. Mark them and label them on the attached Google Earth figure.

9

Name _____

Surficial Processes and the Environment

Landslides

Introduction

These exercises examine the nature and causes of several types of landslides. These include slumps, debris slides, rock slides, and rock falls.

Landslides occur when gravity overcomes the stability of a slope, the slope fails, and Earth materials move downward, usually on slip surfaces. In landslides, numerous factors facilitate the work of gravity. Water increases the hydrostatic pressure; it is a lubricant, which decreases the shearing strength of clays and makes them weak; it adds weight to a potential slide area; when it freezes it exerts an expansive force; as snow it adds weight and melt water; and when snow slides it may induce material below to slide. The *clay content* of the potential slide mass makes it more slippery, and clay, when wet, promotes flow. A clay or shale layer is often the layer on which movement occurs. Joints, faults, foliation, and bedding planes, however, provide zones of weakness that also contribute to downslope movement.

Exercise 1: Slumps

Introduction

Slumps are different from other types of landslides. In slumps, portions of a slope slip downward on a spoon-shaped slip surface. These slump blocks show a backward rotation. Large amounts of earth material may be involved, but displacements are small with respect to the size of the block and when compared with other types of slides. The upper part of the slump is well defined by scarp and slip surfaces. The lower portion of the slump mass, however, is distorted and jumbled (Figure 1).

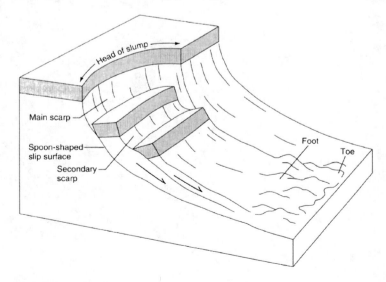

Figure 1. **Block diagram of a slump.**

From *The Lab Book: Problem Solving in Geology, Second Edition,* Sheldon Judson, William E. Bonini, Dallas D. Rhodes, and Lisa A. Rossbacher. Copyright © 2000 by Pearson Education, Inc. Published by Prentice-Hall, Inc. All rights reserved.

Name _____

⊗100'

Figure 2.   An oblique air photo of a slump located along the coast at Point Fermin on the Palos Verdes Peninsula, California. *John S. Shelton*

Name _____

Question Set 1: Point Fermin, California

Figure 2 is an oblique air photo of a slump feature on the coast at Point Fermin on the Palos Verdes Peninsula.

i. Draw lines on the figure along the top of the main scarp and two or three of the minor scarps.

ii. Estimate the maximum displacement in feet along the main scarp. Note elevation in feet marked near top of cliff. Explain how you made this estimation.

iii. Draw a schematic cross section perpendicular to the main scarp through the left center of the scarp to just seaward of the breakers. Label slump features, including scarp, slip surface, and the like, as well as the beach.

iv. How does your section differ from the general pattern of a slump, and why?

v. Does this slump appear to be stabilized for the longer run? If now, why not?

Name _____

Figure 3.   **Slope failure caused by the widening of a railroad right-of-way, Civitella Cesi, Viterbo, Italy.**

Question Set 2: Slope Failure of a Railroad Cut

A railroad is being replaced and the roadbed widened (Figure 3). A backhoe has been used to widen the cut until the slope failure halted the work. The debris from that grading has been left as a ridge yet to be removed.

i. What type of slope failure is this?

ii. Label the graded slope of Figure 3.

iii. Label the scarps of the slope failure and its foot.

iv. What might you expect to happen if construction workers continued to grade the slope as they had on the right side of the photo?

Name _____

Exercise 2:   Debris Slide at Madison Canyon, Montana

Introduction

A magnitude 7.5–7.75 Richter-scale earthquake occurred at 11:37 P.M. on August 17, 1959, at West Yellowstone, Montana, just west of Yellowstone National Park. It triggered a very large and rapid **debris slide** along the Madison River (Figure 4). About 40 million cubic yards of bedrock and soil were involved, traveling at a velocity of greater than 60 miles/hour. The slide traveled about 1,800 feet horizontally and moved some 400 feet up the opposite wall of the canyon above the level of the old channel of the Madison River. Many campers who were bedded down for the night at a campground and along the river were buried. A dam was formed that backed up water to create a lake 6 miles long and 200 feet deep.

Figure 4.   Oblique air photo of the Madison Canyon landslide, Montana, August 26, 1956. View is to the west. *J.R. Stacy, U.S. Gelogical Survey.*

Question Set 3: Madison Canyon Debris Slide, Montana

Figure 4 is an oblique aerial view of the slide. Before the slide, the Madison River was a through-flowing stream in the canyon.

i. What changes resulted from the slide?

ii. What evidence is there in the photo that the slide was of high velocity?

Name _____

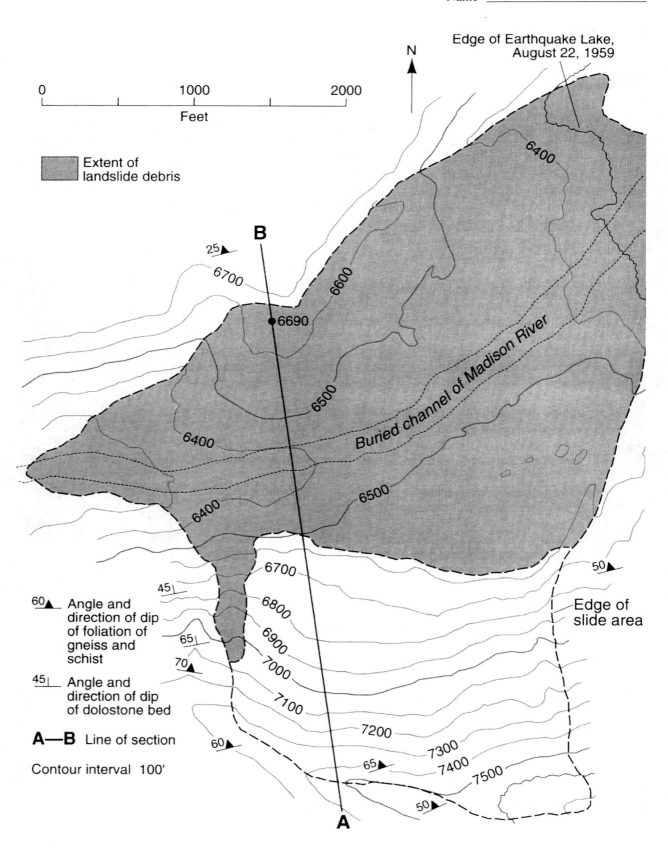

Figure 5. **Topographic map of the Madison Canyon Slide, Montana.** *U.S. Geological Survey.*

Name _____

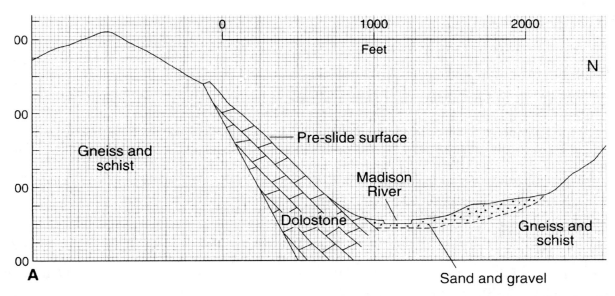

Figure 6.   **Cross section showing pre-slide topography and geology of the Madison Canyon Landslide. See Figure 5 for location.** *Adapted from U.S. Geological Survey.*

Question Set 4: Mapping the Madison Canyon Debris Slide, Montana

i. Referring to Figure 5, note that within the outline of the slide area, the extent of landslide debris is shown in a light gray. Outline in color the area of the slide without fill, that is to say, the area from which the debris has slipped. In addition, highlight each strike-and-dip symbol given on the map for the bedding of the dolostone and the foliation of the gneiss and schist.

ii. Put arrows on the map to indicate the direction of movement of the slide.

iii. Figure 6 is a cross section showing the geology and preslide topography in the Madison Canyon Landslide area. Section A–B is indicated on the topographic map, Figure 5.

    a.   Plot the postslide topography on the profile in Figure 6 using the contour map, Figure 5.

    b.   What is the greatest thickness of landslide debris removed from the mountainside south of the Madison river? _____ feet

    c.   What is the maximum thickness of landslide debris accumulated on the north side of the Madison River? _____ feet

iv. An earthquake triggered the Madison Canyon Landslide, but various preexisting conditions made it possible for the shaking to initiate the landslide. What were they?

Exercise 3:   Rock slide in the Gros Ventre River Valley, Wyoming

Introduction

A **rock slide** of major proportions took place on June 23, 1925, along the south valley wall of the Gros Ventre River valley, east of Jackson Hole, Wyoming. During the movement, detached portions of the sandstone bedrock slid into the valley from the south wall. The debris piled up 350 feet against the north wall to form a natural dam, blocking the river and eventually forming a lake 3 miles long.

The two rock layers most intimately involved in the slide were a sandstone and an underlying clay. The sandstone allows water to percolate slowly through it. The clay is impervious to water. As an old settler who lived along this slope before the slide once said, "If I lay my ear to the ground, I can hear water tricklin' and runnin' underneath. It's runnin' between strata and someday, if we have a wet enough spring, that whole mountain is gonna let loose and slide. Give it a wet enough year and all that rocky strata will just slide right down on the gumbo like a beaver's slickery slide." (Barry Voight, "Lower Gros Ventre Slide, Wyoming," in Barry Voight, ed., *Rockslides and Avalanches,* Vol. 1, p. 116, Elsevier Publishing Co., Amsterdam, 1978)

The fact that there was no break in the dam for nearly two years after the slide had occurred led to the general belief that the dam would hold. In the winter of 1926–27, heavy snows fell in the Gros Ventre Mountains, and a period of rapid melting, together with rain, caused a rapid rise of the lake. On May 18, 1927, the dam was overtopped and rapid erosion of the dam took place, causing a disastrous flood. It wiped out the town of Kelly, population 70, and drowned six or seven people. As it turned out, with prompt action the dam could have been lowered to let water out slowly following the slide, and no lives would have been lost. Thus, although the slide action itself did not result in loss of life, the foot of the slide (the dam) was a life-threatening environmental hazard, unrecognized as such at the time.

Question Set 5: The Gros Ventre Rockslide

Figure 7a is an air photo of the Gros Ventre slide, and Figure 7b is a topographic map of the same area.

i. On the photo and on the figure: Outline in color the area of the slide scar and the slide material. In addition, label the head and the foot of the slide, the dam, and mark in blue the trace of the Gros Ventre River as it passes from the lake, through the dam, and downstream to the west.

ii. Figure 8 is a topographic and geologic cross section of the slide area. The preslide surface is indicated by a dashed line.

   a.   What is the angle of slope of the preslide surface? _____ degrees

   b.   How does it correspond to the bedding beneath? _____

   c.   How do the north slope of the valley and underlying bedding differ from the situation on the south side of the valley?

   d.   There were a number of prehistoric landslides in this area, all occurring on the south side of the Gros Ventre valley. Why?

iii. What are the factors that caused the slide?

Name _____

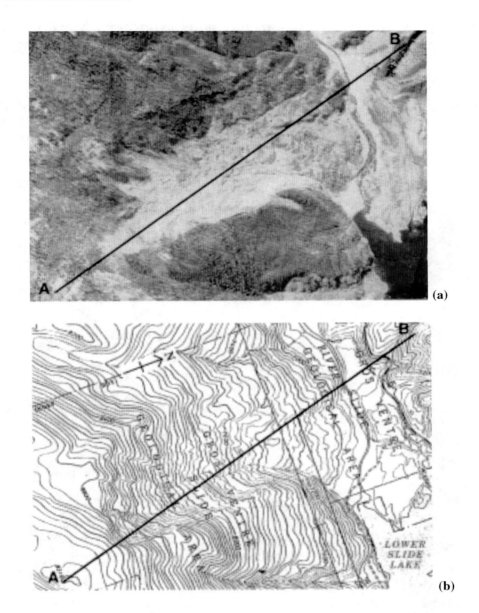

Figure 7.   **(a) Air photo of the Gros Ventre Landslide, Wyoming. (b) Topographic map of the Gros Ventre Landslide.** *U.S. Geological Survey.*

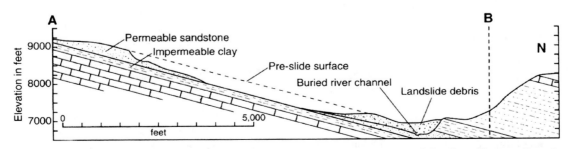

Figure 8.   **Cross-section showing pre- and post-slide topography and geology of the Gros Ventre.** *Based on data from the U.S. Geological Survey.*

Name _____

Exercise 4:   Landslide on the Sherman Glacier, Southern Alaska

Introduction

In this exercise we present two photographs of the Sherman Glacier in southern Alaska taken a year apart. In the interval between the two photos, the Good Friday earthquake (magnitude = 8.6) of March 27, 1964, occurred with an epicenter near Valdez, Alaska, beneath Prince William Sound.

Figure 9.   **The Sherman Glacier as seen on August 26, 1963.** *Austin Post, U.S. Geological Survey.*

Question Set 6: The Sherman Glacier Landslide

i. On Figures 9 and 10 indicate the source of the major landslide.

ii. On the basis of Figure 10 what were some of the characteristics of the main slide?

iii. Indicate on Figure 10 some additional landslides.

Name _____

Figure 10.   **The Sherman Glacier as seen on August 24, 1964.** *Austin Post, U.S. Geological Survey.*

Figure 11.   (a) **The Palisades Cliffs, near Red Lodge, Montana, showing their relation to a house at their base.**
(b) Detail of location of the house at the base of the cliffs in (a).

Exercise 5:   Evaluating a Building Site

Question Set 7: Red Lodge, Montana

Figure 11a shows a house below an outcrop of the Madison Limestone. Figure 11b is a closer view of the house taken from the highway.

i. What evidence suggests that this house has not been placed in an entirely safe location?

Name _____

Figure 12.   **Damage to a tube-tunnel near Buffalo Bill Dam, Shoshone Canyon, Wyoming.**

Exercise 6:   Rock Fall in the Shoshone Canyon, Wyoming

Question Set 8: Shoshone Canyon Rock Fall

Figure 12 is a photo of a concrete tube-tunnel along a cut made in a granite face that allowed tourists to visit the Buffalo Bill Dam, west of Cody, Wyoming. Failure occurred during the winter when no people were present. This access has now been eliminated.

i. Describe this type of failure and suggest how fast it may have moved.

ii. Suggest some feature that caused this failure.

Name _____

Figure 13. **A landslide in the Windgate For-mation along the San Juan River.** *William C. Bradley.*

Figure 14. **A low-angle aerial photo of a landslide in the Pierre Shale along a river in South Dakota.** *D. R. Crandell, U.S. Geological Survey.*

Exercise 7:   Photo Identification of Types of Landslides

Question Set 9: Photo Identification of Landslides

i. a.   What type of landslide is shown in the photo in Figure 13?

    b.   What factors have been involved in this failure?

ii. a.   What type of landslide is shown in the photo in Figure 14?

    b.   What factors were involved in this slope failure?

Name _____

Figure 15.   **Landslide in Carbon County, Idaho.** *John S. Shelton.*

Question Set 10: Photo of a Prehistoric Landslide

Figure 15 is an oblique aerial photo of a prehistoric landslide in Carbon County, Idaho. This landslide is intermediate between a debris slide and a more fluid mud flow.

i. Outline on the photograph the extent of the slide material.

ii. Study the area upslope from the slide and outline the source of the slide material.

10

Shaping Earth's Surface
Running Water and Groundwater

The study of the processes that modify Earth's surface is of major significance to the Earth scientist. By understanding those processes and the features they produce, scientists gain insights into the geologic history of an area and make predictions concerning its future development.

Some of the agents that are responsible for modifying the surface of Earth are running water (Figure 1), groundwater, glacial ice, wind, and volcanic activity. Each produces a unique landscape with characteristic features that can be recognized on topographic maps. This exercise examines several of these agents, the variety of landforms associated with them, and some of the consequences of human interaction with these natural systems.

Objectives

After you have completed this exercise, you should be able to:

1. Sketch, label, and discuss the complete hydrologic cycle.

2. Explain the relation between infiltration and runoff that occurs during a rainfall.

3. Discuss the effect that urbanization has on the runoff and infiltration of an area.

4. Identify on a topographic map the following features that are associated with rivers and valleys: rapids, meanders, floodplain, oxbow lake, and backswamps.

5. Explain the occurrence, fluctuation, use, and misuse of groundwater supplies.

6. Identify on a topographic map the following features associated with karst landscapes: sinkholes, disappearing streams, and solution valleys.

Materials

calculator	hand lens
ruler	

Materials Supplied by Your Instructor

graduated measuring cylinder (100 ml)	coarse sand, fine sand, soil

Figure 1   Mountain stream. (Photo by E.J. Tarbuck)

small funnel	stereoscope
cotton	string
beaker (100 ml)	

Terms

hydrologic cycle	permeability	aquifer
infiltration	hydrograph	karst topography
groundwater	discharge	disappearing
runoff	base level	stream
erosion	meander belt	solution valley
evaporation	zone of saturation	sinkhole
transpiration	water table	cave
porosity	zone of aeration	cavern

From *Applications and Investigations in Earth Science*, Sixth Edition, Edward J. Tarbuck, Frederick K. Lutgens, Kenneth G. Pinzke. Copyright © 2009 by Pearson Education, Inc. Published by Pearson Prentice Hall. All rights reserved.

Introduction

On Earth, the water is constantly being exchanged between the surface and atmosphere. The **hydrologic cycle**, illustrated in Figure 2, describes this continuous movement of water from the oceans to the atmosphere, from the atmosphere to the land, and from the land back to the sea.

A portion of the precipitation that falls on land will soak into the ground via **infiltration** and become **groundwater**. If the rate of rainfall is greater than the surface's ability to absorb it, the additional water flows over the surface and becomes **runoff**. Runoff initially flows in broad sheets; however, it soon becomes confined and is channeled to form streams and rivers. **Erosion** by both groundwater and runoff wears down the land and modifies the shape of Earth's surface. Eventually runoff and groundwater from the continents return to the sea or the atmosphere, continuing the endless cycle.

Examining the Hydrologic Cycle

Figure 2 illustrates Earth's water balance, a quantitative view of the hydrologic cycle. Although the figure correctly implies a uniform exchange of water between Earth's atmosphere and surface on a worldwide basis, factors such as climate, soil type, vegetation, and urbanization often produce local variations.

Use Figure 2 as a reference to answer questions 1–6.

1. On a worldwide basis, more water is evaporated into the atmosphere from the (oceans, land). Circle your answer.

2. Approximately what percent of the total water evaporated into the atmosphere comes from the oceans?

$$\text{Percent from oceans} = \frac{\text{ocean evaporation}}{\text{total evaporation}} \times 100$$

= _____ %

Notice in the figure that more water evaporates from the oceans than is returned directly to them by precipitation.

3. Since sea level is not dropping, what are the other sources of water for the oceans in addition to precipitation?

_____

Over most of Earth, the quantity of precipitation that falls on the land must eventually be accounted for by the sum total of **evaporation**, **transpiration** (the release of water vapor by vegetation), **runoff**, and **infiltration**.

4. Define each of the following four variables.

Evaporation: _____

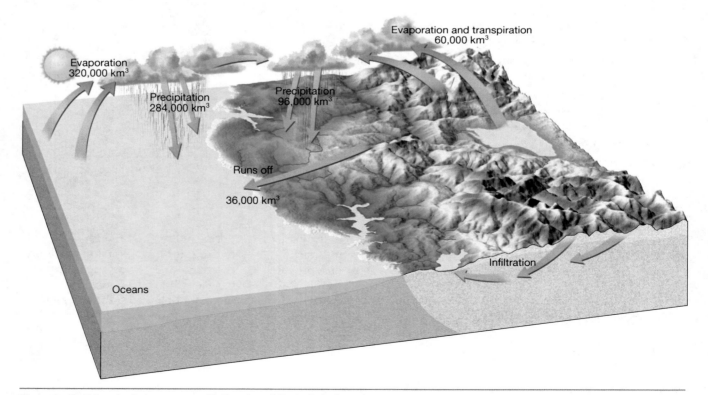

Evaporation and transpiration
60,000 km³

Evaporation
320,000 km³

Precipitation
284,000 km³

Precipitation
96,000 km³

Runs off

36,000 km³

Infiltration

Oceans

Figure 2   Earth's water balance, a quantitative view of the hydrologic cycle.

Transpiration: _____

Runoff: _____

Infiltration: _____

5. On a worldwide basis, about (35, 55, 75) percent of the precipitation that falls on the land becomes runoff. Circle your answer.

6. At high elevations or high latitudes, some of the water that falls on the land does not immediately soak in, run off, evaporate, or transpire. Where is this water being temporarily stored?

_____

_____

Infiltration and Runoff

During a rainfall most of the water that reaches the land surface will infiltrate or run off. The balance between infiltration and runoff is influenced by factors such as the **porosity** and **permeability** of the surface material, slope of the land, intensity of the rainfall, and type and amount of vegetation. After infiltration saturates the land and the ground contains all the water it can hold, runoff will begin to occur on the surface.

7. Describe the difference between the terms *porosity* and *permeability*. Is it possible for a substance to have a high porosity and a low permeability? Why?

_____

_____

_____

_____

Permeability Experiment

To gain a better understanding of how the permeability of various Earth materials affects the flow of groundwater, examine the equipment setup in Figure 3 and conduct the following experiment by completing each of the indicated steps.

Step 1. Obtain the following equipment and materials from your instructor:
  graduated measuring cylinder
  beaker
  small funnel
  piece of cotton
  samples of coarse sand, fine sand, and soil (enough of each to fill the funnel approximately two-thirds full)

Step 2. Place a small wad of cotton in the neck of the funnel.

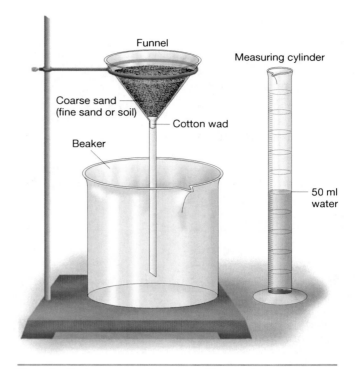

Figure 3 Equipment setup for permeability experiment.

Step 3. Fill the funnel above the cotton about two-thirds full with coarse sand.

Step 4. With the bottom of the funnel placed in the beaker, measure the length of time that it takes for 50 ml of water to drain through the funnel filled with coarse sand. Record the time in the data table, Table 1.

Step 5. Using the measuring cylinder, measure the amount (in milliliters) of water that has drained into the beaker and record the measurement in the data table.

Step 6. Empty and clean the measuring cylinder, funnel, and beaker.

Step 7. Repeat the experiment two additional times, using fine sand and then soil. Record the results of each experiment at the appropriate place in the data table, Table 1. (*Note:* In each case, fill the funnel with the material to the same level that was used for the coarse sand and use the same size wad of cotton.)

Step 8. Clean the glassware and return it to your instructor, along with any unused sand and soil.

Table 1   **Data Table for Permeability Experiment**

	Length of time to drain 50 ml of water through funnel	Milliliters of water drained into beaker
Coarse sand	seconds	ml
Fine sand	seconds	ml
Soil	seconds	ml

8. Questions 8a–8c refer to the permeability experiment.

   a. Of the three materials you tested, the (coarse sand, fine sand, soil) has the greatest permeability. Circle your answer.

   b. Suggest a reason why different amounts of water were recovered in the beaker for each material that was tested.

   _____

   c. Write a brief statement summarizing the results of your permeability experiment.

   _____

   _____

   _____

9. What will be the effect of each of the following conditions on the relation between infiltration and runoff?

   Highly permeable surface material: _____

   _____

   Steep slope: _____

   _____

   Gentle rainfall: _____

   _____

   Dense ground vegetation: _____

   _____

10. What will be the relation between infiltration and runoff in a region with a moderate slope that has a permeable surface material covered with sparse vegetation?

    _____

    _____

    _____

Infiltration and Runoff in Urban Areas

In urban areas much of the land surface has been covered with buildings, concrete, and asphalt. The consequence of covering large areas with impervious materials is to alter the relation between runoff and infiltration of the region.

Figure 4 shows two hypothetical **hydrographs** (plots of stream flow, or runoff, over time) for an area before and after urbanization. The amount of precipitation the area receives is the same after urbanization as before. Runoff is evaluated by measuring the stream **discharge**, which is the volume of water flowing past a given point per unit of time, usually measured in cubic feet per second. Use Figure 4 to answer questions 11–14.

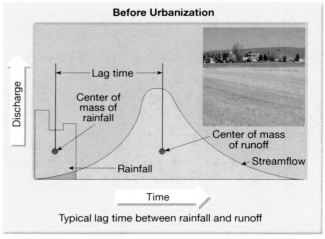

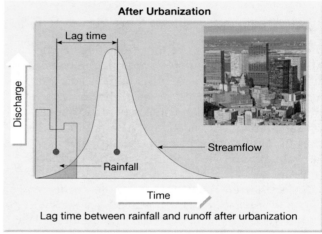

Figure 4   The effect of urbanization on stream flow before urbanization (top) and after urbanization (bottom). (After L. B. Leopold, U.S. Geological Survey Circular 559, 1968)

11. As illustrated in Figure 4, urbanization (increases, decreases) the peak, or maximum, stream flow. Circle your answer.

12. What is the effect that urbanization has on the lag time between the time of the rainfall and the time of peak stream discharge?

    _____

13. Total runoff occurs over a (longer, shorter) period of time in an area that has been urbanized. Circle your answer.

14. Based on what you have learned from the hydrographs, explain why urban areas often experience flash-flooding during intense rainfalls.

    _____

    _____

    _____

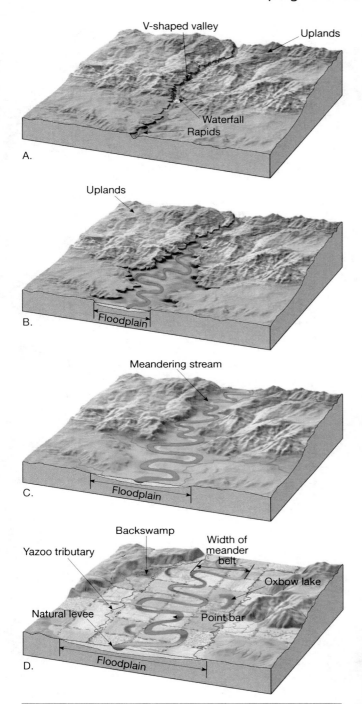

A.

B.

C.

D.

Figure 5 Common features of valleys. **A.** Near the headwaters.
B. and **C.** In the middle. **D.** At the mouth. (After Ward's Natural
Science Establishment, Inc., Rochester, New York)

Running Water

Of all the agents that shape Earth's surface, running
water is the most important. Rivers and streams are responsible for producing a vast array of erosional and
depositional landforms in both humid and arid regions. As illustrated in Figure 5, many of these features
are associated with the *headwaters* of a river, while others typically are found near the *mouth*.

An important factor that governs the flow of a
river is its **base level**. Base level is the lowest point to
which a river or stream may erode. The ultimate base
level is sea level. However, lakes, resistant rocks, and
main rivers often act as temporary, or local, base levels
that control the erosional and depositional activities of
a river for a period of time.

Often the *head*, or source area, of a river is well
above base level. At the headwaters, rivers typically
have steep slopes and downcutting prevails. As the
river deepens its valley it may encounter rocks that are
resistant to erosion and form *rapids* and *waterfalls*. In
arid areas rivers often erode narrow valleys with nearly vertical walls. In humid regions the effect of mass
wasting and slope erosion caused by heavy rainfall
produce typical V-shaped valleys (Figure 5A).

In humid regions downstream from the headwaters, the gradient or slope of a river decreases while its
discharge increases because of the additional water
being added by tributaries. As the level of the channel
begins to approach base level, the river's energy is directed from side to side and the channel begins to follow a sinuous path, or *meanders* (Figure 6). Lateral
erosion by the meandering river widens the valley
floor and a *floodplain* begins to form (Figures 5B and
5C).

Near the mouth of a river where the channel is
nearly at base level, maximum discharge occurs and
meandering often becomes very pronounced. Wide-
spread lateral erosion by the meandering river produces a floodplain that is often several times wider
than the river's *meander belt*. Features such as *oxbow
lakes, natural levees, backswamps* or *marshes*, and *yazoo
tributaries* commonly develop on broad floodplains
(Figure 5D).

Figure 6 This high-attitude image shows incised meanders of the
Delores River in western Colorado. (Courtesy of USDA–ASCS)

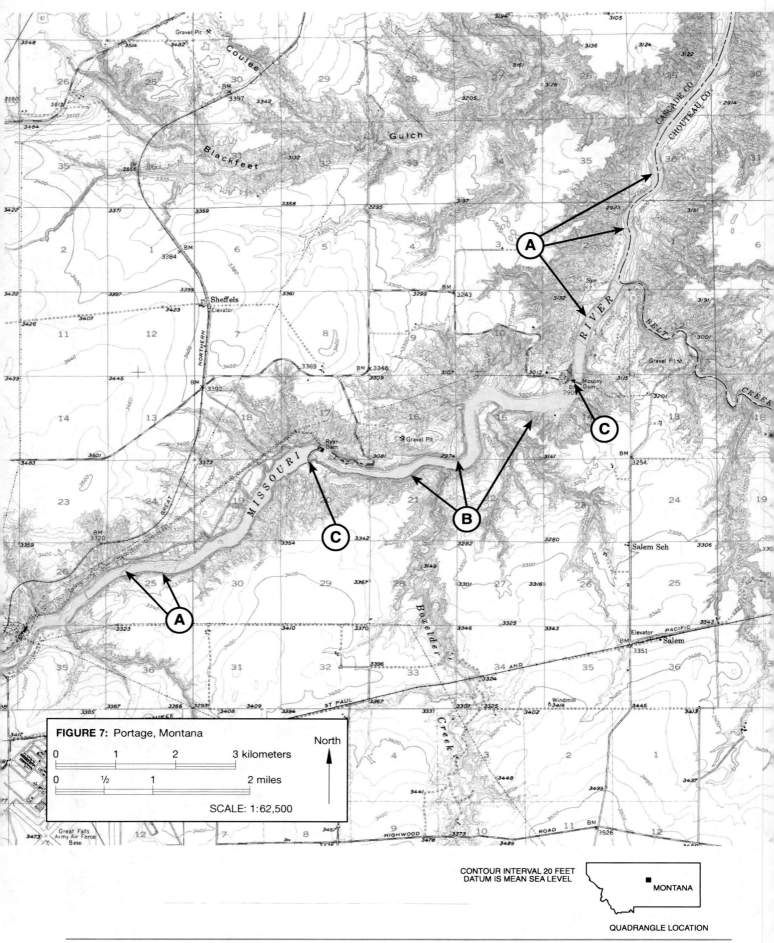

Figure 7 Portion of the Portage, Montana, topographic map. (Map source: United States Department of the Interior, Geological Survey)

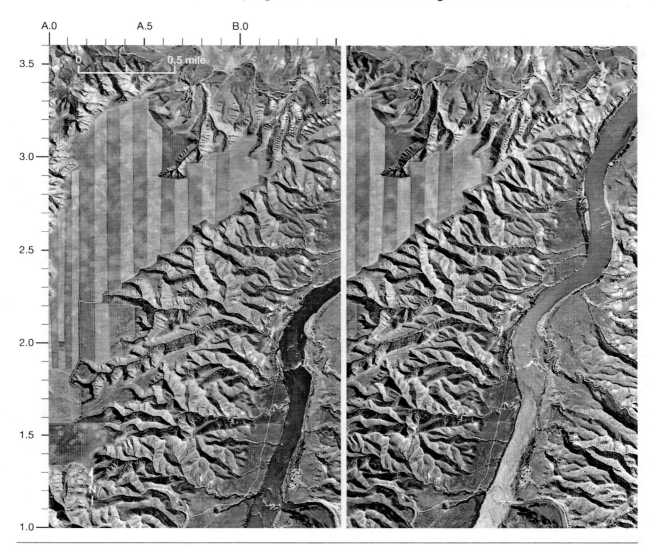

Figure 8   Stereogram of the Missouri River, vicinity of Portage, Montana. (Courtesy of U.S. Geological Survey)

Questions 15–25 refer to the Portage, Montana, topographic map, Figure 7, and stereogram of a portion of the same region, Figure 8. On the map, notice the rapids indicated by A and the steep-sided valley walls of the Missouri River indicated by B.

15. Compare the aerial photograph to the map. Then, on the topographic map, outline the area that is shown in the photo.

16. Use the map to determine the approximate total *relief* (vertical distance between the lowest and highest points of the area represented).

    Highest elevation (_____ ft) – lowest elevation (_____ ft) = total relief (_____ ft).

17. On Figure 9, draw a north–south topographic profile through the center of the map along a line from north of Blackfeet Gulch to south of the Missouri River. Indicate the appropriate elevations on the vertical axis of the profile. Label

Blackfeet Gulch and the Missouri River on the profile.

18. Label the upland areas between stream valleys on the topographic profile in Figure 9 with the word "upland."

19. The upland areas are (broad and flat, narrow ridges). Circle your answer.

20. Approximately what percentage of the area shown on the map is stream valley and what percentage upland?

    Stream valley: _____ %

    Upland: _____ %

21. Approximately how deep would the Missouri River have to erode to reach ultimate base level?

    _____ ft

Figure 9 North–south topographic profile through the center of the Portage, Montana, map.

22. It appears that the Missouri River and its tributaries are, for the most part, actively (eroding, depositing) in the area. Circle your answer.

23. With increasing time, as the tributaries erode and lengthen their courses near the headwaters, what will happen to the upland areas?

_____

_____

Notice the dams located along the Missouri River at C.

24. What effect have the dams had on the width of the river, upriver from their locations?

_____

_____

25. Assuming that climate, base level, and other factors remain unchanged, how might the area look millions of years from now?

_____

_____

Questions 26–31 refer to the Angelica, New York, topographic map, Figure 10.

26. What is the approximate total relief shown on the map?

_____ feet of total relief

27. Draw an arrow on the map indicating the direction that the main river, the Genesee, is flowing. (*Hint:* Use the elevations of the contour lines on the floodplain to determine your answer.)

28. What is the approximate *gradient* (the slope of a river; generally measured in feet per mile) of the Genesee River?

Average gradient = _____ ft/mile

29. The Genesee River (follows a straight course, meanders from valley wall to valley wall). Circle your answer.

30. Most of the areas separating the valleys on the Angelica map are (very broad and flat, relatively narrow ridges). Circle your answer.

31. Assume that erosion continues in the region without interruption. How might the appearance of the area change over a span of millions of years?

_____

_____

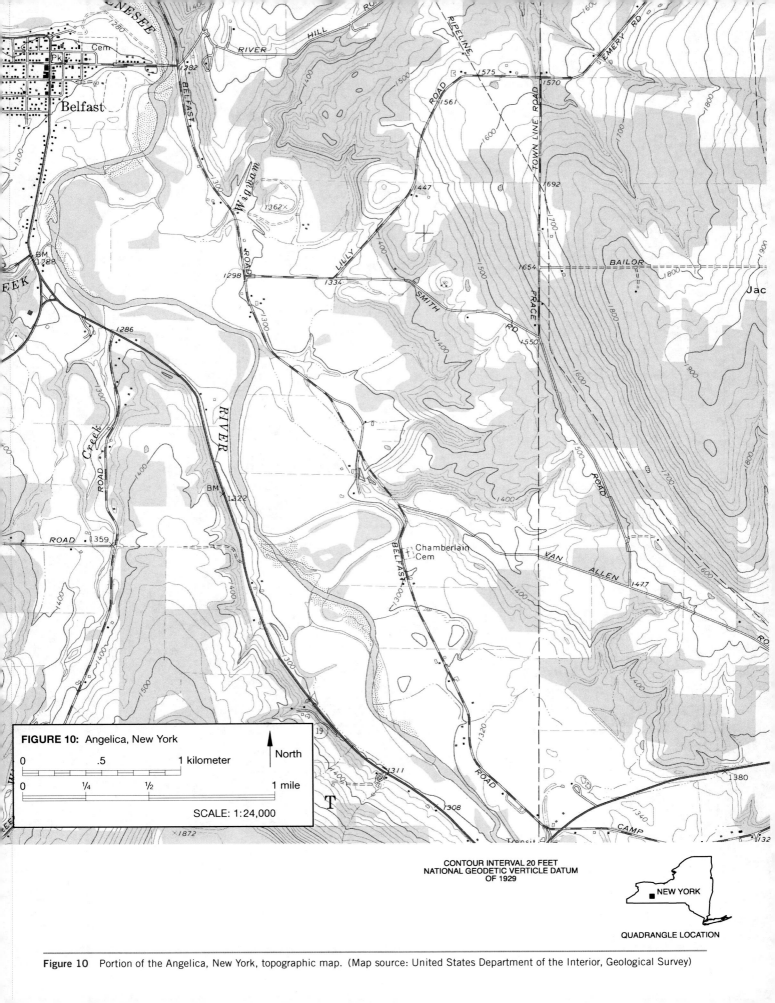

FIGURE 10: Angelica, New York

0   .5   1 kilometer

↑ North

0   ¼   ½   1 mile

SCALE: 1:24,000

CONTOUR INTERVAL 20 FEET
NATIONAL GEODETIC VERTICLE DATUM
OF 1929

NEW YORK

QUADRANGLE LOCATION

Figure 10   Portion of the Angelica, New York, topographic map. (Map source: United States Department of the Interior, Geological Survey)

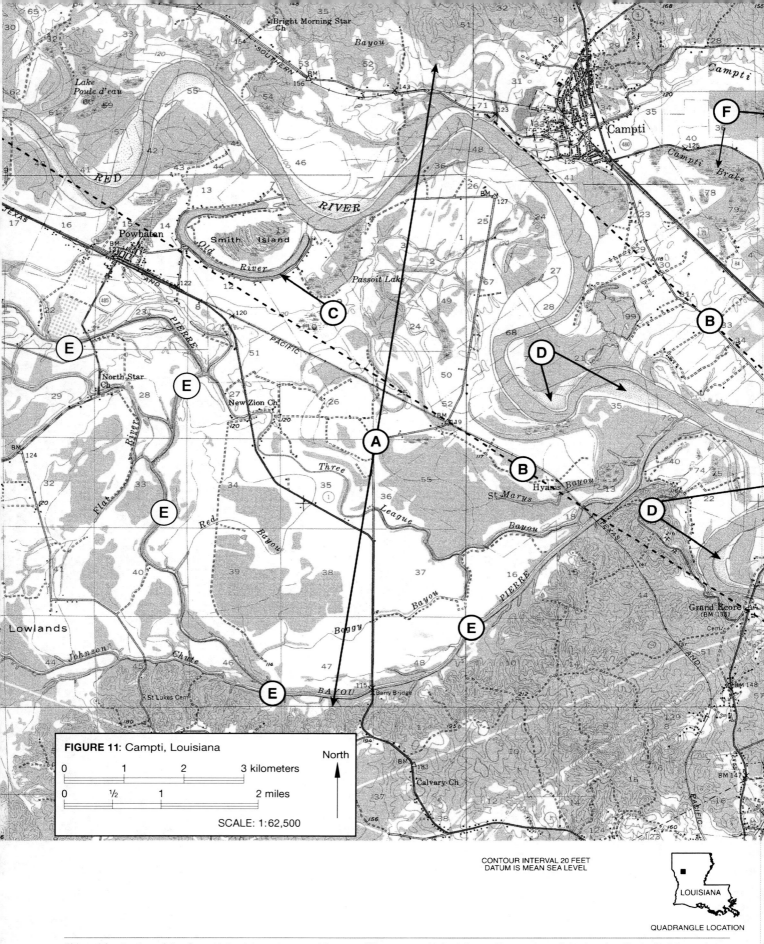

Figure 11 Portion of the Campti, Louisiana, topographic map. (Map source: United States Department of the Interior, Geological Survey)

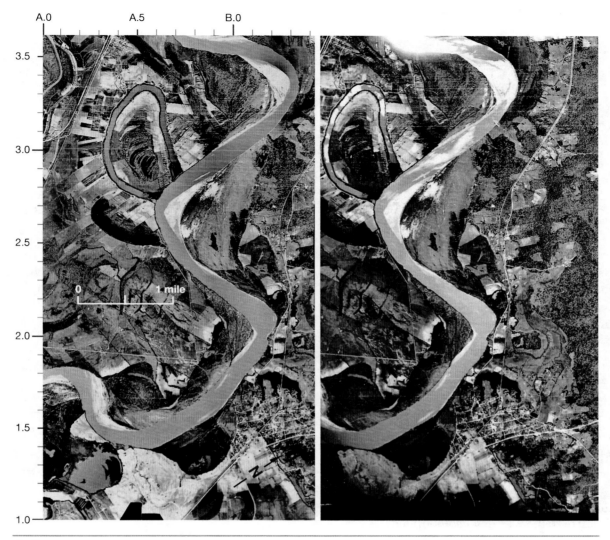

Figure 12   Stereogram of the Campti, Louisiana, area. (Courtesy of U.S. Geological Survey)

Questions 32–39 refer to the Campti, Louisiana, topographic map, Figure 11, and stereogram of the same area, Figure 12. On the map, A indicates the width of the floodplain of the Red River and the dashed lines, B, mark the two sides of the meander belt of the river.

32. Approximately what percentage of the map area is floodplain?

    Floodplain = _____ % of the map area

33. In Figure 13, draw a north–south topographic profile along a line from the south edge of the City of Campti to south of Bayou Pierre. Indicate the appropriate elevations on the vertical axis of the profile. Label the floodplain area and Bayou Pierre on the sketch.

34. Approximately how many feet is the floodplain above ultimate base level?

    _____ feet above ultimate base level

35. Using Figure 5 as a reference, identify the type of feature found at each of the following lettered positions on the map. Also, write a brief statement describing how each feature forms.

    Letter C (in particular, *Old River*): _____

    _____

    Letter D: _____

    _____

    Letter E: _____

    _____

    Letter F: _____

    _____

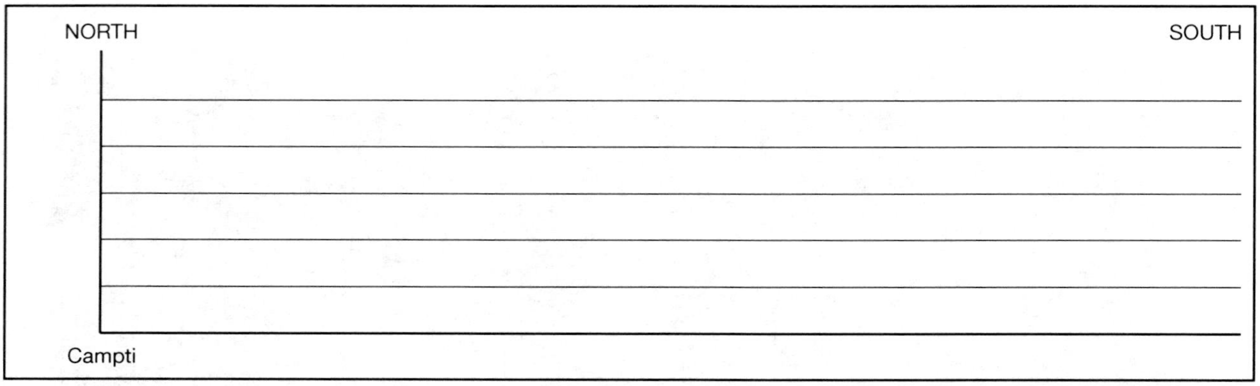

NORTH   SOUTH

Campti

Figure 13   North–south topographic profile of the Campti map.

36. Identify and label examples of a point bar, cut-bank, and an oxbow lake on the stereogram.

37. Write a statement that compares the width of the meander belt of the Red River to the width of its floodplain.

_____

_____

38. (Downcutting, Lateral erosion) is the dominant activity of the Red River. Circle your answer.

39. Assuming that erosion by the Red River continues without interruption, what will eventually happen to the width of its floodplain?

_____

_____

        Answer questions 40–42 by comparing the Portage, Angelica, and Campti topographic maps.

40. On which of the three maps is the gradient of the main river the steepest?

_____

41. Which of the three areas has the greatest total relief (vertical distance between the lowest and highest elevations)?

_____

42. Choosing from the three topographic maps, write the name of the map that is best described by each of the following statements.

Primarily floodplain: _____

_____

River valleys separated by broad, relatively flat upland areas: _____

_____

Most of the area consists of steep slopes:

_____

Greatest number of streams and tributaries:

_____

Poorly drained lowland area with marshes and swamps: _____

_____

Active downcutting by rivers and streams:

_____

Surface nearest to base level: _____

_____

Groundwater

As a resource, groundwater supplies much of our water needs for consumption, irrigation, and industry. On the other hand, as a hazard, groundwater can damage building foundations and aid the movement of materials during landslides and mudflows. In many areas, overuse and contamination of this valuable resource threaten the supply. One of the most serious problems faced by many localities is land subsidence caused by groundwater withdrawal.

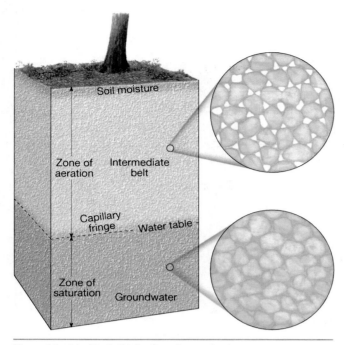

Figure 14   Idealized distribution of groundwater.

Water Beneath the Surface

Groundwater is water that has soaked into Earth's surface and occupies all the pore spaces in the soil and bedrock in a zone called the **zone of saturation**. The upper surface of this saturated zone is called the **water table**. Above the water table in the **zone of aeration**, the pore spaces of the materials are unsaturated and mainly filled with air. (Figure 14)

Figure 15 illustrates a profile through the subsurface of a hypothetical area. Use Figures 14 and 15 to answer questions 43–50.

43. Label the zone of saturation, zone of aeration, and water table on Figure 15.

44. Describe the shape of the water table in relation to the shape of the land surface.

   _____

45. What is the relation of the surface of the water in the stream to the water table?

   _____

46. What is the lowered surface in the water table around the well called? What has caused the lowering of the surface of the water table around the well? What will make it larger or smaller?

   _____

   _____

   _____

47. At point *A* on Figure 15, sketch a small, impermeable pocket of clay that intersects the valley wall.

48. Describe what will happen to water that infiltrates to the depth of the clay pocket at point *A*.

   _____

   _____

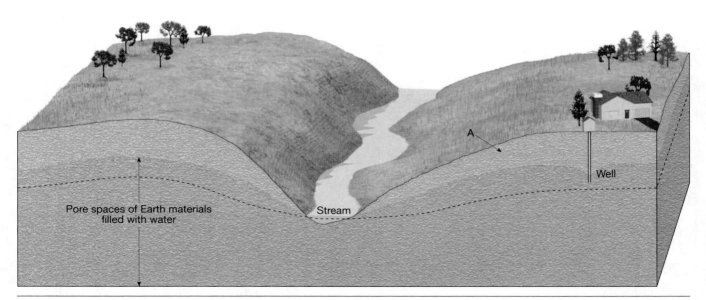

Figure 15   Earth's subsurface showing saturated and unsaturated materials.

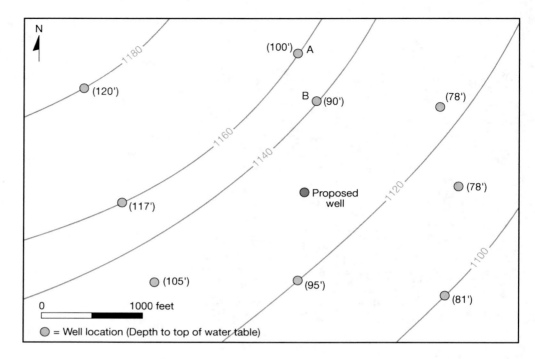

Figure 16 Hypothetical topographic map showing the location of several water walls.

The dashed line in Figure 15 represents the level of the water table during the dry season when infiltration is no longer replenishing the groundwater.

49. What is the consequence of the lower elevation of the water table during the dry season on the operation of the well? How might the problem have been avoided?

_____

_____

50. What are two main sources of pollutants that can contaminate groundwater supplies?

_____

_____

Groundwater Movement

Figure 16 is a hypothetical topographic map showing the location of several water wells. The numbers in parentheses indicate the depth of the water table below the surface in each well.

Questions 51–53 refer to Figure 16.

51. Begin by calculating the elevation of the water table at each indicated well location. Then, using a colored pencil, draw smooth 10-foot contours that illustrate the slope of the water table in the area. Using a different colored pencil, draw arrow(s) on

the map that indicate the direction of the slope of the water table.

a. What is the average amount of slope of the water table in the area? Toward which direction does the water table slope?

_____

_____

b. Referring to the site of the proposed water well, at approximately what depth below the surface should the well drill the water table?

_____

52. Assume that a dye was put into well A at 1 PM on May 10, 1990, and detected in well B at 8 AM on October 1, 1998. What was the velocity of the groundwater movement between the two wells in centimeters per day?

_____

_____

53. Use a different colored pencil to draw dashed 10-ft contour lines on the map that illustrate the configuration of the water table after well B was pumped for a sufficient period of time to lower the water table 22 feet at its location. Assume that an area within a 500-foot radius of well B was affected by the pumping.

The Problem of Ground Subsidence

As the demand for freshwater increases, surface subsidence caused by the withdrawal of groundwater from **aquifers** presents a serious problem for many areas. Several major urban areas such as Las Vegas, Houston-Galveston, Mexico City, and the Central Valley of California are experiencing subsidence caused by over-pumping wells (Figure 17). In Mexico City alone, compaction of the subsurface material resulting from the reduction of fluid pressure as the water table is lowered has caused as much as seven meters of subsidence. Fortunately, in many areas an increased reliance on surface water and replenishing the groundwater supply has slowed the trend.

A classic example of land subsidence caused from groundwater withdrawal is in the Santa Clara Valley, which borders the southern part of San Francisco Bay in California. The graph presented in Figure 18 illustrates the relation between ground subsidence in the valley and the level of water in a well in the same area.

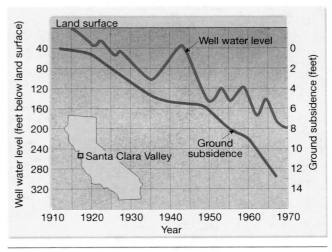

Figure 18   Ground subsidence and water level in a well in the Santa Clara Valley, California. (Data courtesy of U.S. Geological Survey)

Figure 17   The marks on this utility pole indicate the level of the surrounding land in preceding years. Between 1925 and 1977 this part of the San Joaquin Valley, CA subsided almost 9 meters because of the withdrawal of groundwater and the resulting compaction of sediments. (Photo courtesy of U.S. Geological Survey)

Questions 54–58 refer to Figure 18.

54. What is the general relation between the ground subsidence and level of water in the well illustrated on the graph?

_____

_____

55. What was the total ground subsidence and total drop in the level of water in the well during the period shown on the graph?

Total ground subsidence = _____ ft

Total drop in well level = _____ ft

56. During the period shown on the graph, on an average, about (1 ft, 5 ft, 10 ft) of land subsidence occurred with each 20-ft decrease in the level of water in the well. Circle your answer.

57. The ground subsidence that took place during the twenty years before 1950 was (less, greater) than the subsidence that took place between 1950 and 1970. Circle your answer.

58. Notice that minimal subsidence took place between 1935 and 1950. After referring to the well water level during the same period of time, suggest a possible reason for the reduced rate of subsidence between 1935 and 1950.

_____

_____

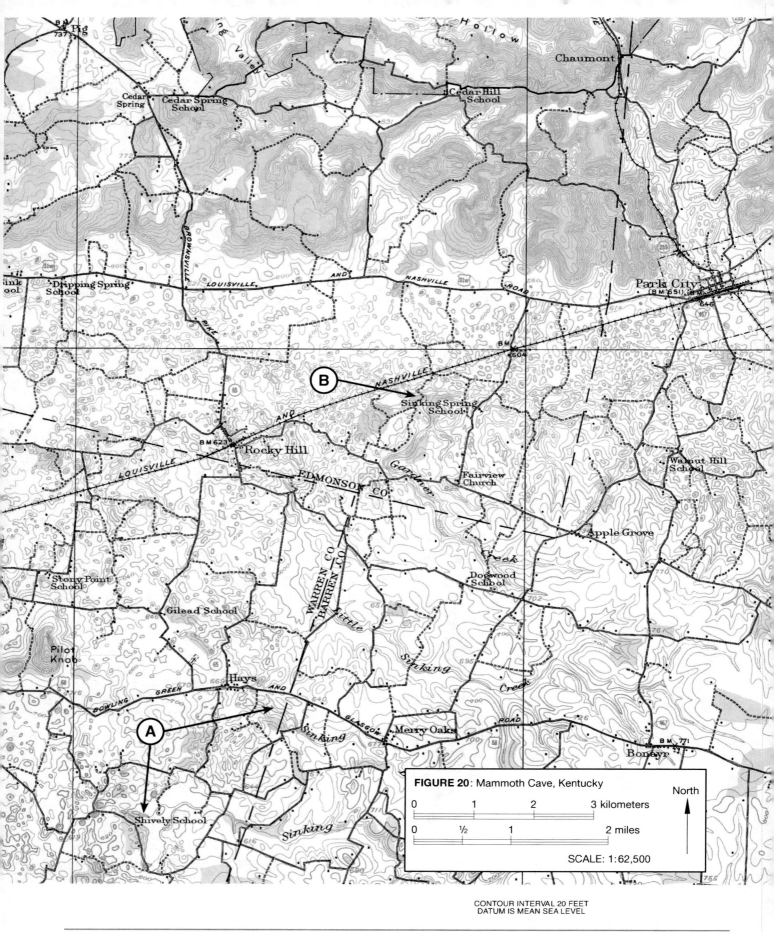

Figure 20 Portion of the Mammoth Cave, Kentucky, topographic map. (Map source: United States Department of the Interior, Geological Survey)

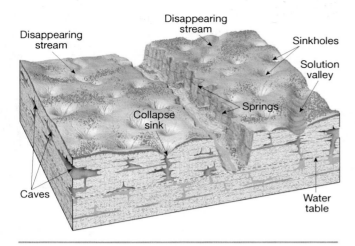

Figure 19 Generalized features of an advanced stage of karst topography.

Examining a Karst Landscape

Landscapes that are dominated by features that form from groundwater dissolving the underlying rock are said to exhibit **karst topography** (Figure 19). On the surface, karst topography is characterized by irregular terrain, springs, **disappearing streams**, **solution valleys**, and depressions called **sinkholes** (Figure 19). Beneath the surface, dissolution of soluble rock may result in **caves** and **caverns**.

One of the classic karst regions in the United States is the Mammoth Cave, Kentucky, area. Locate and examine the Mammoth Cave, Kentucky, topographic map, Figure 20. An insoluble sandstone layer is the surface rock that forms the upland area in the northern quarter of the map. Underneath the sandstone layer is a soluble limestone. Erosion has removed all the sandstone in the southern three fourths of the map and exposed the limestone. On the limestone surface, numerous sinkholes, indicated by closed contour lines with hachures, are present, as well as several disappearing streams (letter A).

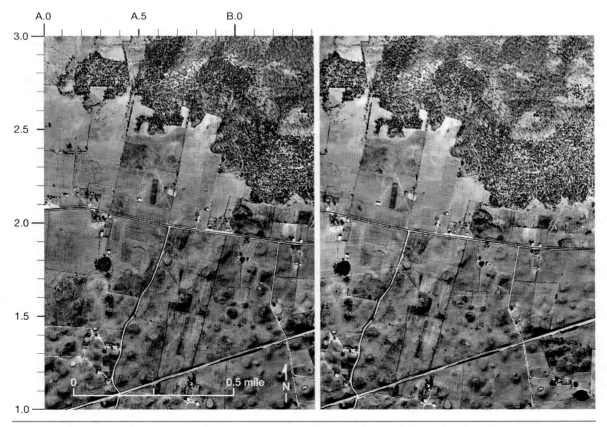

Figure 21 Stereogram of the Mammoth Cave, Kentucky, area. (Courtesy of the U.S. Geological Survey)

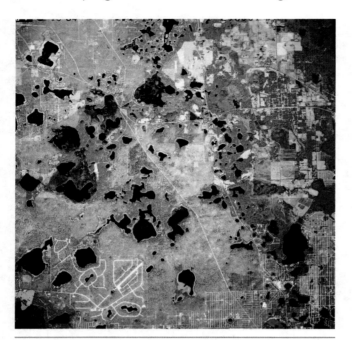

Figure 22 This high-altitude infrared image shows an area of karst topography in central Florida. The numerous lakes occupy sinkholes. (Courtesy of USDA–ASCS)

Use the Mammoth Cave topographic map, Figure 20, the stereogram of the same area, Figure 21, and Figure 22 to answer questions 59–63.

59. On the topographic map, outline the area that is shown on the stereogram.

60. What does the absence of water in the majority of sinkholes indicate about the depth of the water table in the area?

_____

61. Examine both the stereogram and map. Then describe the difference in appearance between the northern quarter and southern three-fourths of the mapped area.

_____

_____

_____

_____

62. Describe what is happening to Gardner Creek in the area indicated with the letter B on the map.

_____

63. List two ways that sinkholes commonly form.

a. _____

b. _____

Running Water and Groundwater on the Internet

Apply the concepts from this exercise to investigate the hydrology of a river and the groundwater resources in your home state by completing the corresponding on-line activity on the *Applications & Investigations in Earth Science* website at http://prenhall.com/earthsciencelab

Shaping Earth's Surface
Running Water and Groundwater

Date Due: _____

Name: _____

Date: _____

Class: _____

After you have finished this exercise, complete the following questions. You may have to refer to the exercise for assistance or to locate specific answers. Be prepared to submit this summary/report to your instructor at the designated time.

1. Write a statement that describes the movement of water through the hydrologic cycle, citing several of the processes that are involved.

_____

_____

_____

2. Assume you are assigned a project to determine the quantity of infiltration that takes place in an area. What are the variables you must measure or know before you can arrive at your answer?

_____

_____

3. Write a brief paragraph summarizing the results of your permeability experiment in question 8 of the exercise.

_____

_____

_____

4. Describe the effects that urbanization has on the stream flow of a region.

_____

Figure 23   River and valley features. (Photo by Michael Collier)

5. On Figure 23, identify and label as many features of the river and valley as possible. Write a brief paragraph describing the area and its relation to base level.

_____

_____

_____

_____

_____

159

6. Refer to the proportion of water that either infiltrates or runs off. Why does a soil-covered hillside with sparse vegetation often experience severe soil erosion? What are some soil conservation methods that could be used to reduce the erosion?

_____

_____

_____

7. Name and describe two features you would expect to find on the floodplain of a widely meandering river near its mouth.

Feature   Description

_____   _____

_____   _____

8. Assume you have decided to drill a water well. What are at least two factors concerning the water table and zone of saturation that should be considered prior to drilling?

_____

_____

9. What is the average slope of the water table illustrated on Figure 16?

_____

10. What was the velocity of the groundwater movement between wells A and B in Figure 16?

_____

11. How might a rapidly growing urban area that relies on groundwater as a freshwater source avoid the problem of land subsidence from groundwater withdrawal?

_____

_____

12. Name and describe two features you would expect to find in a region with karst topography.

Feature   Description

_____   _____

_____   _____

11

Coastal Processes, Landforms, Hazards, and Risks

•CONTRIBUTING AUTHORS•

James G. Titus • *U.S. Environmental Protection Agency*

Donald W. Watson • *Slippery Rock University*

OBJECTIVES

A. Identify and interpret natural shoreline landforms.

B. Distinguish between emergent and submergent shorelines.

C. Know the common types of artificial structures that are used to modify shorelines and understand their effects on coastal environments.

D. Be aware of the probability of global sea-level rise and the coastal hazards and increased risks that this sea-level rise may cause.

MATERIALS

Pencils, eraser, ruler, set of colored pencils, and pocket stereoscope.

INTRODUCTION

The shorelines of lakes and oceans are among the most rapidly changing parts of the Earth's surface. All coastlines are subject to *erosion* (wearing away) by waves. A coastline comprised of loose sediment can be eroded easily and rapidly. A coastline composed of dense bedrock or plastic-like mud erodes much more slowly.

Several factors determine the characteristic landforms of shorelines. They include the shape of the shoreline, the materials that comprise the shoreline (rock, plastic mud, loose sediment, concrete), the source and supply of sediments, the direction that currents move along the shoreline, and the effects of major storms.

Most coastlines also are affected by changes in mean (average) sea level:

- A *rising* sea level creates a **submergent coastline**—one that is flooding and receding (*retrogradational*). Sea level rise is caused either by the water level actually rising (called *transgression*), or by the land getting lower (called *subsidence*).

- A *falling* sea level creates an **emergent coastline**—one that is being elevated above sea level and building out into the water (*progradational*). Sea level fall is caused either by the water level actually falling (called *regression*), or by rising of the land (called *uplift*).

Submergent coastlines may display some emergent features, and vice versa. For example, the Louisiana coastline is submergent, enough so that dikes and levees have been built to keep the ocean from flooding New Orleans. However, the Mississippi Delta is progradational—building out into the water—a feature of most emergent coastlines. It is progradational because of the vast supply of sediment being carried there and deposited by the Mississippi River.

Thus, *sediment supply* is a major factor in determining whether a coastline is progradational or retrogradational, regardless of vertical changes of land level or water level.

From *Laboratory Manual in Physical Geology*, Eighth Edition, American Geological Institute, National Association of Geoscience Teachers, Richard M. Busch, Dennis Tasa.

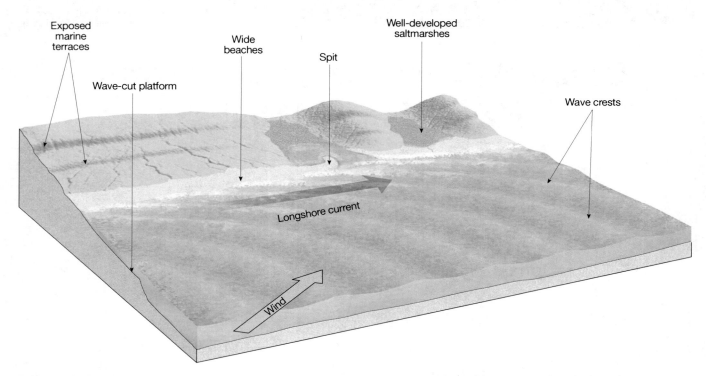

FIGURE 1 *Emergent* coastline features. An emergent coastline is caused by sea-level lowering, the land rising, or both. Emergence causes tidal flats and coastal wetlands to expand, wave-cut terraces are exposed to view, deltas prograde at faster rates, and wide stable beaches develop.

Sediment transport and the effects of major storms also are very important agents of shoreline change. A single storm can completely change the form of a coastline.

Figures 1 and 2 illustrate some features of *emergent* and *submergent* shorelines. Study these features and their definitions below.

- **Barrier island**—a long, narrow island that parallels the mainland coastline and is separated from the mainland by a lagoon, tidal flat, or salt marsh.

- **Beach**—a gently sloping deposit of sand or gravel along the edge of a shoreline.

- **Berm crest**—the highest part of a beach; it separates the *foreshore* (seaward part of the shoreline) from the *backshore* (landward part of the shoreline).

- **Washover fan**—a fan-shaped deposit of sand or gravel transported and deposited landward of the beach during a storm or very high tide.

- **Estuary**—a river valley flooded by a rise in the level of an ocean or lake. (A flooded glacial valley is called a *fjord*.)

- **Longshore current**—a water current in the *surf zone* (zone where waves break). It flows slowly parallel to shoreline, driven by waves that were caused by wind.

- **Delta**—a sediment deposit at the mouth of a river where it enters an ocean or lake.

- **Headland**—projection of land that extends into an ocean or lake and generally has cliffs along its water boundary.

- **Spit**—a sand bar extending from the end of a beach into the mouth of an adjacent bay.

- **Tidal flat**—muddy or sandy area that is covered with water at high tide and exposed at low tide.

- **Saltmarsh**—a marsh that is flooded by ocean water at high tide.

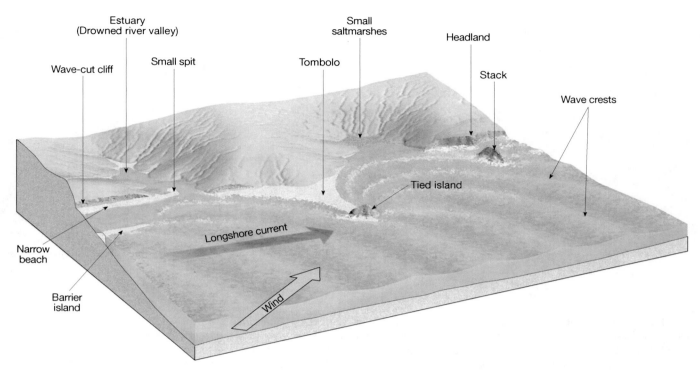

FIGURE 2 *Submergent* (drowning) coastline features. A submergent coastline is caused by sea-level rising (transgression), sinking of the land, or both. As the land is flooded, the waves cut cliffs, valleys are flooded to form estuaries, wetlands are submerged, deep bays develop, beaches narrow, and islands are created.

- **Wave-cut cliff** (or *sea cliff*)—seaward-facing cliff along a steep shoreline, produced by wave erosion.

- **Wave-cut platform**—a bench or shelf at sea level (or lake level) along a steep shore, and formed by wave erosion.

- **Marine terrace**—an elevated platform that is bounded on its seaward side by a cliff or steep slope (and formed when a wave-cut platform is elevated by uplift or regression).

- **Stack**—an isolated rocky island near a headland cliff.

- **Tombolo**—a sand bar that connects an island with the mainland or another island.

- **Tied island**—an island connected to the mainland or another island by a tombolo.

Humans build several common types of coastal structures in order to protect harbors, build up sandy beaches, or extend the shoreline. Study these four kinds of structures and their effects both in Figure 3 and below.

- **Sea wall**—an embankment of boulders, reinforced concrete, or other material constructed against a shoreline to prevent erosion by waves and currents.

- **Breakwater**—an offshore wall constructed parallel to a shoreline to break waves. The longshore current is halted behind such walls, so the sand accumulates there and the beach widens. Where the breakwater is used to protect a harbor from currents and waves, sand often collects behind the breakwater and may have to be dredged.

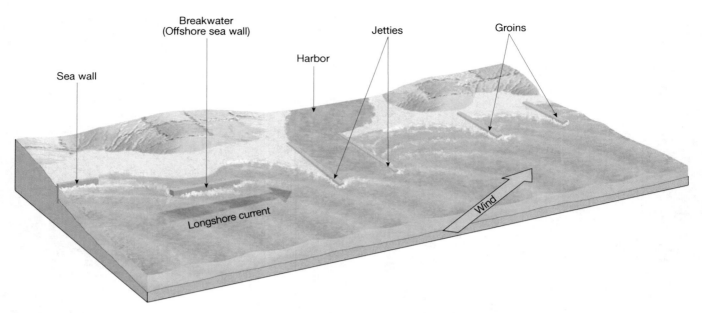

FIGURE 3   Coastal structures—sea walls, breakwaters, groins, and jetties. **Sea walls** are constructed along the shore to stop erosion of the shore or extend the shoreline (as sediment is used to fill in behind them). **Breakwaters** are a type of offshore sea wall constructed parallel to shoreline. The breakwaters stop waves from reaching the beach, so the longshore drift is broken and sand accumulates behind them (instead of being carried down shore with the longshore current). **Groins** are short walls constructed perpendicular to shore. They trap sand on the side from which the longshore current is carrying sand against them. **Jetties** are long walls constructed at entrances to harbors to keep waves from entering the harbors. However, they also trap sand just like groins.

- **Groin** (or *groyne*)—a short wall constructed perpendicular to shoreline in order to trap sand and make or build up a beach. Sand accumulates on the up-current side of the groin in relation to the longshore current.

- **Jetties**—long walls extending from shore at the mouths of harbors and used to protect the harbor entrance from filling with sand or being eroded by waves and currents. Jetties are usually constructed of boulders and in pairs (one on each side of a harbor or inlet).

PART A: DYNAMIC NATURAL COASTLINES

Refer to the Space Shuttle photograph of the Po Delta, Italy (Figure 4). The city of Adria, on the Po River in northern Italy, was a thriving seaport

during Etruscan times (600 B.C.). Adria had such fame as to give its name to the Adriatic Sea, the gulf into which the Po River flows. Over the years, the Po River has deposited sediment at its mouth in the Po Delta. Because of the Po Delta's progradation, Adria is no longer located on the shoreline of the Adriatic Sea. The modern shoreline is far downstream from Adria.

Questions

1. What has been the average annual rate of Po Delta progradation in centimeters per year (cm/yr) since Adria was a thriving seaport on the coastline of the Adriatic Sea?

2. Based on the average annual rate calculated in Question 1, how many centimeters would the Po Delta prograde during the lifetime of someone who lived to be 60 years old?

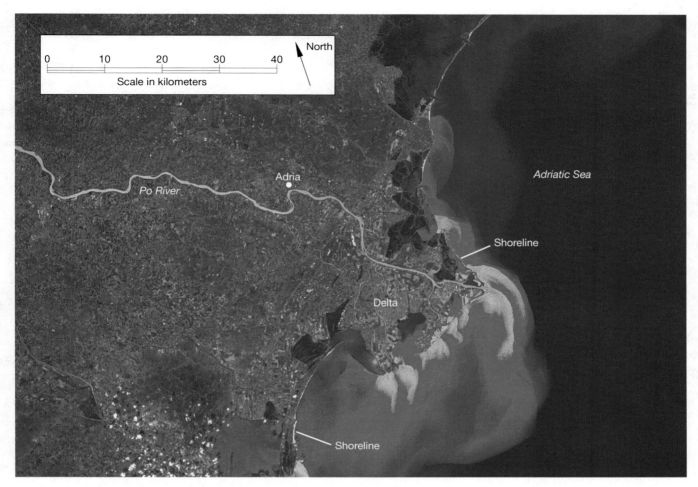

FIGURE 4   Space Shuttle photograph of the Po Delta region, northern Italy.
(Courtesy of NASA)

Refer to the Oceanside, California, quadrangle (Figure 5) and complete Questions 3 and 4.

3. If you climb inland from the Pacific Ocean at South Oceanside to Fire Mountain, you will cross a series of relatively flat surfaces located at successively higher elevations and separated by steep hills or cliffs. All together, they resemble a sort of giant staircase.

   a. About how many of these coastal features are there?

   b. What are the approximate elevations of the flat surfaces, from lowest to highest?

   c. What are these coastal features called, and what is their probable origin?

4. Is this a coastline of emergence or of submergence? Why?

Refer to the Point Reyes, California, quadrangle (Figure 6). Point Reyes is a subtriangular landmass bounded on the west by the Pacific Ocean, on the south by Drakes Bay, and on the east by the San Andreas Fault. The fault runs along Sir Francis Drake Road in the northeast corner of the map.

5. Which area is *more* resistant to wave erosion: Point Reyes or Point Reyes Beach? Why?

6. How did Drakes Estero (Spanish: "estuary") form?

7. What is the direction of longshore drift in Drakes Bay? How can you tell?

8. If a groin was constructed from Limantour Spit, at the "n" in Limantour, then on what side of the groin would sand accumulate (east or west)? Why?

9. Is this a coastline of emergence or submergence? Explain.

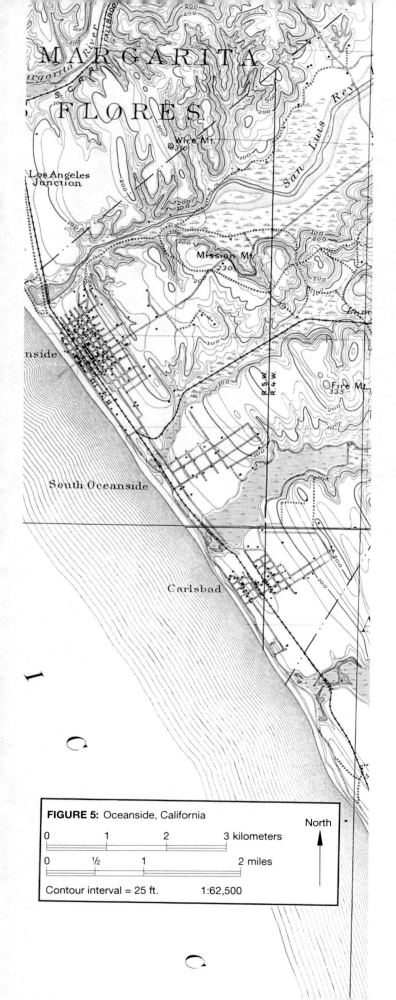

Refer to the map and photographs of Saint Catherines Island, Georgia (Figure 7). Note that on the east-central portion of the island there is a large area of salt-marsh mud. Living saltmarsh plants are present there, as shown on the right (west) in Figures 7A and B. Also, note the linear sandy beach in Figures 7A and B, bounded on its seaward side (left) by another strip of saltmarsh mud. However, all of the living, surficial saltmarsh plants and animals have been stripped from this area. This is called **relict** saltmarsh mud (mud remaining from an ancient saltmarsh).

10. What type of sediment is probably present beneath the beach sands in Figures 7A and B?

11. Explain how you think the beach sands became located landward of the relict saltmarsh mud.

12. Portions of the living saltmarsh (wetland) in Figure 7C recently have been buried by bodies of white sand that was deposited from storm waves that crashed over the beach and sand dunes. What is the name given to such sand bodies?

13. Photograph 7C was taken from a landform called Aaron's Hill. It is the headland of this part of the island. What will eventually happen to Aaron's Hill? Why?

14. Based upon your answer in Question 13, would Aaron's Hill be a good location for a resort hotel?

15. Based upon your inferences, observations, and explanations in Questions 11, 12, and 13, what will eventually happen to the living saltmarsh in Figures 7B and C?

16. What can you infer about global sea level, based on your answers to Questions 4, 9, and 15?

FIGURE 5: Oceanside, California

North

| 0 | | 1 | | 2 | | 3 kilometers |

| 0 | ½ | 1 | | 2 miles |

Contour interval = 25 ft.   1:62,500

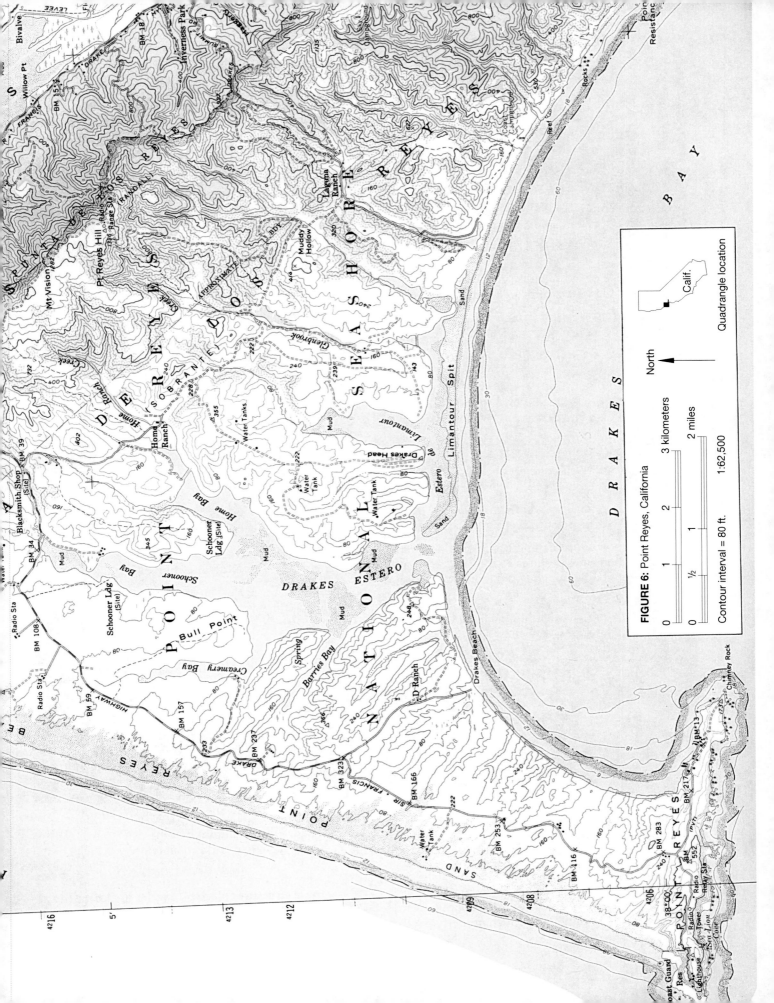

FIGURE 6: Point Reyes, California

North

Quadrangle location

Calif.

0   1   2   3 kilometers

0   ½   1   2 miles

Contour interval = 80 ft.   1:62,500

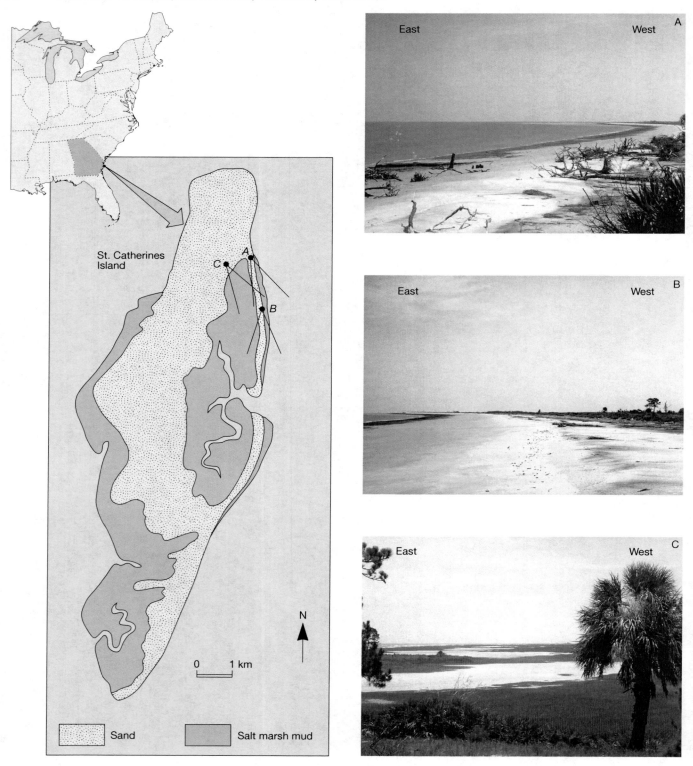

FIGURE 7   Saint Catherines Island, Georgia: coastal features and distribution of sand and saltmarsh mud. **A.** View south–southeast from point **A** on map, at low tide. Dark-brown "ribbon" adjacent to ocean is salt-marsh mud. Light-colored area is sand. **B.** View south from point **B** on map at low tide. **C.** View southeast from point **C** (Aaron's Hill) on map. (Photos by R. Busch)

PART B: HUMAN MODIFICATION OF SHORELINES

Examine the portion of the Ocean City, Maryland, topographic quadrangle map provided in Figure 8. Purple features show changes made in 1972 to a 1964 map, so you can see how the coastline changed from 1964–1972. Also note the outline of the barrier island as it appeared in 1849 according to the U.S. Geological Survey.

Ocean City is located on a long, narrow barrier island called Fenwick Island. During a severe hurricane in 1933, the island was breached by tidal currents that formed Ocean City Inlet and split the barrier island in two. Ocean City is still located on what remains of Fenwick Island. The city is a popular vacation resort that has undergone much property development over the past 50 years. The island south of Ocean City Inlet is called Assateague Island. It has remained undeveloped, as a state and national seashore.

Questions

17. After the 1933 hurricane carved out Ocean City Inlet, the Army Corps of Engineers constructed a pair of jetties on each side of the inlet to keep it open. The southern jetty is labeled "seawall" on the map. Sand filled in behind the northern jetty, so it is now a sea wall forming the straight southern edge of Ocean City on Fenwick Island (a straight black line on the map). Based on this information, would you say that the longshore current is traveling north to south, or south to north? Explain.

18. Notice that Assateague Island has migrated landward (west), relative to its 1849 position. This migration began in 1933.

    a. Why did Assateague Island migrate landward?

    b. Field inspection of the west side of Assateague Island reveals that muds of the lagoon (Sinepuxent Bay) are being covered up by the westward-advancing island. What is the rate of Assateague Island's westward migration in feet/year and meters/year?

    c. Based on your last answer (Question 18b), predict the approximate year in which the west side of Assateague Island will merge with saltmarshes around Ocean City Harbor. What natural processes and human activities could prevent this?

19. Notice the groins (short black lines) that have been constructed on the east side of Fenwick Island (Ocean City) in the northeast corner of the map.

    a. Why do you think these groins have been constructed there?

    b. What effect could these groins have on the beaches around Ocean City's Municipal Pier? Why?

20. Hurricanes normally approach Ocean City from the south–southeast. In 1995, one of the largest hurricanes ever recorded (Hurricane Felix) approached Ocean City but miraculously turned back out into the Atlantic Ocean. How does the westward migration of Assateague Island increase the risk of hurricane damage to Ocean City?

21. The westward migration of Assateague Island could be halted and probably reversed if all of the groins, jetties, and sea walls around Ocean City were removed. How would removal of all of these structures place properties in Ocean City at greater risk to environmental damage than they now face?

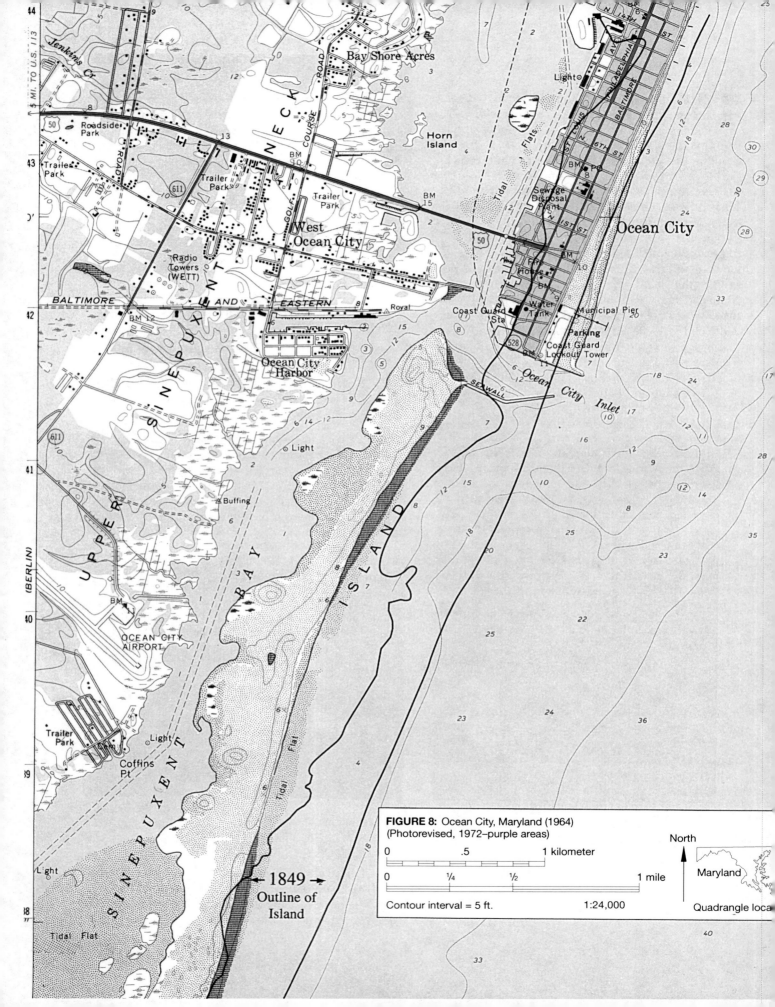

FIGURE 8: Ocean City, Maryland (1964)
(Photorevised, 1972–purple areas)

0   .5   1 kilometer

0   1/4   1/2   1 mile

Contour interval = 5 ft.   1:24,000

North

Maryland

Quadrangle loca...

PART C: THE THREAT OF RISING SEAS

All of the topographic maps in this laboratory manual rely on a zero reference datum of *mean sea level*. Sea level actually fluctuates both above and below mean sea level during daily tidal cycles and storm surges. A **storm surge** is a bulge of water pushed landward by abnormally high winds and/or low atmospheric pressure associated with storms. Storm surges cause the ocean to rise by about 2–24 feet, depending on the magnitude of the storm. However, except for hurricanes, most storm surges are in the range of 2–3 feet.

Given the fact that daily tides cause sea level to fluctuate 2–3 feet above and below mean sea level, and most storm surges are in the range of 2–3 feet, it might be wise to generally not build dwellings and businesses on elevations less than 6 feet near marine coastlines.

Notice that Ocean City, Maryland (Figure 8) has not followed this rule of thumb. Dense construction (pink areas on Figure 8) has occurred in many areas less than 5 feet above mean sea level. Therefore, Ocean City is at a high risk of flooding from rising sea levels even during normal winter storms. One of these storms flooded most of the city in 1962, and a hurricane could submerge the entire city (because the city's highest elevation is only 10 feet above mean sea level).

A more long-term hazard to coastal cities is the threat that mean sea level may rise significantly over the coming decades. A report on *The Probability of Sea Level Rise* was issued by the U.S. Environmental Protection Agency (EPA) in 1996, and was based on data from dozens of the most respected researchers in this field throughout the world. The report demonstrates that mean sea level is already rising at rates of 2.5–3.0 mm/yr (10–12 inches per century) along U.S. coastlines, and these rates are expected to increase. According to this comprehensive study, there is a 50% probability that sea level will rise 34 cm (about 13 inches) over the next century. A 50% probability is the same probability that you will get heads if you flip a coin. The EPA study also suggests that there is only a 1% probability (1 chance in 100) that sea level will rise 104 cm (well over 3 feet) over the next century.

In planning for safe and economical coastal development, planning commissions and real estate developers could "play it safe" and assume that sea level could rise about 1 meter (about 3 feet) in the next century.

Questions

22. From our discussion on storm surges and the threat of actual sea-level rise, it seems logical that there are two main rules of planning for safe and economical coastal development in relation to the threat of property damage from coastal flooding. Planners should account for the probability that storm surges will normally cause sea level to rise approximately 6 feet above mean sea level. Planners should also account for the long-term probability that mean sea level will actually rise approximately 3 feet over the next century. Given the fact that most existing topographic maps of coastal areas have contour intervals of 5 feet, what would you suggest as the contour line below which construction should not occur along coastlines? Explain.

23. Let us assume that dwellings constructed at elevations less than 10 feet above mean sea level are at increasingly high risk to flooding over the next century. Using a blue colored pencil, color in all of the land areas in Figure 9 (Charleston, South Carolina) that are now at elevations less than and equal to 10 feet above mean sea level.

    a. What amount of the new buildings (purple buildings in Figure 9) in Charleston have been built in this high-risk, 10-foot zone?

    b. Why do you think that so much new construction has occurred in the high-risk, 10-foot zone around Charleston?

    c. What effect would a 10-foot sea level rise have on the abundant saltmarshes (wetlands) in the Charleston region?

24. Study the map of Miami, Florida (Figure 10), and list some of the significant properties that are now located within the high-risk, 10-foot zone where flood hazards will increase over the next century.

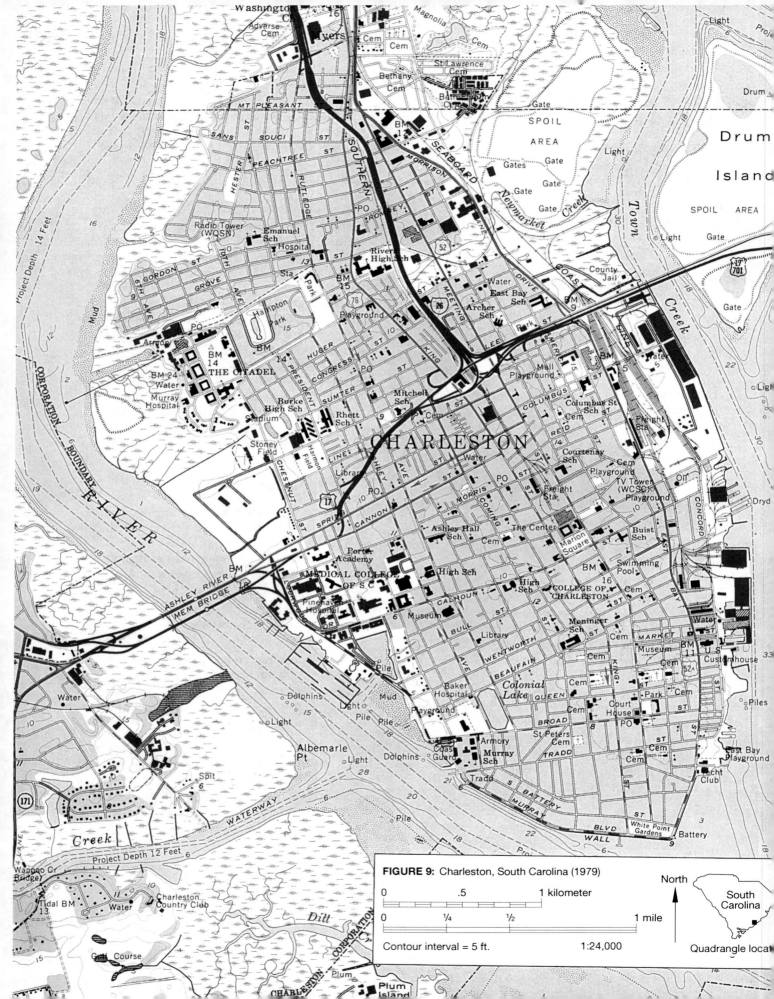

FIGURE 9: Charleston, South Carolina (1979)

| 0 | .5 | 1 kilometer |

| 0 | 1/4 | 1/2 | 1 mile |

Contour interval = 5 ft.   1:24,000

North

South
Carolina

Quadrangle loca

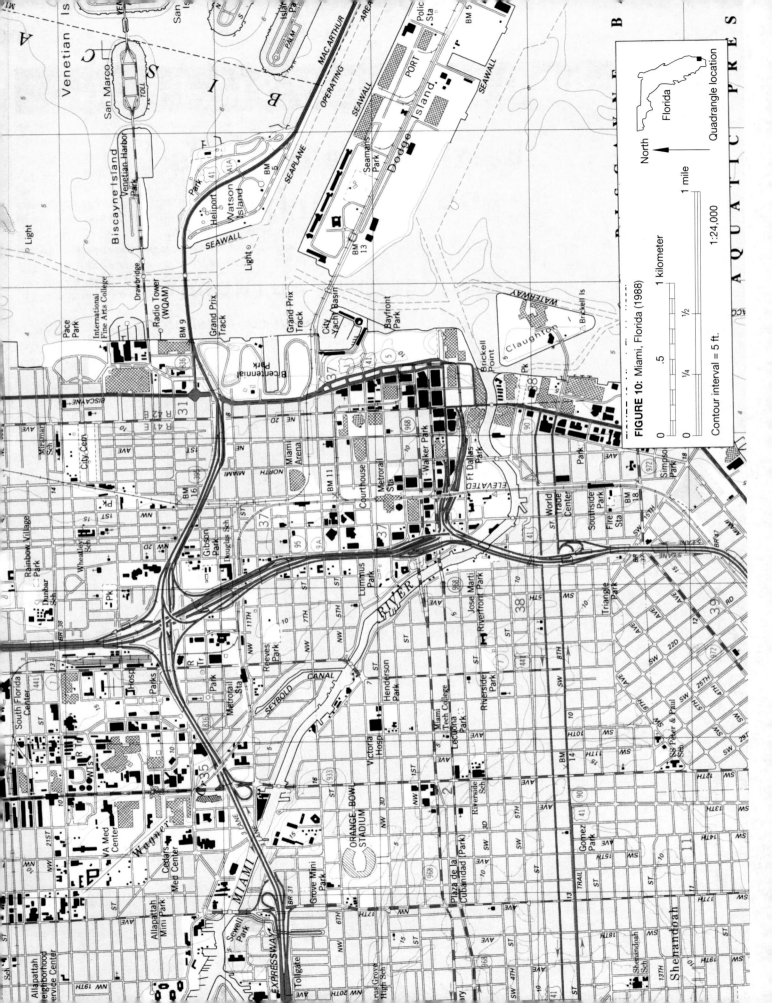

FIGURE 10: Miami, Florida (1988)

12

Introduction to Oceanography

The global ocean covers nearly three quarters of Earth's surface and **oceanography** is an important focus of Earth science studies. This exercise investigates some of the physical characteristics of the oceans. To establish a foundation for reference, the extent, depths, and distribution of the world's oceans are the first topics examined. Salinity and temperature, two of the most important variables of seawater, are studied to ascertain how they influence the density of water and the deep ocean circulation (Figure 1).

Objectives

After you have completed this exercise, you should be able to:

1. Locate and name the major water bodies on Earth.
2. Discuss the distribution of land and water in each hemisphere.
3. Locate and describe the general features of ocean basins.
4. Explain the relation between salinity and the density of seawater.
5. Describe how seawater salinity varies with latitude and depth in the oceans.
6. Explain the relation between temperature and the density of seawater.
7. Describe how seawater temperature varies with latitude and depth in the oceans.

Materials

colored pencils   ruler

Materials Supplied by Your Instructor

measuring cylinder (100 ml, clear, Pyrex or plastic)	world wall map, globe, or atlas	test tubes dye
	ice	salt
salt solutions	beaker	rubber band

Figure 1 The deep-diving submersible *Alvin* is 7.6 meters long, weighs 16 tons, has a cruising speed of 1 knot, and can reach depths as great as 4000 meters. A pilot and two scientific observers are along during a normal 6- to 10-hour dive. (Courtesy of Rod Catanach/Woods Hole Oceanographic Institution)

Terms

oceanography	deep-ocean trench	submarine
continental shelf	mid-ocean ridge	canyons
continental slope	density	turbidity
abyssal plain	density current	currents
seamount	salinity	

Extent of the Oceans

1. Refer to a globe, wall map of the world, or world map in an atlas and identify each of the oceans

From *Applications and Investigations in Earth Science,* Sixth Edition, Edward J. Tarbuck, Frederick K. Lutgens, Kenneth G. Pinzke. Copyright © 2009 by Pearson Education, Inc. Published by Pearson Prentice Hall. All rights reserved.

and major water bodies listed below. Locate and label each on the world map, Figure 2.

Oceans	Other Major Water Bodies	
A. Pacific	1. Caribbean Sea	11. Arabian
B. Atlantic	2. North Sea	Sea
C. Indian	3. Coral Sea	12. Weddell
D. Arctic	4. Sea of Japan	Sea
	5. Sea of Okhotsk	13. Bering Sea
	6. Gulf of Mexico	14. Red Sea
	7. Persian Gulf	15. Bay of
	8. Mediterranean Sea	Bengal
	9. Black Sea	16. Caspian
	10. Baltic Sea	Sea

Area

The area of Earth is about 510 million square kilometers (197 million square miles). Of this, approximately 360 million square kilometers (140 million square miles) are covered by oceans and marginal seas.

2. What percentage of Earth's surface is covered by oceans and marginal seas?

$$\frac{\text{Area of oceans and marginal seas}}{\text{Area of Earth}} \times 100$$

$$= \underline{\hspace{1cm}} \% \text{ oceans}$$

3. What percentage of Earth's surface is land?

_____ % land

Distribution of Land and Water by Hemisphere

Answer questions 4–7 by examining either a globe, wall map of the world, world map in an atlas, or Figure 2.

4. **a.** Which hemisphere, Northern or Southern, could be called the "water" hemisphere and which the "land" hemisphere?

"Water" hemisphere: _____

"Land" hemisphere: _____

b. The oceans become (wider, more narrow) as you go from the equator to the pole in the Northern Hemisphere. Circle your answer.

c. In the Southern Hemisphere the width of the oceans (increases, decreases) from the equator to the pole.

5. Follow a line around a globe, world map, and Figure 3 at the latitudes listed on the following page and estimate what percentage of Earth's surface is ocean at each latitude.

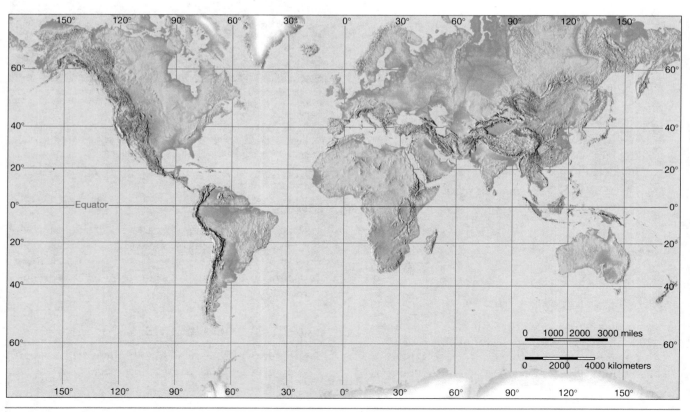

Figure 2 World map.

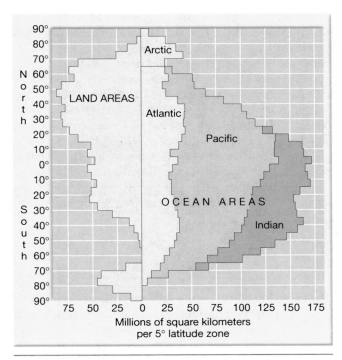

Figure 3   Distribution of land and water in each 5° latitude belt. (After M. Grant Gross, *Oceanography: A View of the Earth,* 2nd ed., Englewood Cliffs, NJ: Prentice-Hall, 1977)

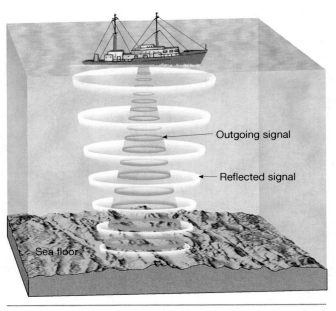

Figure 4   An echo sounder determines the water depth by measuring the time interval required for an acoustic wave to travel from a ship to the seafloor and back. The speed of sound in water is 1,500 m/sec. Therefore, depth = 1/2(1500 m/sec × echo travel time).

	NORTHERN HEMISPHERE	SOUTHERN HEMISPHERE
40°:	_____ % ocean	_____ % ocean
60°:	_____ % ocean	_____ % ocean

6. Which ocean covers the greatest area?

   _____

7. Which ocean is almost entirely in the Southern Hemisphere?

   _____

Measuring Ocean Depths

Charting the shape or topography of the ocean floor is a fundamental task of oceanographers. In the 1920s a technological breakthrough for determining ocean depths occurred with the invention of electronic depth-sounding equipment. The **echo sounder** (also referred to as *sonar,* an acronym for *so*und *na*vigation *a*nd *r*anging) works by measuring the precise time that a sound wave, traveling at about 1,500 meters per second in water, takes to reach the ocean floor and return to the instrument (Figure 4). Today, in addition to using sophisticated echo sounders such as *multibeam sonar,*

oceanographers are also using satellites to map the ocean floor.

8. Using the formula in Figure 4, calculate the depth of the ocean for each of the following echo soundings.

   5.2 seconds: _____

   6.0 seconds: _____

   2.8 seconds: _____

   Ships generally don't make single depth soundings. Rather, as the ship makes a traverse from one location to another, it is continually sending out sound impulses and recording the echoes. In this way, oceanographers obtain many depth recordings from which a *profile* (side view) of the ocean floor can be drawn.

   The data in Table 1 were gathered by a ship equipped with an echo sounder as it traveled the North Atlantic Ocean eastward from Cape Cod, Massachusetts. The depths were calculated using the same technique used in question 8.

9. Use the data in Table 1 to construct a generalized profile of the ocean floor in the North Atlantic on Figure 5. Begin by plotting each point at its proper distance from Cape Cod, at the indicated depth. Complete the profile by connecting the depth points.

Table 1 Echo Sounder Depths Eastward from Cape Cod, MA

POINT	DISTANCE (KM)	DEPTH (M)
1	0	0
2	180	200
3	270	2700
4	420	3300
5	600	4000
6	830	4800
7	1100	4750
8	1130	2500
9	1160	4800
10	1490	4750
11	1770	4800
12	1800	500
13	1830	4850
14	2120	4800
15	2320	4000
16	2650	3000
17	2900	1500
18	2950	1000
19	2960	2700
20	3000	2700
21	3050	1000
22	3130	1900

Ocean Basin Topography

Various features are located along the continental margins and on the ocean basin floor (Figure 6). **Continental shelves**, flooded extensions of the continents, are gently sloping submerged surfaces extending from the shoreline toward the ocean basin. The seaward edge of the continental shelf is marked by the **continental slope**, a relatively steep structure (as compared with the shelf) that marks the boundary between continental crust and oceanic crust. Deep, steep-sided valleys known as **submarine canyons**, eroded in part by the periodic downslope movements of dense, sediment-laden water called **turbidity currents**, are often cut into the continental slope. The ocean basin floor, which constitutes almost 30% of Earth's surface, in-

cludes remarkably flat areas known as **abyssal plains**, tall volcanic peaks called **seamounts**, **oceanic plateaus** generated by mantle plumes, and **deep-ocean trenches**, which are deep linear depressions that occasionally border some continents, primarily in the Pacific Ocean basin. Near the center of most oceanic basins is a topographically elevated feature, characterized by extensive faulting and numerous volcanic structures, called the **oceanic (or mid-ocean) ridge**. Using Figure 6 and a wall map or atlas as references, briefly describe each of these features in questions 10–15. Label one or more examples of each feature on Figure 5 and the ocean floor map of the North Atlantic Ocean basin, Figure 7.

10. Continental shelf: _____

_____

a. What is the approximate average ocean depth along the continental shelves bordering North America?

_____

b. Write a brief statement comparing the width of the continental shelf along the east coast, west coast, and gulf coast of North America.

_____

_____

11. Continental slope: _____

_____

a. Briefly describe the origin of submarine canyons and label at least one on Figure 7.

_____

_____

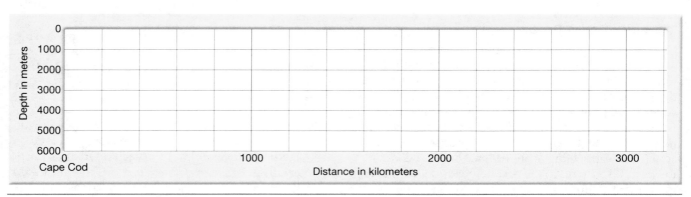

Figure 5 North Atlantic Ocean floor profile (exaggerated).

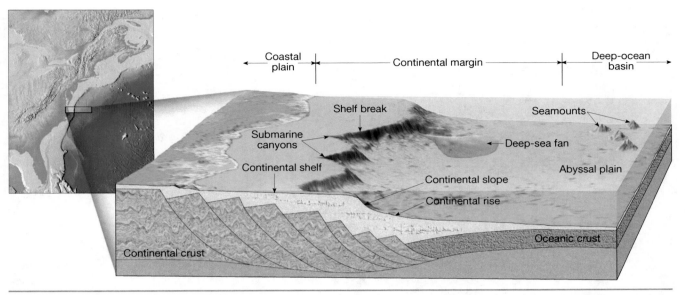

Figure 6 Generalized continental margin. Note that the slopes shown for the continental shelf and continental slope are greatly exaggerated. The continental shelf has an average slope of one tenth of 1 degree, while the continental slope has an average of about 5 degrees.

12. Abyssal plain: _____

_____

   a. The general topography of abyssal plains is (flat, irregular). Circle your answer.

   b. How do abyssal plains form and what is their composition?

_____

_____

13. Seamount: _____

_____

14. Deep-ocean trench (not shown on Figure 5):

_____

_____

_____

   a. Approximately how deep is the Puerto Rico trench?

_____ meters

   b. Use a map or globe to locate three deep-ocean trenches in the western Pacific Ocean. Give the name, location, and depth of each.

Trench 1: _____

_____

Trench 2: _____

_____

Trench 3: _____

_____

15. Mid-ocean ridge: _____

_____

   a. Examine the mid-ocean ridge system on a world map. Follow the ridge eastward from the Atlantic Ocean into the Indian Ocean and then into the Pacific. Describe what happens to the ridge along the southwest coast of North America.

_____

   b. Approximately how high above the adjacent ocean floor does the Mid-Atlantic Ridge rise?

_____ meters

16. Note that Figures 5 and 7 illustrate only the western side of the North Atlantic floor. Using a globe or map, write a brief statement comparing the to-

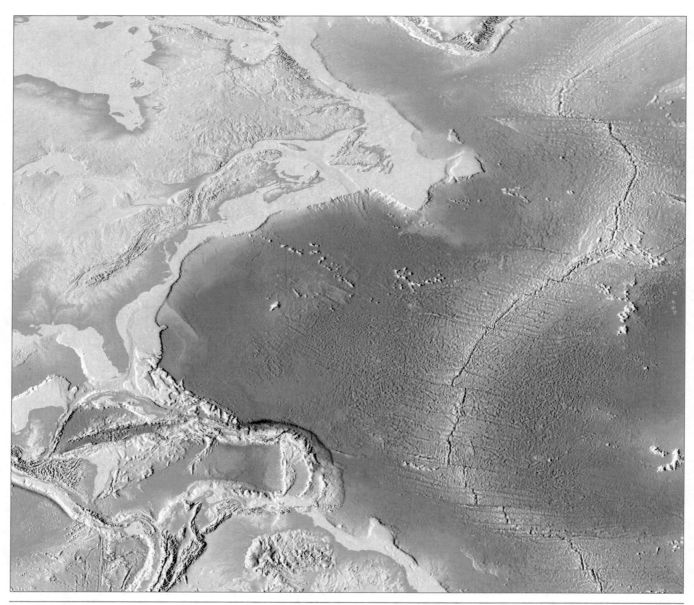

Figure 7 North Atlantic basin.

pography of the North Atlantic Ocean floor east of the mid-ocean ridge to that on the west side.

_____

_____

_____

_____

Characteristics of Ocean Water

Ocean circulation has two primary components: surface ocean currents and deep-ocean circulation. While surface currents like the famous Gulf Stream are driven primarily by the prevailing world winds, the deep-ocean circulation is largely the result of differences in ocean water **density** (mass per unit volume of a substance). A **density current** is the movement (flow) of one body of water over, under, or through another caused by density differences and gravity. Variations in **salinity** and temperature are the two most important factors in creating the density differences that result in the deep-ocean circulation.

Salinity

Salinity is the amount of dissolved solid material in water, expressed as parts per thousand parts of water. The symbol for parts per thousand is 0/00. Although

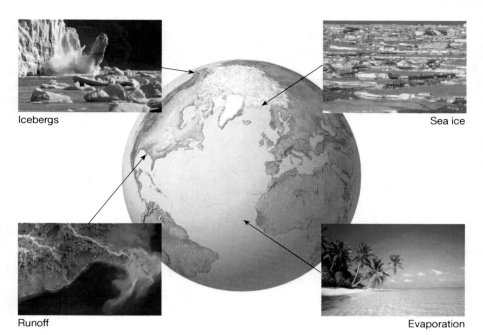

Icebergs

Sea ice

Runoff

Evaporation

Figure 8 Processes affecting seawater salinity. Processes that *decrease* seawater salinity include precipitation, runoff, icebergs melting, and sea ice melting. Processes that *increase* seawater salinity include formation of sea ice and evaporation. Source: (upper left) Tom Bean/Tom and Susan Bean, Inc., (upper right) Wolfgang Kaehler Photography, (lower left) NASA Headquarters, (lower right) Paul Steel/Corbis/Stock Market.

there are many dissolved salts in seawater, sodium chloride (common table salt) is the most abundant.

Variations in the salinity of seawater are primarily a consequence of changes in the water content of the solution. In regions where evaporation is high, the proportionate amount of dissolved material in seawater is increased by removing the water and leaving behind the salts. On the other hand, in areas of high precipitation and high runoff, the additional water dilutes seawater and lowers the salinity. Since the factors that determine the concentration of salts in seawater are not constant from the equator to the poles, the salinity of seawater also varies with latitude and depth (Figure 8).

Salinity–Density Experiment

To gain a better understanding of how salinity affects the density of water, examine the equipment in the lab (see Figure 9) and conduct the following experiment by completing each of the indicated steps.

Step 1. Fill the measuring cylinder with cool tap water up to the rubber band or other marker near the top of the cylinder.

Step 2. Fill a test tube about half full of solution A (saltwater) and pour it slowly into the cylinder. Observe and describe what happens.

Observations: _____

_____

Step 3. Repeat steps 1 and 2 two additional times and measure the time required for the front edge of the saltwater to travel from the rubber band to the bottom of the cylinder. Record the times

for each test in the data table, Table 2. *Make certain* that you drain the cylinder after each trial and refill it with fresh water and use the same amount of solution with each trial.

Step 4. Determine the travel time two times for solution B exactly as you did with solution A and enter your measurements in Table 2.

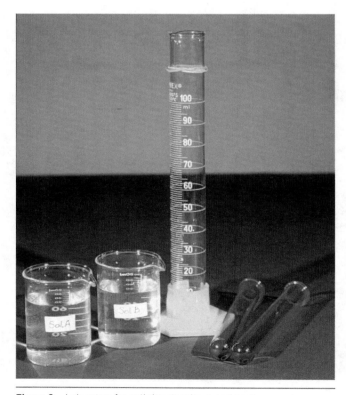

Figure 9 Lab setup for salinity–density experiment.

Table 2   Salinity–Density Experiment Data Table

SOLUTION	TIMED TRIAL #1	TIMED TRIAL #2	AVERAGE OF BOTH TRIALS
A			
B			
Solution B plus salt		XXXX	XXXX

Step 5. Fill a test tube about half full of solution B and add to it some additional salt. Then shake the test tube vigorously. Determine the travel time of this solution and enter your results in Table 2.

Step 6. Clean all your glassware.

17. Questions 17a and 17b refer to the salinity–density experiment.

   a. Write a brief summary of the results of your salinity–density experiment.

   _____

   _____

   b. Since the solution that traveled fastest has the greatest density, solution (A, B) is most dense. Circle your answer.

   Table 3 lists the approximate surface water salinity at various latitudes in the Atlantic and Pacific Oceans. Using the data, construct a salinity curve for each ocean on the graph, Figure 10. *Use a different-colored pencil for each ocean.* Then answer questions 18–22.

Table 3   Ocean Surface Water Salinity in Parts per Thousand (0/00) at Various Latitudes in the Atlantic and Pacific Oceans

LATITUDE	ATLANTIC OCEAN	PACIFIC OCEAN
60°N	33.0 0/00	31.0 0/00
50°	33.7	32.5
40°	34.8	33.2
30°	36.7	34.2
20°	36.8	34.2
10°	36.0	34.4
0°	35.0	34.3
10°	35.9	35.2
20°	36.7	35.6
30°	36.2	35.7
40°	35.3	35.0
50°	34.3	34.4
60°S	33.9	34.0

18. At which latitudes are the highest surface salinities located?

   _____

19. What are two factors that control the concentration of salts in seawater?

   _____ and _____

20. Refer to the factors listed in question 19. What is the cause of the difference in surface water salinity between equatorial and subtropical regions in the Atlantic Ocean?

   _____

   _____

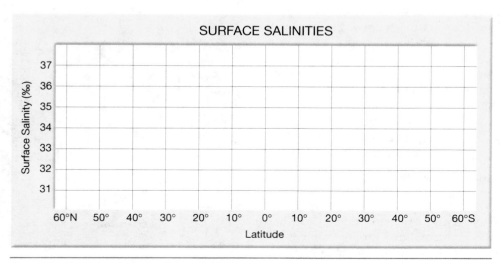

Figure 10   Graph for plotting surface salinities.

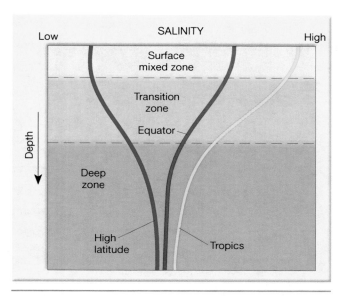

Figure 11 Ocean water salinity changes with depth at high latitudes, equatorial regions, and the tropics.

21. Of the two oceans, the (Atlantic, Pacific) Ocean has higher average surface salinities. Circle your answer.

22. Suggest a reason(s) for the difference in average surface salinities between the oceans.

_____

_____

_____

Figure 11 shows how ocean water salinity varies with depth at different latitudes. Use the figure to answer questions 23–26.

23. In general, salinity (increases, decreases) with depth in the equatorial and tropical regions and (increases, decreases) with depth at high latitudes. Circle your answers.

24. Why are the surface salinities higher than the deepwater salinities in the lower latitudes?

_____

The *halocline* (*halo*-salt, *cline*-slope) is a layer of ocean water where there is a rapid change in salinity with depth.

25. Label the halocline on Figure 11. Where does it occur?

_____

26. Below the halocline the salinity of ocean water (increases rapidly, remains fairly constant, decreases rapidly). Circle your answer.

Ocean Water Temperatures

Seawater temperature is the most extensively determined variable of the oceans because it is easily measured and has an important influence on marine life. Like salinity, ocean water temperatures vary from the equator to poles and also changes with depth.

Temperature, like salinity, also affects the density of seawater. However, the density of seawater is more sensitive to temperature fluctuations than salinity.

Temperature–Density Experiment

To illustrate the effects of temperature on the density of water, examine the equipment in the lab (see Figure 12) and then conduct the following experiment by completing each of the indicated steps.

Step 1. Fill a measuring cylinder with *cold* tap water up to the rubber band.

Step 2. Put 2–3 drops of dye in a test tube and fill it half full with *hot* tap water.

Step 3. Pour the contents of the test tube *slowly* into the cylinder and then record your observations.

Observations: _____

_____

_____

Figure 12 Lab setup for temperature–density experiment.

Step 4. Empty the cylinder and refill it with *hot* water.

Step 5. Add a test tube full of cold water and 2–3 drops of dye to some ice in a beaker. Stir the solution for a few seconds. Fill the test tube three-fourths full with some liquid (no ice) from your beaker. Pour this cold liquid *slowly* into the cylinder. Then record your observations.

Observations: _____

_____

_____

Step 6. Clean the glassware and return it along with the other materials to your instructor.

27. Questions 27a and 27b refer to the temperature–density experiment.

   a. Write a brief summary of your temperature–density experiment.

_____

_____

_____

   b. Given equal salinities, (cold, warm) seawater would have the greatest density. Circle your answer.

Table 4 shows the average surface temperature and density of seawater at various latitudes. Using the data, plot a line on the graph in Figure 13 for temperature and a separate line for density using a different color. Then answer questions 28–30.

28. (Warm, Cool) surface temperatures and (high, low) surface densities occur in the equatorial regions. While at high latitudes, (warm, cool) surface temperatures and (high, low) surface densities are found. Circle your answers.

Table 4   Idealized Ocean Surface Water Temperatures and Densities at Various Latitudes

LATITUDE	SURFACE TEMPERATURE (C°)	SURFACE DENSITY (g/cm³)
60°N	5	1.0258
40°	13	1.0259
20°	24	1.0237
0°	27	1.0238
20°	24	1.0241
40°	15	1.0261
60°S	2	1.0272

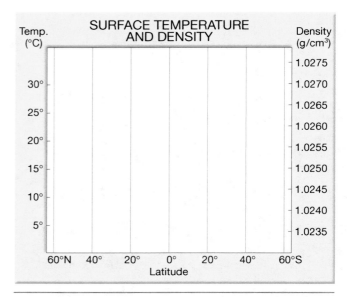

Figure 13   Graph for plotting surface temperatures and densities.

29. What is the reason for the fact that higher average surface densities are found in the Southern Hemisphere?

_____

In question 18 you concluded that surface salinities were greatest at about latitudes 30°N and 30°S.

30. Refer to the density curve in Figure 13. What evidence supports the fact that the temperature of seawater is more of a controlling factor of density than salinity?

_____

_____

Figure 14 shows how ocean water temperature varies with depth at different latitudes. Use the figure to answer questions 31–33.

31. Temperature decreases most rapidly with depth at (high, low) latitudes. Circle your answer and give the reason that the decrease with depth is most rapid at these latitudes.

_____

The layer of water where there is a rapid change of temperature with depth is called the *thermocline* (*thermo* = heat, *cline* = slope). The thermocline is a very important structure in the ocean because it creates a vertical barrier to many types of marine life.

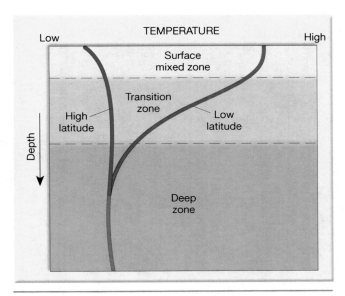

Figure 14 Ocean water temperature changes with depth at high and low latitudes.

32. Label the thermocline on Figure 14. Where does it occur?

_____

33. Below the thermocline the temperature of ocean water (increases rapidly, remains fairly constant, decreases rapidly). Circle your answer.

Oceanography on the Internet

Continue your exploration of the oceans by applying the concepts in this exercise to investigate real-time ocean water characteristics on the *Applications & Investigations in Earth Science* website at http://prenhall.com/earthsciencelab

Notes and calculations.

Introduction to Oceanography

Date Due: _____

Name: _____

Date: _____

Class: _____

After you have finished this exercise, complete the following questions. You may have to refer to the exercise for assistance or to locate specific answers. Be prepared to submit this summary/report to your instructor at the designated time.

1. Give the approximate latitude and longitude of the centers of each of the following water bodies.

    Mediterranean Sea: _____

    Sea of Japan: _____

    Indian Ocean: _____

2. Write a brief statement comparing the distribution of water and land in the Northern Hemisphere to the distribution in the Southern Hemisphere.

    _____

    _____.

3. On the ocean basin profile in Figure 15, label the continental shelf, continental slope, abyssal plain, seamounts, mid-ocean ridge, and deep-ocean trench.

4. List the names and depths of two Pacific Ocean trenches.

NAME	DEPTH
_____	_____
_____	_____

5. Explain how an echo sounder is used to determine the shape or topography of the ocean floor.

    _____

    _____

    _____

    _____

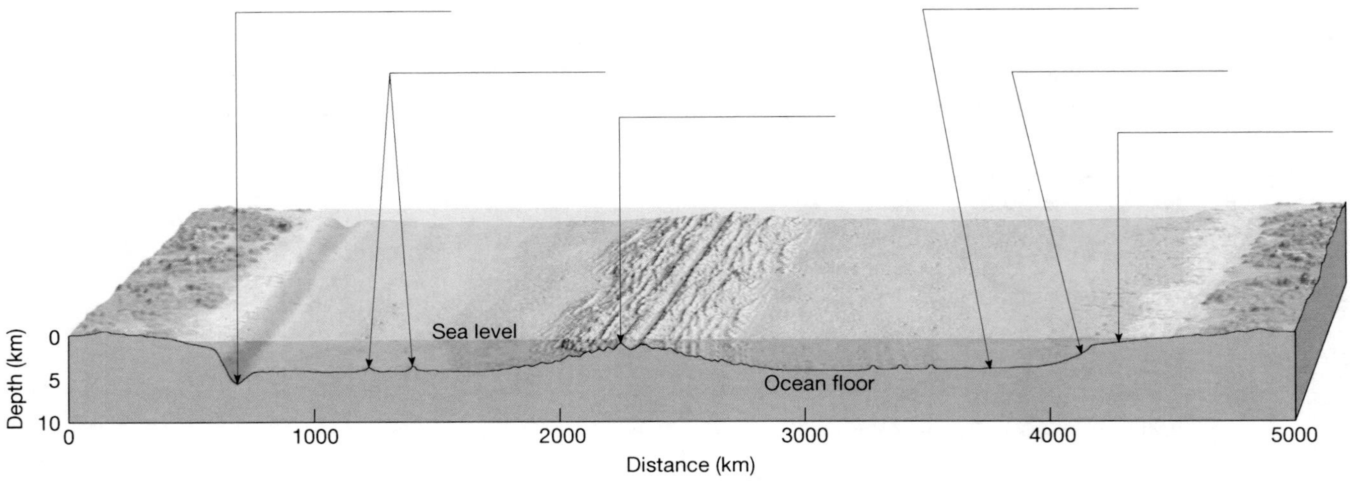

Figure 15 Hypothetical ocean basin.

6. The following are some short statements. Circle the most appropriate response.

   a. The higher the salinity of seawater, the (lower, higher) the density.

   b. The lower the temperature of seawater, the (lower, higher) the density.

   c. Surface salinity is greatest in (polar, subtropical, equatorial) regions.

   d. (Temperature, Salinity) has the greatest influence on the density of seawater.

   e. (Warm, Cold) seawater with (high, low) salinity would have the greatest density.

   f. Vertical movements of ocean water are most likely to begin in (equatorial, subtropical, polar) regions, because the surface water there is (most, least) dense.

7. Summarize the results of your salinity–density and temperature–density experiments.

   Salinity–density experiment: _____

   _____

   _____

   _____

   Temperature–density experiment: _____

   _____

   _____

   _____

8. Why is the surface salinity of an ocean higher in the subtropics than in the equatorial regions?

   _____

   _____

   _____

9. Given your understanding of the relation between ocean water temperature, salinity, and density, where in the Atlantic Ocean would you expect surface water to sink and initiate a subsurface flow? List the reason(s) for your choice(s).

   _____

   _____

   _____

   _____

10. Refer to the salinity–density experiment you conducted. Solution (A, B) had the greatest density. Circle your answer.

11. Describe the change in salinity *and* temperature with depth that occurs at low latitudes.

    Salinity: _____

    _____

    _____

    Temperature: _____

    _____

    _____

12. Are the following statements true or false? Circle your response. If the statement is false, correct the word(s) so that it reads as a true statement.

    T F **a.** The Atlantic Ocean covers the greatest area of all the world oceans.

    T F **b.** Continental shelves are part of the deep-ocean floor.

    T F **c.** Deep-ocean trenches are located in the middle of ocean basins.

    T F **d.** High evaporation rates in the subtropics cause the surface ocean water to have a lower than average salinity.

13

Atmospheric Heating

The quantity of radiation from the Sun that strikes the outer edge of Earth's atmosphere at any one place is not constant but varies with the seasons. This exercise examines, step by step, what happens to **solar radiation** as it passes through the atmosphere, is absorbed at Earth's surface, and is reradiated by land and water back to the atmosphere (Figure 1). Investigating the journey of solar radiation and how it is influenced and modified by air, land, and water will provide a better understanding of one of the most basic weather elements, atmospheric temperature.

Objectives

After you have completed this exercise, you should be able to:

1. Explain how Earth's atmosphere is heated.
2. Describe the effect that the atmosphere has on absorbing, scattering, and reflecting incoming solar radiation.
3. List the gases in the atmosphere that are responsible for absorbing long-wave radiation.
4. Explain how the heating of a surface is related to its albedo.
5. Discuss the differences in the heating and cooling of land and water.
6. Summarize the global pattern of surface temperatures for January and July.
7. Describe how the temperature of the atmosphere changes with increasing altitude.
8. List the cause of a surface temperature inversion.
9. Determine the effect that wind speed has on the windchill equivalent temperature.

Materials

calculator
colored pencils

Figure 1   Solar radiation and atmospheric heating. (Photo by E. J. Tarbuck)

Materials Supplied by Your Instructor

light source	wood splints
black and silver	beaker of sand
containers	beaker of water
two thermometers	

Terms

solar radiation	albedo	isotherm
greenhouse	environmental	windchill
effect	lapse rate	equivalent
terrestrial	temperature	temperature
radiation	inversion	

Introduction

Temperature is an important element of weather and climate because it greatly influences air pressure, wind, and the amount of moisture in the air. The unequal heating that takes place over the surface of Earth is what sets the atmosphere in motion, and the movement of air is what brings changes in our weather.

The single greatest cause for temperature variations over the surface of Earth is differences in the reception of solar radiation. Secondary factors such as the differential heating of land and water, ocean currents, and altitude can modify local temperatures.

The amount of solar energy (radiation) striking Earth is not constant throughout the year at any particular place, nor is it uniform over the face of Earth at any one time. However, the total amount of radiation that the planet intercepts from the Sun equals the total radiation that it loses back to space. It is this balance between incoming and outgoing radiation that keeps Earth from becoming continuously hotter or colder.

Solar Radiation at the Outer Edge of the Atmosphere

The two factors that control the amount of solar radiation that a square meter receives at the outer edge of the atmosphere, and eventually Earth's surface, are the Sun's *intensity* and its *duration*. You may want to review the exercise "Earth-Sun Relations."

1. Briefly define solar intensity and duration.

   Intensity of solar radiation: _____

   _____

   Duration of solar radiation: _____

   _____

2. Complete Table 1 by calculating the angle that the noon Sun would strike the outer edge of the atmosphere at each of the indicated latitudes on the specified date. How many hours of daylight would each place experience on these dates?

Table 1   Noon Sun Angle and Length of Day

	March 21		June 21	
	NOON SUN ANGLE	LENGTH OF DAY	NOON SUN ANGLE	LENGTH OF DAY
40°N:	___°	___ hrs	___°	___ hrs
0°:	___°	___ hrs	___°	___ hrs
40°S:	___°	___ hrs	___°	___ hrs

3. Explain the reason why the intensity and duration of solar radiation received at the outer edge of the atmosphere is not constant at any particular latitude throughout the year.

_____

_____

Atmospheric Heating

Atmospheric heating is a function of (1) the ability of atmospheric gases to absorb radiation, (2) the amount of solar radiation that reaches Earth's surface, and (3) the nature of the surface material. Of the three, selective absorption of radiation by the atmosphere provides an insight into the mechanism of atmospheric heating. The quantity of radiation that reaches Earth's surface and the ability of the surface to absorb and reradiate the radiation determine the extent of atmospheric heating.

The atmosphere is rather selective and efficiently absorbs long-wave radiation that we detect as heat while allowing the transmission of most of the short wavelengths—a process called the **greenhouse effect**. The short-wave radiation that reaches Earth's surface and is absorbed ultimately returns to the atmosphere in the form of long-wave, **terrestrial radiation**. As the radiation travels up from the surface through the atmosphere, it is absorbed by atmospheric gases, heating the atmosphere from below. Since terrestrial radiation supplies most of the long-wave radiation to the atmosphere, it is the primary source of heat. The fact that temperature typically decreases with an increase in altitude in the lower atmosphere is clear evidence supporting this mechanism of atmospheric heating.

Solar Radiation Received at Earth's Surface

As solar radiation travels through the atmosphere, it may be reflected, scattered, or absorbed. The effect of the atmosphere on incoming solar radiation and the amount of radiation that ultimately reaches the surface is primarily dependent upon the angle at which the solar beam passes through the atmosphere and strikes Earth's surface.

Figure 2 illustrates the atmospheric effects on incoming solar radiation for an average noon Sun angle. Answer questions 4–7 by examining the figure and supplying the correct response.

4. _____ % of the incoming solar radiation is reflected and scattered back to space.

5. _____ % of the incoming solar radiation is absorbed by gases in the atmosphere and clouds.

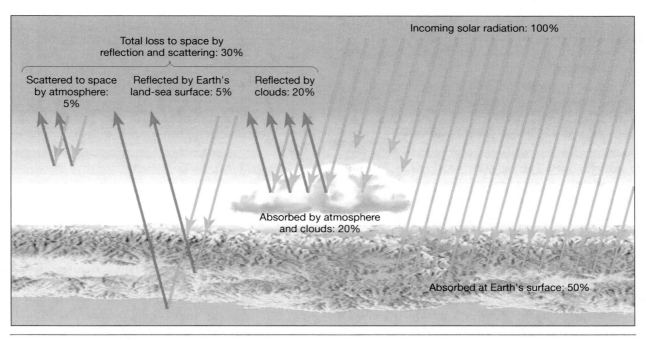

Figure 2 Solar radiation budget of the atmosphere and Earth.

6. _____ % of the incoming solar radiation is absorbed at Earth's surface.

7. (Two and a half, Four) times as much incoming radiation is absorbed by Earth's surface than by the atmosphere and clouds. Circle your answer.

Figure 3 illustrates the effects of the atmosphere on various wavelengths of radiation. Use Figure 3 to answer questions 8–11 by circling the correct response.

8. The incoming solar radiation that passes through the atmosphere and is absorbed at Earth's surface is primarily in the form of (ultraviolet, visible, infrared) wavelengths.

9. When the surface releases the solar radiation it has absorbed, this terrestrial radiation is primarily (ultraviolet, visible, infrared) wavelengths.

10. (Ultraviolet, Visible, Infrared) wavelengths of radiation are absorbed efficiently by oxygen and ozone in the atmosphere.

11. Oxygen and ozone are (good, poor) absorbers of infrared radiation.

12. (Nitrogen, Carbon dioxide) and (water vapor, ozone) are the two principal gases that absorb most of the terrestrial radiation in the atmosphere.

Assume Figure 2 represents the atmospheric effects on incoming solar radiation for an average noon Sun angle of about 50°. Answer questions 13–16 concerning other noon Sun angles by circling the appropriate responses.

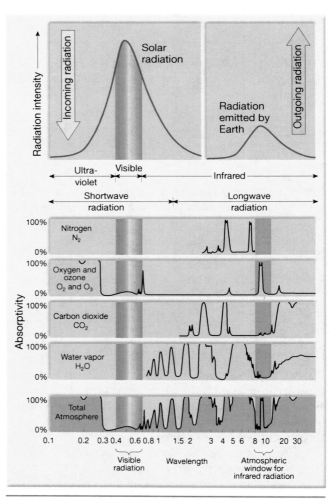

Figure 3 The absorptivity of selected gases of the atmosphere and the atmosphere as a whole.

13. If the noon Sun angle is 90°, solar radiation would have to penetrate a (greater, lesser) thickness of atmosphere than with an average noon Sun angle.

14. The result of a 90° noon Sun angle would be that (more, less) incoming radiation would be reflected, scattered, and absorbed by the atmosphere and (more, less) radiation would be absorbed and reradiated by Earth's surface to heat the atmosphere.

15. If the noon Sun angle is 20°, solar radiation would have to penetrate a (greater, lesser) thickness of atmosphere than with an average noon Sun angle.

16. The result of a 20° noon Sun angle would be that (more, less) incoming radiation would be reflected, scattered, and absorbed by the atmosphere and (more, less) radiation would be absorbed and reradiated by Earth's surface to heat the atmosphere.

17. How is the angle (intensity) at which the solar beam strikes Earth's surface related to the quantity of solar radiation received by each square meter?

_____

_____

18. How is the length of daylight related to the quantity of solar radiation received by each square meter at the surface?

_____

_____

19. Write a brief statement summarizing the mechanism responsible for heating the atmosphere.

_____

_____

_____

The Nature of Earth's Surface

The various materials that comprise Earth's surface play an important role in determining atmospheric heating. Two significant factors are the **albedo** of the surface and the different abilities of land and water to absorb and reradiate radiation.

Albedo is the reflectivity of a substance, usually expressed as the percentage of radiation that is reflected from the surface. Since surfaces with high albedos are not efficient absorbers of radiation, they cannot return much long-wave radiation to the atmosphere for heating.

Albedo Experiment

To better understand the effect of color on albedo, observe the equipment in the laboratory (Figure 4) and then conduct the following experiment by completing each of the indicated steps.

Step 1: Write a brief hypothesis stating the heating and cooling of light-versus dark-colored surfaces.

_____

_____

_____

Step 2: Place the black and silver containers (with lids and thermometers) about six inches away from the light source. Make certain that both containers are of equal distance from the light and are not touching one another.

Step 3: Record the starting temperature of both containers on the albedo experiment data table, Table 2.

Step 4: Turn on the light and record the temperature of both containers on the data table at about 30-second intervals for 5 minutes.

Step 5: Turn off the light and continue to record the temperatures at 30-second intervals for another 5 minutes.

Step 6: Plot the temperatures from the data table on the albedo experiment graph, Figure 5. Use a different color line to connect the points for each container.

Figure 4   Albedo experiment lab equipment.

Table 2   Albedo Experiment Data Table

	STARTING TEMPERATURE	30 SEC	1 MIN	1.5 MIN	2 MIN	2.5 MIN	3 MIN	3.5 MIN	4 MIN	4.5 MIN	5 MIN	5.5 MIN	6 MIN	6.5 MIN	7 MIN	7.5 MIN	8 MIN	8.5 MIN	9 MIN	9.5 MIN	10 MIN
Black container																					
Silver container																					

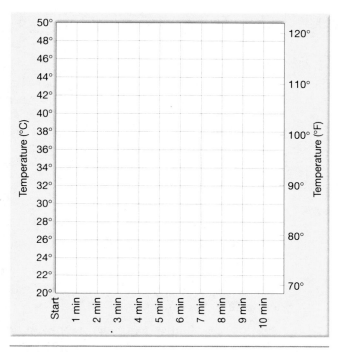

Figure 5 Albedo experiment graph.

20. For each container, calculate the *rate of heating* (change in temperature divided by the time the light was on) and the *rate of cooling* (change in temperature divided by the time the light was off).

	Heating Rate	Cooling Rate
Silver can:	_____	_____
Black can:	_____	_____

21. Write a statement that summarizes and explains the results of your albedo experiment.

_____

_____

_____

_____

_____

22. What are some Earth surfaces that have high albedos and some that have low albedos?

High albedos: _____

Low albedos: _____

23. Given equal amounts of radiation reaching the surface, the air over a snow-covered surface will be (warmer, colder) than air above a dark-colored, barren field. Circle your answer. Then explain your choice fully in terms of what you have learned about albedo.

_____

_____

24. If you lived in an area with long, cold winters, a (light-, dark-) colored roof would be the best choice for your house. Circle your answer. Explain the reasons for your choice.

_____

_____

Land and Water Heating Experiment

Land and water influence the air temperatures above them in different manners because they do not absorb and reradiate energy equally.

Investigate the differential heating of land and water by observing the equipment in the laboratory (Figure 6) and conducting the following experiment by completing each of the indicated steps.

Step 1: Fill one beaker three-quarters full with dry sand and a second beaker three-quarters full with water at room temperature.

Step 2: Using a wood splint, suspend a thermometer in each beaker so that the bulbs are *just below* the surfaces of the sand and water.

Step 3: Hang a light from a stand so it is equally as close as possible to the top of the two beakers.

Step 4: Record the starting temperatures for both the dry sand and water on the land and water heating data table, Table 3.

Figure 6 Land and water heating experiment lab equipment.

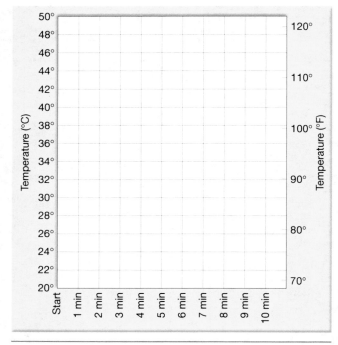

Figure 7 Land and water heating graph.

ferent color line to connect the points for each material.

25. Questions 25a and 25b refer to the land and water heating experiment.

a. How do the abilities to change temperature differ for dry sand and water when they are exposed to equal quantities of radiation?

_____

_____

b. How do the abilities to change temperature differ for dry sand and damp sand when they are exposed to equal quantities of radiation?

_____

_____

Step 5: Turn on the light and record the temperature on the data table at about one-minute intervals for 10 minutes.

Step 6: Turn off the light for several minutes. Dampen the sand with water and record the starting temperature of the damp sand on the data table. Turn on the light and record the temperature of the damp sand on the data table at about one-minute intervals for 10 minutes.

Step 7: Plot the temperatures for the water, dry sand, and damp sand from the data table on the land and water heating graph, Figure 7. Use a dif-

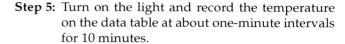

Table 3	Land and Water Heating Data Table										
	STARTING TEMPERATURE	**1 MIN**	**2 MIN**	**3 MIN**	**4 MIN**	**5 MIN**	**6 MIN**	**7 MIN**	**8 MIN**	**9 MIN**	**10 MIN**
Water											
Dry sand											
Damp sand											

26. Suggest several reasons for the differential heating of land and water.

_____

_____

_____

_____

Figure 8 presents the annual temperature curves for two cities, A and B, that are located in North America at approximately 37°N latitude. On any date both cities receive the same intensity and duration of solar radiation. One city is in the center of the continent, while the other is on the west coast. Use Figure 8 to answer questions 27–34.

27. In Figure 8, city (A, B) has the highest mean monthly temperature. Circle your answer.

28. City (A, B) has the lowest mean monthly temperature.

29. The greatest *annual temperature range* (difference between highest and lowest mean monthly temperatures) occurs at city (A, B).

30. City (A, B) reaches its maximum mean monthly temperature at an earlier date.

31. City (A, B) maintains a more uniform temperature throughout the year.

32. Of the two cities, city A is most likely located (along a coast, in the center of a continent).

33. The most likely location for city B is (coastal, mid-continent).

34. Describe the effect that the location, along the coast or in the center of a continent, has on the temperature of a city.

_____

_____

Atmospheric Temperatures

Air temperatures are not constant. They normally change (1) through time at any one location, (2) with latitude because of the changing sun angle and length of daylight, and (3) with increasing altitude in the lower atmosphere because the atmosphere is primarily heated from the bottom up.

Daily Temperatures

In general, the daily temperatures that occur at any particular place are the result of long-wave radiation being released at Earth's surface. However, secondary factors, such as cloud cover and cold air moving into the area, can also cause significant variations.

Questions 35–42 refer to the daily temperature graph, Figure 9.

35. The coolest temperature of the day occurs at _____. Fill in your answer.

36. The warmest temperature occurs at _____.

37. What is the *daily temperature range* (difference between maximum and minimum temperatures for the day)?

Daily temperature range: _____ °F (_____ °C).

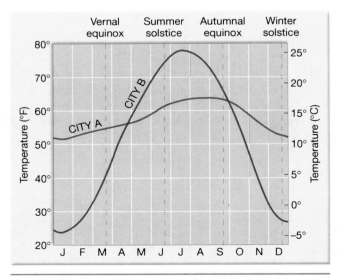

Figure 8 Mean monthly temperatures for two North American cities located at approximately 37°N latitude.

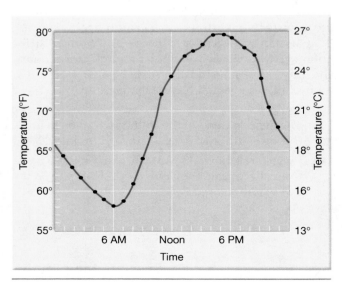

Figure 9 Typical daily temperature graph for a mid-latitude city during the summer.

38. What is the *daily temperature mean* (average of the maximum and minimum temperatures)?

    Daily temperature mean: _____ °F (_____ °C).

39. Refer to the mechanism for heating the atmosphere. Why does the warmest daily temperature occur in mid-to-late afternoon rather than at the time of the highest Sun angle?

    _____

    _____

40. Why does the coolest temperature of the day occur about sunrise?

    _____

    _____

41. How would cloud cover influence daily maximum and minimum temperatures?

    _____

    _____

42. On Figure 9 sketch and label a colored line that best represents a daily temperature graph for a typical cloudy day.

Global Pattern of Temperature

The primary reason for global variations in surface temperatures is the unequal distribution of radiation over the Earth. Among the most important secondary factors are differential heating of land and water, ocean currents, and differences in altitude.

Questions 43–55 refer to Figure 10, "World Distribution of Mean Surface Temperatures (°C) for January and July." The lines on the maps, called **isotherms**, connect places of equal surface temperature.

43. The general trend of the isotherms on the maps is (north–south, east–west). Circle your answer.

44. In general, how do surface temperatures vary from the equator toward the poles? Why does this variation occur?

    _____

    _____

    _____

45. The warmest and coldest temperatures occur over which countries or oceans?

    Warmest global temperature: _____

    _____

    Coldest global temperature: _____

    _____

46. The locations of the warmest and coldest temperatures are over (land, water).

47. Calculate the *annual temperature range* at each of the following locations:

    Coastal Norway at 60°N: _____ °C (_____ °F)

    Siberia at 60°N, 120°E: _____ °C (_____ °F)

    On the equator over the center of the Atlantic Ocean: _____ °C (_____ °F)

48. Explain the large annual range of temperature in Siberia.

    _____

    _____

49. Why is the annual temperature range smaller along the coast of Norway than at the same latitude in Siberia?

    _____

    _____

50. Why is temperature relatively uniform throughout the year in the tropics?

    _____

    _____

51. Using the two maps in Figure 10, calculate the approximate average annual temperature range for your location. How does your temperature range compare with those in the tropics and Siberia?

    Average annual temperature range:

    _____ °C (_____ °F)

    _____

    _____

52. Trace the path of the 5°C isotherm over North America in January. Explain why the isotherm de-

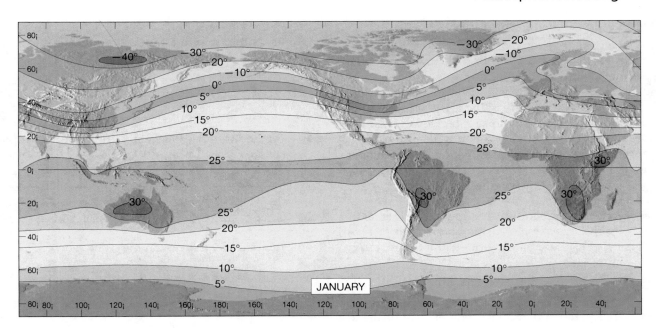

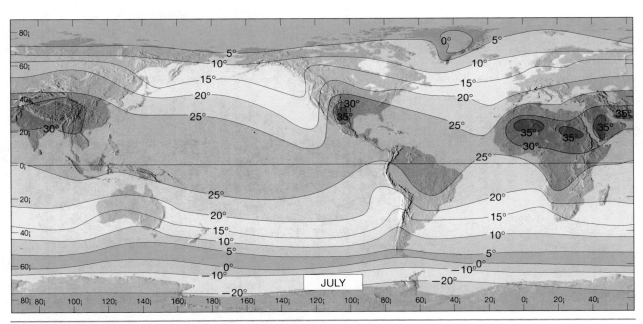

Figure 10   World distribution of mean surface temperatures (°C) for January and July.

viates from a true east–west trend where it crosses from the Pacific Ocean onto the continent.

_____

_____

53. Trace the path of the 20°C isotherm over North America in July. Explain why the isotherm deviates from a true east–west trend where it crosses from the Pacific Ocean onto the continent.

_____

_____

54. Why do the isotherms in the Southern Hemisphere follow a true east–west trend more closely than those in the Northern Hemisphere?

_____

_____

55. Why does the entire pattern of isotherms shift northward from the January map to the July map?

_____

_____

Temperature Changes with Altitude

Since the primary source of heat for the lower atmosphere is Earth's surface, the normal situation found in the lower 12 kilometers of the atmosphere is a decrease in temperature with increasing altitude. This temperature decrease with altitude in the lower atmosphere is called the **environmental lapse rate**. However, at altitudes from about 12 to 45 kilometers, the atmospheric absorption of incoming solar radiation causes temperature to increase.

Use Figure 11 to answer questions 56–60.

56. Using the temperature curve as a guide, label the *troposphere, mesosphere, stratosphere,* and *thermosphere* on the atmospheric temperature curve, Figure 11.

57. On Figure 11, mark with a line and label the *tropopause, mesopause,* and *stratopause.*

58. What is the approximate temperature of the atmosphere at each of the following altitudes?

    10 km: _____ °C (_____ °F)

    50 km: _____ °C (_____ °F)

    80 km: _____ °C (_____ °F)

59. Using Figure 11, calculate the average decrease in temperature with altitude of the troposphere in both °C/km and °F/mi.

    _____

60. Explain the reason for each of the following:

    Temperature decrease with altitude in the troposphere:

    _____

    _____

    Temperature increase in the stratosphere:

    _____

    _____

    Temperature increase in the thermosphere:

    _____

    _____

Figure 11   Atmospheric temperature curve.

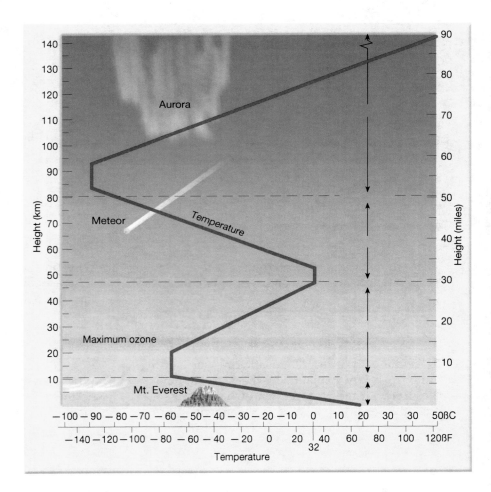

61. Of what importance is the gas *ozone* in the stratosphere? What will be the effect on radiation received at Earth's surface of a decrease of ozone in the stratosphere?

_____

_____

_____

Assume the average, or normal, environmental lapse rate (temperature decrease with altitude) in the troposphere is 3.5°F per 1,000 feet (6.5°C per kilometer).

62. If the surface temperature is 60°F (16°C), what would be the approximate temperature at 20,000 feet (6,000 meters)?

_____ °F (_____ °C)

63. If the surface temperature is 80°F (27°C), at approximately what altitude would a pilot expect to find each of the following atmospheric temperatures?

50°F: _____ feet (10°C: _____ meters)

0°C: _____ meters (32°F: _____ feet)

Periodically, the temperature near the surface of Earth increases with altitude. This situation, which is opposite from the normal condition, is called a **temperature inversion**.

64. Suggest a possible cause for a surface temperature inversion.

_____

_____

Windchill Equivalent Temperature

Windchill equivalent temperature is the term applied to the sensation of temperature that the human body feels, in contrast to the actual temperature of the air as recorded by a thermometer. Wind cools by evaporating perspiration and carrying heat away from the body. When temperatures are cool and the wind speed increases, the body reacts as if it were being subjected to increasingly lower temperatures—a phenomenon known as *windchill*.

65. Refer to the windchill equivalent temperature chart, Figure 12. What is the windchill equivalent temperature sensed by the human body in the following situations?

Air Temperature (°F)	Wind Speed (mph)	Windchill Equivalent Temperature (°F)
30°	10	_____
−5°	20	_____
−20°	30	_____

66. Write a brief summary of the effect of wind speed on how long a person can be exposed before frostbite develops.

_____

_____

_____

Atmospheric Heating on the Internet

Research current and historical atmospheric temperatures at your location by completing the corresponding online activity on the *Applications & Investigations in Earth Science* website at http://prenhall.com/ earthsciencelab

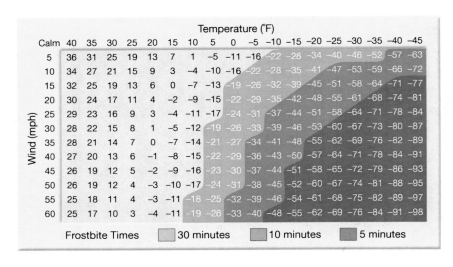

Figure 12 This windchill chart came into use in November 2001. Fahrenheit temperatures are used here because this is how the National Weather Service and the news media in the United States commonly report windchill information. The shaded areas on the chart indicate frostbite danger. Each shaded zone shows how long a person can be exposed before frostbite develops. (*After NOAA, National Weather Service*)

Notes and calculations.

Atmospheric Heating

Date Due: _____

Name: _____

Date: _____

Class: _____

After you have finished this exercise, complete the following questions. You may have to refer to the exercise for assistance or to locate specific answers. Be prepared to submit this summary/report to your instructor at the designated time.

1. Assume an average noon Sun angle. What percentage of the solar radiation will be absorbed by the atmosphere and what percentage will be absorbed by Earth's surface?

   Atmospheric absorption: _____ %

   Absorption by Earth's surface: _____ %

2. What will be the atmospheric effect of each of the following?

   Less ozone in the stratosphere:

   _____

   _____

   More carbon dioxide in the atmosphere:

   _____

   _____

   A surface with a high albedo:

   _____

   _____

3. Briefly explain how Earth's atmosphere is heated.

   _____

   _____

   _____

4. What are the primary heat-absorbing gases in the atmosphere? In general, what wavelength of radiation do they absorb?

   _____

   _____

5. What were the starting and 5-minute temperatures you obtained for the black and silver containers in the albedo experiment?

	STARTING TEMPERATURE	5-MINUTE TEMPERATURE
Black container:	_____	_____
Silver container:	_____	_____

6. Summarize the effect of color on the heating of an object.

   _____

   _____

7. What were the starting and ending temperatures you obtained for the water and dry sand in the land and water heating experiment?

	STARTING TEMPERATURE	ENDING TEMPERATURE
Water:	_____	_____
Dry sand:	_____	_____

8. Summarize the effects that equal amounts of radiation have on the heating of land and water.

_____

_____

9. Where are the highest and lowest average monthly temperatures located on Earth?

Highest average monthly temperature:

_____

_____

Lowest average monthly temperature:

_____

_____

10. Why does the Northern Hemisphere experience a greater annual range of temperature than the Southern Hemisphere?

_____

_____

11. Define each of the following:

Environmental lapse rate:

_____

_____

Windchill equivalent temperature:

_____

_____

Troposphere:

_____

_____

12. Referring to the average temperature graphs for Spokane and Seattle, Washington, shown in Figure 13, discuss the reason(s) why the two graphs are dissimilar, even though both cities are at about the same latitude.

_____

_____

_____

_____

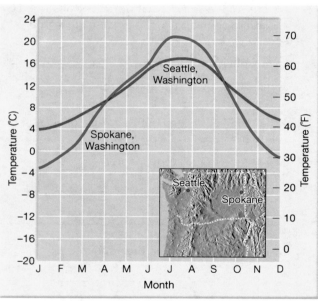

Figure 13   Temperature graphs for Spokane and Seattle, WA.

14

CLIMATE VARIABILITY AND CHANGE

Introduction

Is our climate changing? How can we tell? With recent interest in global warming, climatic variability and change have become popular topics. This interest has, however, highlighted the uncertainty involved in our understanding of the climate. It can be difficult to identify climate variability and change and to determine their specific causes. Moreover, the very way we collect data may influence the historic climate record. Added to these difficulties, climate change often involves times scales extending beyond our written climate records, requiring scientists to develop proxy measures for past climates. This lab will focus on some of the methods climatologists use to detect climate changes and some of the problems they have with their data.

Hypothetical Temperature Curves

With statistics, we can examine a time series—i.e., how a particular climate variable changes over time. One way of examining a time series is to break out its component parts. Statistical analysis can reveal different aspects of the time series. There may be a regular *cycle* present (Figure 1), an *upward trend* (Figure 2), or *sudden changes* (Figure 3). The goal of statisti-

cal analysis is to uncover a link between these components and the factors that may influence or force them, as the forcing factors themselves may exhibit similar cycles, trends, and sudden changes. The process is complicated because there usually is a *random* component (Figure 4) to each time series.

1. *Name and explain any mechanisms that could produce cyclical climate fluctuations, a linear trend, or a sudden increase or decrease in temperature.*

2. *Figure 5 shows a sample temperature time series. Rather than analyzing this time series statistically, see if you can visually detect any of the components discussed previously. Label those you find.*

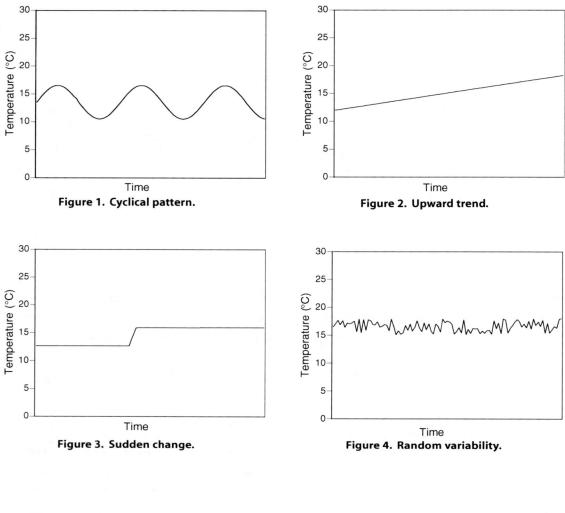

Figure 1. Cyclical pattern.

Figure 2. Upward trend.

Figure 3. Sudden change.

Figure 4. Random variability.

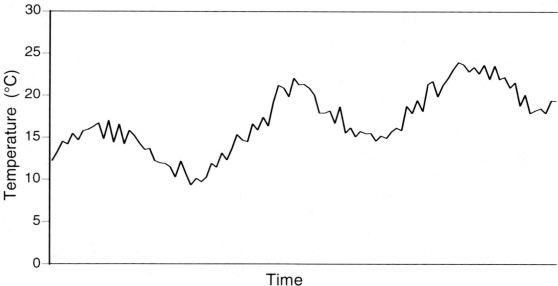

Figure 5. Temperature time series.

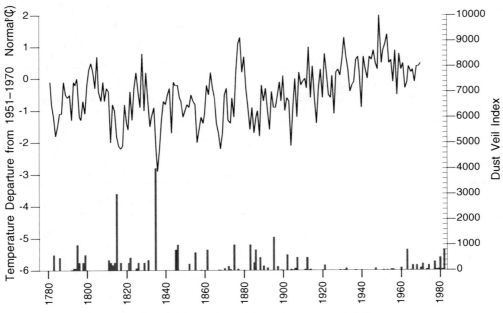

Figure 6. New Haven, CT, annual temperature variability.

3. Examine the New Haven, Connecticut, annual temperature anomaly curve (Figure 6). The data are plotted as °C deviations from the 1951–1970 mean. Negative values show below-normal temperatures, positive values above-normal temperatures. Comment on any patterns in the data such as cycles, gradual trends, or dramatic changes.

4. Which century was generally warmer, the 19th or the 20th?

5. The bars in Figure 6 show the annual dust veil index, a proxy for volcanic activity. The two largest spikes correspond to the eruptions of Mts. Tambora, Indonesia (1815), and Coseguina, Nicaragua (1835). For how long and by how much does the New Haven temperature record respond to those events?

Figure 7 shows Northern Hemisphere temperature estimates for the past millennium. The values used to construct the figure were derived from tree rings, ice cores, coral, and a variety of other techniques. They were compiled by P. D. Jones and M. E. Mann and were published in *Reviews of Geophysics* (2004). Figure 8 shows estimates of three factors influencing the earth's radiation budget. These *radiative forcings* can be viewed as increasing or decreasing radiation at the top of the atmosphere.

6. Using Figure 8, briefly describe changes in the solar forcing during the past 400 years. Do you detect a relationship between this forcing factor and Northern Hemisphere temperatures? Explain.

7. Briefly describe changes in greenhouse gas forcing during the past 400 years. Describe the correlation between this forcing factor and the reconstructed Northern Hemisphere temperature estimates.

8. What is the relationship between greenhouse gas forcing and aerosol forcing?

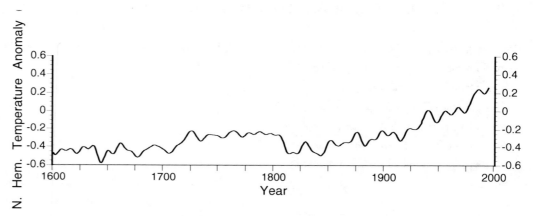

Figure 7. Northern Hemisphere temperature estimates.

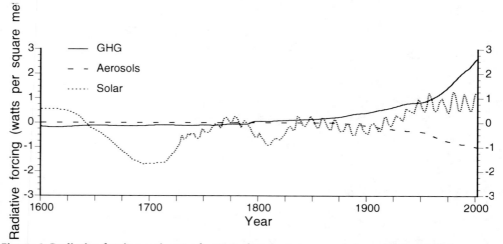

Figure 8. Radiative forcing estimates for greenhouse gases, aerosols, and solar radiation.

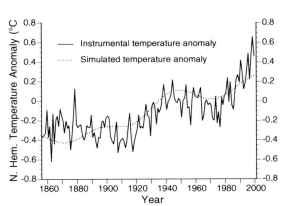

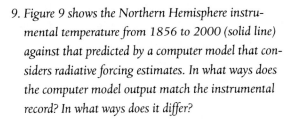

Figure 9. Simulated vs. instrumental temperature.

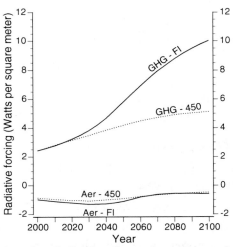

Figure 10. Estimates of greenhouse gas and aerosol forcing for two different scenarios.

9. *Figure 9 shows the Northern Hemisphere instrumental temperature from 1856 to 2000 (solid line) against that predicted by a computer model that considers radiative forcing estimates. In what ways does the computer model output match the instrumental record? In what ways does it differ?*

Figure 10 shows the radiative forcing of greenhouse gases and aerosols that would result from two future scenarios. One labeled "450" attempts to achieve a stabilization of carbon dioxide at 450 parts per million by the year 2100. It requires that carbon emissions begin decreasing in 2005 and reach half the 1990 emission levels by 2100. The other labeled "FI" assumes that fossil-fuel emissions will continue to increase at current rates until 2050, then increase at a slightly slower rate from 2050 to 2100. The forcings are projected on the same scale as those in Figure 8.

10. *Describe the magnitude of the projected radiative forcing changes (Figure 10) relative to those shown for the past 400 years (Figure 8).*

Table 1. Sample differences between urban and rural environments.

Variable	Urban Environment Compared with Rural Environment
Temperature	0.5°–1.5°C higher
Solar radiation	15%–30% less
Precipitation	5%–15% more
Wind speed	25% lower

The Effect of Urbanization

Estimates of climatic variability and change during the past 150 years are primarily derived from the instrumental record (i.e., compiled from direct observations with instruments). This record is more precise than indirect evidence, but it is not without problems. Sites in Europe and North America are disproportionately represented in the early part of the record and perhaps skew what we know about global climate. The growth of cities during this period also creates problems with the record, since urban climates differ significantly from surrounding rural areas (Table 1).

11. *Why would average temperature generally be higher in the city than in surrounding rural areas?*

12. *Table 1 shows that regional-scale urban winds are generally lower than those in surrounding rural areas. What do you think causes this? By contrast, the microscale winds around buildings can be relatively fast. Why? How could low wind speeds contribute to the urban heat island?*

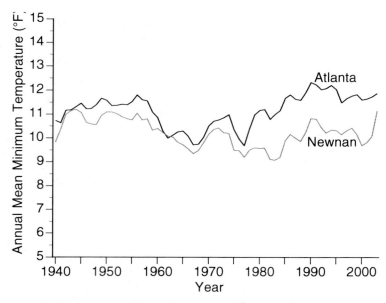

Figure 11. Atlanta and Newnan minimum temperatures, 3-year running mean, 1940–2004.

Figure 11 shows a 65-year record of annual mean minimum temperature for the Atlanta airport and Newnan, Georgia, located in a more rural setting approximately 45 km southwest of Atlanta.

13. *Using Figure 11, develop an argument supporting the idea that over time Atlanta's temperature has increasingly been influenced by an urban heat island.*

14. *How could urban heat islands influence our understanding of temperature changes during the past 150 years?*

Data from a study in Orlando, Florida, show how a city can affect diurnal temperatures. Figure 12 below compares the January 11 and 12 hourly temperatures at stations in Orlando's urban core with those from park locations on the outskirts of the metropolitan area.

15. *During what hours is the urban heat island most prominent? Why do you think it is more clearly defined during certain times of the day?*

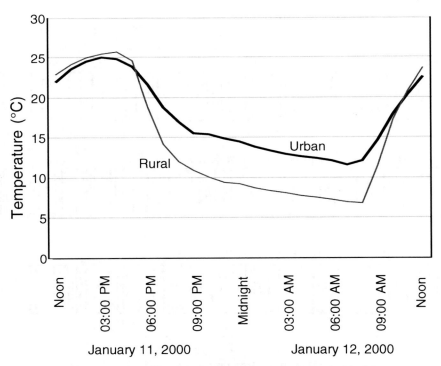

Figure 12. Rural vs. urban temperatures in Orlando, Florida.

Reconstructing Past Climate

Many of the physical mechanisms producing climate change act over long time periods and are, therefore, not evident in the relatively short instrumental climate record encompassing approximately the last 100 years. To uncover the details of past climate we must reconstruct the climate record using proxy data. Such reconstruction relies on the sensitivity of certain phenomena to climate. Plant and animal species, for example, respond to certain climate conditions, and their thresholds and their fossil record can indicate the presence of these conditions.

Tree-ring analysis has been used to reconstruct the climate over decades, centuries, and even millennia. It assumes that annual tree growth is limited or augmented by a particular climatic variable—such as summer temperature or winter and spring precipitation. For example, a narrow annual growth ring might indicate a dry year, a wide ring a wet year.

Tree ring analysis often requires cross-dating, i.e., comparing two or more cores to confirm the conditions of a given year. Cross-dating can also be used to extend the climate record into the past. Consider the three tree ring cores in Figure 13, all taken from an area where precipitation affects annual tree growth. The top core was taken in December 1990 from a living tree, and its outermost ring represents the growth in that year. Core 2 is from a beam of a house built in 1950. Core 3 is taken from a house built in 1912. The cores are read from right to left, so that the extreme left represents the oldest portion of each core.

16. *Examine the first core and label the newest ring 1990. Then mark every tenth ring, labeling them 1980, 1970, 1960, etc. Match the rings in the second core to the overlapping years in core 1 and continue marking every tenth ring, labeling the appropriate years. Do the same for the overlapping years between cores 2 and 3 to extend the record further into the past.*

17. *Which decades have unusually dry conditions?*

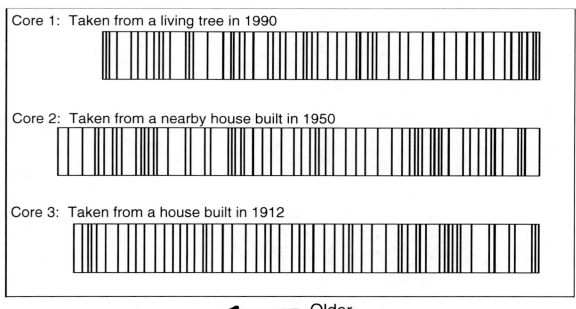

Figure 13. Tree ring cores.

Data from an Iowa tree ring study provide an example. Two researchers, Daniel Duvick and T. J. Blasing, cored white oak trees in south-central Iowa and correlated their annual ring width with precipitation during the preceding 12 months. Notice the relationship between precipitation and annual growth for the period 1880–1980 (Figure 14).

18. *Is the relationship stronger during wet years or dry years? (Hint: Circle the four driest seasons and the four wettest seasons and examine the corresponding ring width. Do the driest years correspond to the most narrow rings? Do the wettest years correspond to the widest rings?)*

Although tree rings provide detailed records for relatively recent climate history, many factors causing climatic change operate at longer time scales. The advance and retreat of glaciers, for example, have periods of tens of thousands of years or more. Fortunately, ocean fossils and ice cores preserve climate records at these longer time scales. Scientists have used two oxygen isotopes, ^{18}O and ^{16}O, found in ocean fossils as evidence of climatic change. Since ^{16}O evaporates more readily than ^{18}O, oceans are richer in ^{18}O during glacial advance, when water moves from oceans to continental glaciers. The shells of microorganisms produced during these periods preserve the ocean's higher ^{18}O concentrations. Ice cores from Greenland and Antarctica also preserve evidence of past climate or factors that influence climate. Air bubbles trapped in the ice, for example, can reveal past concentrations of greenhouse gases.

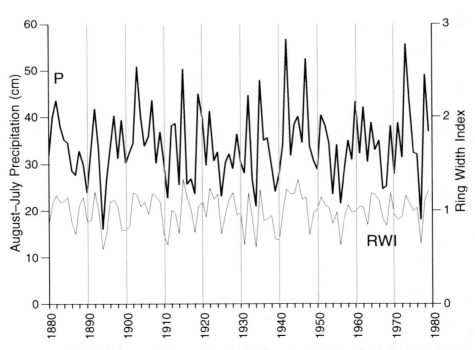

Figure 14. Tree-ring analysis: precipitation (dark solid line) vs. tree ring width (light dashed line).

Long-term variations in the path, tilt, and precession of the earth's orbit (Milankovitch cycles) strongly influence glacial advance and retreat. Glaciers retreat when these cycles combine to amplify the seasons in the Northern Hemisphere, creating relatively warm summers and relatively cool winters. Glaciers advance when the seasons are moderated—i.e., have relatively cool summers and relatively warm winters.

Figure 15 shows estimates of ice volume, CO_2 concentrations, and June insolation at 60° N latitude for the past 160,000 years. Use it to answer questions 19–23.

19. *When was the last time we had as little ice as we have today?*

20. *Examine the last glacial advance, 20,000 years ago. Was June insolation relatively high or relatively low at this time? How would a relatively cool summer contribute to glacial advance?*

21. *How could the CO_2 concentrations 20,000 years ago contribute to a global temperature that is cooler than today's?*

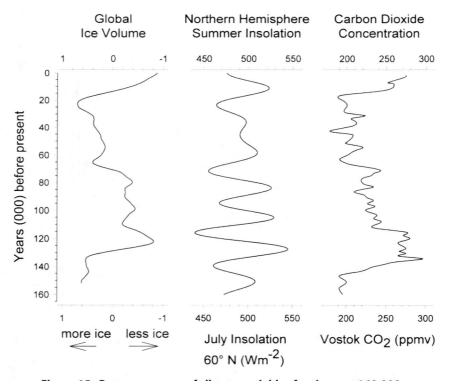

Figure 15. Proxy measures of climate variables for the past 160,000 years.

22. *Scientists examining paleoclimate records are often curious about which variables lead and which lag. How does the timing of June insolation minima relate to glacial ice volume at 135,000, 65,000, and 20,000 years before present? Which variable leads and which lags?*

23. *How is the relative timing of changes in ice volume and CO_2 more complicated?*

Optional Exercise: The Climate Record in Your Area

Examine the instrumental climate record for your area. You may want to collect data from the National Oceanic and Atmospheric Administration (NOAA) Climatological Data Series, which is found in many government documents libraries and is also available from various Internet sources (e.g., http://cdiac.esd.ornl.gov/r3d/ushcn/ushcn.html). Does the instrumental record show any special patterns over time? Can you make any general statements about climatic variability and change for your area?

You may be interested in the local climate during times preceding the instrumental record. Perhaps there are resources in a historical library such as records of missionaries, traders, or early settlers that could help you to reconstruct the climate. Often, diaries provide information about general temperature and precipitation patterns of the past.

Can you think of some other way that you could learn about the past climate of a particular area?

Review Questions

What challenges face climatologists interested in reconstructing the climate of the past?

Which of the two future emissions scenarios shown in Figure 10 seems more likely to you? Why?

Past climates could provide clues to future changes, but how does predicting the future climate become more complicated than simply extrapolating from past records?

What is the basis for using tree-ring analysis to reconstruct the climate? What are the potential advantages and disadvantages of this method?

15

HOW BIG IS YOUR ECOLOGICAL FOOTPRINT?

This project is best done as a homework assignment after Lab 14 or 15, which addresses the major greenhouse gases and their sources. This assignment requires that you assess your ecological footprint by answering a series of questions on-line at the following website: http://www.myfootprint.org/ .

Questions:

1. Before you begin guess how many Earth's would be needed to support the world's population if everyone live as you do.

My best guess is: _____ Earth's

2. Take note as you complete the quiz how you compare to your country's average. Your running tally is a small box on the right of the screen. Which variables seem to change your footprint the most in each category?

       Carbon footprint: _____

       Food footprint: _____

       Housing footprint: _____

       Goods and services footprint: _____

3. For each of the four categories how does your footprint compare to the American Average?

Carbon - American Average: _____My Footprint: _____

Food: - American Average: _____My Footprint: _____

Housing - American Average: _____My Footprint: _____

Goods/services - American Average: _____My Footprint: _____

4. On which biome is your footprint the strongest? Weakest?

5. Were there any questions, which you did not expect to have an influence on your ecological footprint?

6. What is an ecological footprint?

7. So, how big is your ecological footprint? How many Earth's would be needed to support the world's population if everyone live as you do.

_____ Earth's

16

Patterns in the Solar System

Although composed of many diverse objects, the solar system (Figure 1) exhibits various degrees of order and several regular patterns. To simplify the investigation of planetary sizes, masses, etc., the planets can be arranged into two distinct groups, with the members of each displaying similar attributes. This exercise examines the physical properties and motions of the planets with the goal of summarizing these characteristics in a few general, easily remembered statements.

Objectives

After you have completed this exercise, you should be able to:

1. Describe the appearance of the solar system when it is viewed along the plane of the ecliptic.
2. Summarize the distances and spacing of the planets in the solar system.

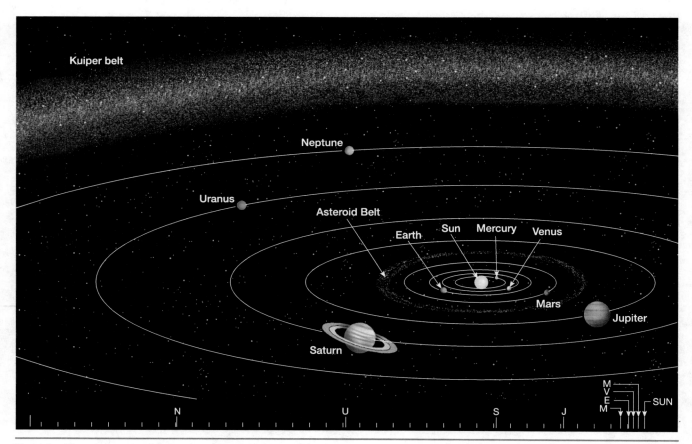

Figure 1   The solar system showing the orbits of the planets to scale. A different scale has been used for the sizes of the Sun and planets. Therefore, the diagram is not a true scale model representation of the solar system.

3. Summarize and compare the physical characteristics of the terrestrial and Jovian planets.

4. Describe the motions of the planets in the solar system.

Materials

ruler
colored pencils
calculator

Materials Supplied by Your Instructor

4-meter length of adding
   machine paper
meterstick
light source
   (150-watt bulb)

black containers
   with covers and
   thermometers

Terms

nebula
terrestrial planets
Jovian planets
dwarf planets
plane of the ecliptic

mass
density
weight
rotation

revolution
Kepler's laws
astronomical unit

Introduction

The order that exists within the solar system is directly related to the laws of physics that governed its formation. Astronomers have determined that the Sun and planets originated approximately 4.6 billion years ago from an enormous cloud of dust and gas. As this **nebula** contracted, it began to rotate and flatten. Eventually the temperature and pressure in the center of the cloud was great enough to initiate nuclear fusion and form the Sun.

Near the center of the nebula, the planets Mercury, Venus, Earth, and Mars evolved under nearly the same conditions and consequently exhibit similar physical properties. Because these planets are rocky objects with solid surfaces, they are collectively called the **terrestrial (Earth-like) planets**.

The outer planets, Jupiter, Saturn, Uranus, and Neptune, being farther from the Sun than the terrestrial planets, formed under much colder conditions and are gaseous objects with central cores of ices and rock. Since the four planets are very similar, they are often grouped together and called the **Jovian (Jupiterlike) planets**.

The **dwarf planets**, which include, among other celestial objects, Pluto and the former asteroid Ceres, are not included with either the terrestrial or Jovian planets.

Table 1 illustrates many of the individual characteristics of the planets in the solar system.

1. Examine the data in Table 1, then

   a. Draw lines on the upper and lower parts of Table 1 that separate the terrestrial planets from the Jovian planets. Label the lines "Belt of Asteroids."

Table 1 Planetary data.

| Planet | Symbol | Mean Distance from Sun | | | Period of Revolution | Inclination of Orbit | Orbital Velocity | |
		AU	Millions of Miles	Millions of Kilometers			mi/s	km/s
Mercury	☿	0.387	36	58	88^d	7°00'	29.5	47.5
Venus	♀	0.723	67	108	224.7^d	3°24'	21.8	35.0
Earth	⊕	1.000	93	150	365.25^d	0°00'	18.5	29.8
Mars	♂	1.524	142	228	687^d	1°51'	14.9	24.1
Jupiter	♃	5.203	483	778	11.86^{yr}	1°18'	8.1	13.1
Saturn	♄	9.539	886	1427	29.46^{yr}	2°29'	6.0	9.6
Uranus	♅	19.180	1783	2870	84^{yr}	0°46'	4.2	6.8
Neptune	♆	30.060	2794	4497	165^{yr}	1°46'	3.3	5.3

| Planet | Period of Rotation | Diameter | | Relative Mass (Earth = 1) | Average Density (g/cm^3) | Polar Flattening (%) | Mean Temperature (°C) | Number of Known Satellites |
		Miles	Kilometers					
Mercury	59^d	3015	4854	0.056	5.4	0.0	167	0
Venus	244^d	7526	12,112	0.82	5.2	0.0	464	0
Earth	23^{h}56^{m}04^s	7920	12,751	1.00	5.5	0.3	15	1
Mars	24^{h}37^{m}23^s	4216	6788	0.108	3.9	0.5	−65	2
Jupiter	9^{h}50^m	88,700	143,000	317.87	1.3	6.7	−110	63
Saturn	10^{h}14^m	75,000	121,000	95.14	0.7	10.4	−140	56
Uranus	17^{h}14^m	29,000	47,000	14.56	1.2	2.3	−195	27
Neptune	16^{h}03^m	28,900	46,529	17.21	1.7	1.8	−200	13

b. On both parts of the table write the word "terrestrial" next to Mercury, Venus, Earth, and Mars and the word "Jovian" next to Jupiter, Saturn, Uranus, and Neptune.

The "Shape" of the Solar System

When the solar system is viewed from the side, the orbits of the planets all lie in nearly the same plane, called the **plane of the ecliptic** (Figure 1). The column labeled "Inclination of Orbit" in Table 1 lists how many degrees the orbit of each planet is inclined from the plane. Answer questions 2–4 by referring to Table 1.

2. Other than Mercury, whose orbit is inclined (4, 7, 10) degrees, the orbits of the remaining planets are all within (4, 7, 10) degrees of the plane of the ecliptic. Circle your answers.

3. The orbit of the dwarf planet Pluto is inclined 17° to the plane. When compared to the eight planets, Pluto's orbit is:

_____

4. Considering the nebular origin of the solar system, suggest a reason why the orbits of the planets are nearly all in the same plane.

_____

_____

Distance and Spacing of the Planets

An examination of any scale-model solar system reveals that the distances from the Sun and the spacing between the planets appear to follow a regular pattern. Although many ancient astronomers were concerned with planetary distances and spacing, it was not until the mid-1700s that astronomers found a simple mathematical relation that described the arrangement of the planets known at the time.

A Scale Model of Planetary Distances

Perhaps the best way to examine distance and spacing of the planets in the solar system is to use a scale model.

5. Prepare a distance scale model of the solar system according to the following steps.

Step 1: Obtain a 4-meter length of adding machine paper and a meterstick from your instructor.

Step 2: Draw an "X" about 10 centimeters from one end of the adding machine paper and label it "Sun."

Step 3: Using the mean distances of the planets from the Sun in miles presented in Table 1 and the following scale, draw a small circle for each planet at its proper scale mile distance from the Sun. Use a different colored pencil for the terrestrial and Jovian planets and write the name of the planet next to its position.

SCALE

1 millimeter =   1 million miles

1 centimeter =   10 million miles

1 meter = 1,000 million miles

Step 4: Write the word "asteroids" 258 million scale miles from the Sun.

Answer questions 6–9 using the distance scale model you constructed in question 5.

6. What feature of the solar system separates the terrestrial planets from the Jovian planets?

_____

7. Observe the scale model diagram and summarize the spacing for each of the two groups of planets.

Spacing of the terrestrial planets: _____

_____

Spacing of the Jovian planets: _____

_____

8. Write a brief statement that describes the spacing of the planets in the solar system.

_____

_____

9. Which planet(s) vary the most from the general pattern of spacing?

_____

Comparing the Terrestrial and Jovian Planets

The physical characteristics such as diameter, density, and mass of the terrestrial planets are very similar and can be summarized in a few statements. Likewise, the characteristics exhibited by the Jovian planets as a group can also be generalized.

To gain an understanding of the similarities of the planets within each of the two groups and the contrasts between the two groups, complete the following sections using the planetary data presented in Table 1.

Size of the Planets

The similarities in the diameters of the planets within each of the two groups and the contrast between the groups are perhaps the most obvious patterns in the solar system. The diameter of each planet is given in both miles and kilometers in Table 1.

10. To visually compare the relative sizes of the planets and Sun, complete the following steps using the unmarked side of your 4-meter length of adding machine paper.

Step 1: Determine the radius of each planet in kilometers by dividing its diameter (in kilometers) by 2. List your answers in the "Radius" column of Table 2.

Step 2: Use a scale of 1 cm = 2,000 km. Determine the scale model radius of each planet and list your answer in the "Scale Model Radius" column of Table 2.

Step 3: Draw an "X" about 10 cm from one end of the adding machine paper and label it "Starting point."

Step 4: Using the scale model radius in Table 2, begin at the starting point and mark the radius of each planet with a line on the paper. Use a different colored pencil for the terrestrial and Jovian planets. Label each line with the planet's name.

Step 5: The diameter of the Sun is approximately 1,350,000 kilometers. Using the same scale as you used for the planets (1 cm = 2000 km), determine the scale model radius of the Sun. Mark the Sun's radius on the adding machine paper using a different colored pencil from the two planet groups. Label the line "Sun."

Table 2   Planetary Radii with Scale Model Equivalents

Planet	Radius (in kilometers)	Scale Model Radius
Mercury	_____	_____ cm
Venus	_____	_____ cm
Earth	_____	_____ cm
Mars	_____	_____ cm
Jupiter	_____	_____ cm
Saturn	_____	_____ cm
Uranus	_____	_____ cm
Neptune	_____	_____ cm

Answer questions 11–17 using both Table 1 and the scale model radius diagram you constructed in question 10.

11. Which is the largest of the terrestrial planets and what is its diameter?

    _____, _____ miles

12. Which is the smallest Jovian planet and what is its diameter?

    _____, _____ miles

13. Complete the following statement.

    The smallest Jovian planet, _____, is _____ times larger than the largest terrestrial planet.

14. Summarize the sizes of the planets within each group.

    The diameters of the terrestrial planets: _____

    _____

    The diameters of the Jovian planets: _____

    _____

15. Write a general statement that compares the sizes of the terrestrial planets to those of the Jovian planets.

    _____

    _____

16. Complete the following statement.

    The Sun is _____ times larger than Earth and _____ times larger than Jupiter.

17. The diameter of the dwarf planet Pluto is approximately 1,500 miles, which is about (one-third, one-half, twice) the diameter of the smallest planet. Circle your answer.

Mass and Density of the Planets

Mass is a measure of the quantity of matter an object contains. In Table 1 the masses of the planets are given in relation to the mass of Earth. For example, the mass of Mercury is given as 0.056, which means that it consists of only a small fraction of the quantity of matter that Earth contains. On the other hand, the Jovian planets all contain several times more matter than Earth.

Density is the mass per unit volume of a substance. In Table 1 the average densities of the planets are expressed in grams per cubic centimeter (g/cm^3). As a reference, the density of water is approximately one gram per cubic centimeter.

Using the relative masses of the planets given in Table 1, answer questions 18–22.

18. Complete the following statements:

    a. The planet _____ is the most massive planet in the solar system. It is _____ times more massive than Earth.

    b. The least massive planet is _____, which contains only _____ as much mass as Earth.

The gravitational attraction of a planet is directly related to its mass.

19. Which planet exerts the greatest, and which the least, pull of gravity? Explain your answer.

    _____

    _____

Your **weight** is a function of the gravitational attraction of an object on your mass.

20. The surface gravities of Mars and Jupiter are respectively about 0.4 and 2.5 that of Earth. What would be your approximate weight on each of these planets?

    _____

21. Which of the two groups of planets would have the greatest ability to hold large quantities of gas as part of their compositions? Explain your answer.

    _____

    _____

22. Write a general statement comparing the masses and gravitational attractions of the terrestrial planets to those of the Jovian planets.

    _____

    _____

Diameter versus Density

To visually compare the diameters and densities of the planets, use the data in Table 1 to complete the diameter versus density graph, Figure 2, according to the procedure in question 23.

23. Plot a point on the diameter verses density graph, Figure 2, for each planet where its diameter intersects its density. Label each point with the planet's name. Use a different colored pencil for the terrestrial and Jovian planets.

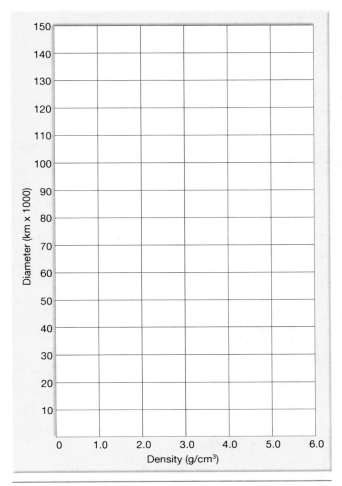

Figure 2   Diameter verses density graph.

Answer questions 24–34 using Table 1 and the diameter verses density graph you constructed in question 23.

24. What general relation exists between a planet's size and its density?

    _____

25. Consider the fact that the densities of the two rocks that form the majority of Earth's surface, the igneous rocks granite and basalt, are each about 3.0 g/cm³. Therefore, the average density of the terrestrial planets is (greater, less than) the density of Earth's surface. Circle your answer.

26. The term (rocky, gaseous) best describes the terrestrial planets. Circle your answer.

27. The average density of Earth is about 5.5 g/cm³. Considering that the densities of the surface rocks are much less than the average, what does this suggest about the density of Earth's interior?

    _____

28. Which of the planets has a density less than water and therefore would "float"?

_____

29. Write a brief statement comparing the densities of the Jovian planets to the density of water.

_____

_____

30. The Jovian planets can be best described as (rocky, ice, and gas) worlds. Circle your answer.

31. Explain why Jupiter can be such a massive object and yet have such a low density.

_____

32. Write a general statement comparing the densities of the terrestrial planets to the Jovian planets.

_____

_____

33. Why are the densities of the terrestrial and Jovian planets so different?

_____

_____

34. The mass of Pluto, about 0.002 that of Earth's, is most like the masses of the (terrestrial, Jovian) planets, while its density of approximately 2.0 gm/cm^3 is similar to the (terrestrial, Jovian) planets. This suggests that this dwarf planet is made of (solid rock, a rock and ice mixture, all gas). Circle the correct responses.

Number of Moons of the Planets

The column labeled "Number of Known Satellites" in Table 1 indicates the number of known moons orbiting each planet.

35. Write a brief statement comparing the number of known moons of the terrestrial planets to the number orbiting the Jovian planets.

_____

_____

36. What is the general relation between the number of moons a planet has compared to its mass? Suggest a reason for the relation.

_____

_____

_____

Rotation and Revolution of the Planets

Rotation is the turning of a planet about its axis that is responsible for day and night. When the solar system is viewed from above the Northern Hemisphere of Earth, the planets, with the exception of Venus, rotate in a counterclockwise direction. Venus exhibits a very slow clockwise rotation. The time that it takes for a planet to complete one 360° rotation on its axis is called the *period of rotation*. The units used to measure a planet's period of rotation are Earth hours and days.

Revolution is the motion of a planet around the Sun. The time that it takes a planet to complete one revolution about the Sun is the length of its year, called the *period of revolution*. The units used to measure a planet's period of revolution are Earth days and years. Without exception, the direction of revolution of the planets is counterclockwise around the Sun when the solar system is viewed from above the Northern Hemisphere of Earth.

Use the planetary data in Table 1 to answer questions 37–46.

37. If you could live on Venus or Jupiter, approximately how long would you have to wait between sunrises?

On Venus a sunrise would occur every _____ days.

On Jupiter a sunrise would occur every _____ hours.

38. Write a statement comparing the periods of rotation of the terrestrial planets to those of the Jovian planets.

_____

_____

The giant planet Jupiter rotates once on its axis approximately every 10 hours. If an object were on the equator of the planet and rotating with it, it would travel approximately 280,000 miles (the equatorial circumference or distance around the equator) in about 10 hours.

39. Calculate the equatorial rotational velocity of Jupiter using the following formula.

$$\text{Velocity} = \frac{\text{Distance}}{\text{Time}} = \frac{\text{_____ mi}}{\text{_____ hr}}$$

$$= \text{_____ mi/hr}$$

40. The equatorial circumference of Earth is about 24,000 miles. What is the approximate equatorial rotational velocity of Earth?

_____ miles/hour

41. How many times faster is Jupiter's equatorial rotational velocity than Earth's?

_____ times faster

42. Compare the planets' periods of rotation to their periods of revolution and then complete the following statement by circling the correct responses.

The terrestrial planets all have (long, short) days and (long, short) years, while the Jovian planets all have (long, short) days and (short, long) years.

43. In one Earth year, how many revolutions will the planet Mercury complete and what fraction of a revolution will Neptune accomplish?

Mercury: _____ revolutions in one Earth year

Neptune: _____ of a revolution in one Earth year

44. On Venus, how many days (sunrises) would there be in each of its years?

_____ day(s) per year

45. How many days (rotations) will Mercury complete in one of its years?

Mercury: _____ Mercury days in one Mercury year

46. Explain the relation between a planet's period of rotation and period of revolution that would cause one side of a planet to face the Sun throughout its year.

_____

_____

In the early 1600s Johannes Kepler set forth three laws of planetary motion. According to Kepler's third law, the period of revolution of a planet, measured in Earth years, is related to its distance from the Sun in astronomical units (one **astronomical unit (AU)** is defined as the average distance from the Sun to Earth—93 million miles or 150 million kilometers). The law states that a planet's orbital period squared is equal to its mean solar distance cubed ($p^2 = d^3$).

47. Applying Kepler's third law, what would be the period of revolution of a hypothetical planet that is 4 AUs from the Sun? Show your calculation in the following space.

_____

_____

_____

Terrestrial Planet Temperatures

The temperature of an object is related to the intensity of the heat source, its distance from the source, and the nature of the material it is composed of. To better understand how these variables influence the temperatures of the terrestrial planets, observe the equipment in the laboratory (Figure 3) and then complete the following steps. Answer questions 48–51 after you complete your investigation.

Step 1: Working in groups of four or more, obtain four *identical* light (heat) sources and four *identical* black containers with covers and thermometers.

Step 2: Conduct four experiments simultaneously, one by each member of the group. Do one experiment with the covered can and thermometer 15 cm from the light source, another with the can 30 cm from the light source, the third 45 cm, and the fourth 60 cm.

Step 3: Note the starting temperature for each container on Table 3; the temperatures should all be the same.

Step 4: For each of the four setups, turn on the light and record the temperature of the container exactly 10 minutes later. Record the temperatures in Table 3.

Step 5: Using the temperature scale on the left axis of the graph, plot the temperatures from Table 3

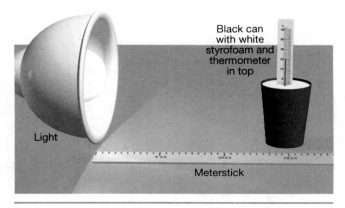

Figure 3 Terrestrial planet temperatures lab-equipment setup.

Table 3 Temperature Data

Distance from Light Source (cm)	Starting Temperature (°C)	10-minute Temperature
15		
30		
45		
60		

on the graph in Figure 4. Connect the points and label the graph "temperature change with distance."

Step 6: In Table 1, notice the mean temperatures for the planets. Plot the mean temperatures of the terrestrial planets at their proper locations on the graph, Figure 4. Assume a scale of 40 cm equals 1 AU and use the temperature scale on the right axis of the graph. Label each point with the planet's name. Connect the points and label the graph "mean terrestrial planet temperatures."

48. The "temperature change with distance" graph represents how you would expect that, everything else being equal, the temperature of a planet would be related to its distance from the Sun.

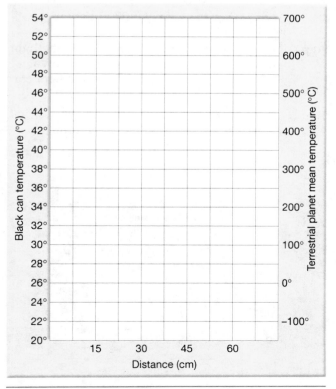

Figure 4 Terrestrial planet temperatures graph.

In the following space, write a brief description of the "temperature change with distance" graph.

_____

_____

_____

49. The "mean terrestrial planet temperatures" graph represents the real mean temperatures of the planets. Compare this graph to the theoretical "temperature change with distance graph." How are the graphs similar? How are they different?

_____

_____

_____

_____

50. Write a brief statement suggesting the reason(s) for the difference(s) between the two graphs you noted in question 49.

_____

_____

_____

51. Complete your investigation by writing a statement describing the mean temperatures of the terrestrial planets and the variables that determine those temperatures.

_____

_____

_____

_____

The Solar System on the Internet

Continue your analyses of the topics presented in this exercise by completing the corresponding online activity on the *Applications & Investigations in Earth Science* website at http://prenhall.com/earthsciencelab

Patterns in the Solar System

Date Due: _____

Name: _____

Date: _____

Class: _____

After you have finished this exercise, complete the following questions. You may have to refer to the exercise for assistance or to locate specific answers. Be prepared to submit this summary/report to your instructor at the designated time.

1. On Figure 5, prepare a sketch illustrating the planets Mercury, Venus, Earth, and Mars at their approximate distance from the Sun. View the solar system from above the Northern Hemisphere of Earth. Draw arrows around each planet to illustrate its direction of rotation. Also, draw an arrow in the orbit of each planet that shows the direction of revolution.

2. Briefly describe the spacing of the planets in the solar system.

_____

_____

_____

3. Define the following terms:

Terrestrial planets: _____

_____

Jovian planets: _____

_____

Plane of the ecliptic: _____

_____

Rotation: _____

_____

Mass: _____

_____

Astronomical unit: _____

_____

Figure 5   Spacing and motion of the terrestrial planets.

4. Referring to the nebular origin of the solar system, describe and explain the direction of revolution of the planets.

_____

_____

_____

5. Write a brief statement for each of the following characteristics that compares the terrestrial to the Jovian planets.

Diameter: _____

_____

_____

Density: _____

_____

Period of rotation: _____

_____

_____

Number of moons: _____

_____

_____

Mass: _____

_____

_____

6. If you knew the distance of a planet from the Sun, explain how you would calculate its period of revolution.

_____

_____

_____

7. How does a planet's distance from the Sun affect the solar radiation the planet receives? Why?

_____

_____

_____

8. How are the mean temperatures of the terrestrial planets related to the solar radiation they intercept? What is the explanation for any discrepancy?

_____

_____

_____

_____

9. Considering what you have learned about general patterns in the solar system, after reexamining the characteristics of Pluto, discuss why this former planet was reclassified as a dwarf planet in 2006.

_____

_____

_____

17

EXERCISE

Examining the Terrestrial Planets

Of the terrestrial planets, Earth exhibits the most complex and diverse topography (Figure 1). Fortunately, living on the planet allows us the opportunity to investigate in detail those geologic processes that continuously modify its surface. However, scientists are also painfully aware that the processes active on today's Earth have also removed much of the record of our planet's geologic history.

With the use of increasingly more sophisticated earthbound instruments, and during recent decades, complex spacecraft, early speculation about the nature of the objects that comprise the solar system has given way to detailed scientific investigation. In this investigation you will explore those natural processes that shape not only our planet, Earth, but, to some degree, all the terrestrial planets.

Objectives

After you have completed this exercise, you should be able to:

1. List and describe the geologic processes that have shaped the landforms of the terrestrial planets.
2. Give an example of a feature on Earth or the Moon produced by each of the geologic processes that have shaped the landforms of the terrestrial planets.
3. List the primary geologic processes that have shaped the landforms on each of the terrestrial planets.
4. Describe the procedure for determining the relative ages of a planet's surface features.

Materials

ruler
colored pencils
calculator

Figure 1   The terrestrial planets. (Image courtesy of NASA)

Terms

volcanism	gradation
tectonism	impact cratering

Geologic Processes of the Terrestrial Planets

The forces that drive Earth's evolution and contour its surface also operate elsewhere in the solar system. Thanks to detailed investigations of our Moon and neighbor planets, scientists are now examining how the

From *Applications and Investigations in Earth Science,* Sixth Edition, Edward J. Tarbuck, Frederick K. Lutgens, Kenneth G. Pinzke. Copyright © 2009 by Pearson Education, Inc. Published by Pearson Prentice Hall. All rights reserved.

four main geologic processes that act on Earth's surface (volcanism, tectonism, gradation, and impact cratering) have shaped the exteriors of other members of the solar system. Since each of these processes often produces distinctive landforms or surface features, by identifying and analyzing these objects it is possible to begin to unravel the geologic history of a planetary surface.

Volcanism and tectonism are driven by a planet's internal forces, with both tending to increase the relief and enhance the topography of a planet. The process of **volcanism** is the eruption of molten rock material (*magma*) and its associated gases onto a planet's surface. Steep, conical hills with summit *craters,* or large *calderas,* and regions covered by rock that appears to have at one time flowed are distinctive as volcanic in origin. **Tectonism** involves the movement of crustal rock by fracturing, faulting, or folding. The process is responsible for the major structural or deformational features of a planet. Landforms produced by tectonism are typically straight or gently curving and include mountain ranges, ridges, and fault scarps.

Gradation, the process that levels a surface to a common elevation by erosion and deposition, is controlled by the surface environment of a planet. Gravity, temperature, and the presence of an atmosphere all play key roles. The major agents of gradation include running water, gravity, wind, and ice.

The fourth geologic process acting on a planet's surface, **impact cratering**, is the consequence of rapidly moving *meteoroids* from space striking the surface. Large craters resulting from such impacts often have central pinnacles (peaks) and are surrounded by a blanket of material, called *ejecta,* which has been thrown from the crater.

Our understanding of the geologic histories of the planets and their satellites is based on observations of their surfaces. This exercise investigates and compares the surfaces of Mercury, Venus, Earth (and the Moon), and Mars at both global and detailed scales. At a global scale, only the largest and most prominent landforms and terrains—such as large volcanoes, canyons, mountains, etc.—are visible. However, detailed examination of a landform and its relation to the surrounding landscape can be used to understand a single feature's specific evolution.

Geologic Landforms on Earth

Geologic processes frequently result in distinctive landforms, which can be identified based on their shapes and forms. For example, the characteristic shapes of volcanoes or impact craters, and the branching pattern of a river system.

Begin your investigation of geologic processes by examining those at work on Earth and its Moon. Use the photographs in Figure 2 to answer questions 1–10.

1. Selecting from the lettered photographs (Figure 2a–j), list the letter of one or more examples of features produced by each of the four geologic processes that modify the surfaces of Earth and/or its Moon.

   Volcanism: _____

   Tectonism: _____

   Gradation: _____

   Impact cratering: _____

   Photographs 2a, b, and h are representative of gradational processes on Earth. The major agents of gradation are running water, wind, gravity, and ice.

2. Indicate the agent responsible for the feature in each photo (Figure 2a, b, and h) by writing the name of the agent by the image.

   Figure 2i is Meteor Crater, an impact crater in Arizona. Figure 2c is of Mount Capulin, a volcanic cone in New Mexico.

3. Describe the general shape of the impact crater compared to that of the volcanic cone.

   _____

   _____

   Meteor Crater has a diameter of approximately 1,200 meters. It is estimated that the object that produced it was about 25 meters across.

4. How many times greater is the size of the crater than the object that produced it? Suggest a reason(s) why such a comparatively small object can form such a large hole.

   _____

   _____

   _____

5. Meteor Crater, one of the best preserved impact craters on Earth, has been somewhat eroded. Describe the evidence for this erosion.

   _____

   _____

6. It is very likely that at one time Meteor Crater had a central peak. What might have happened to this feature?

   _____

   _____

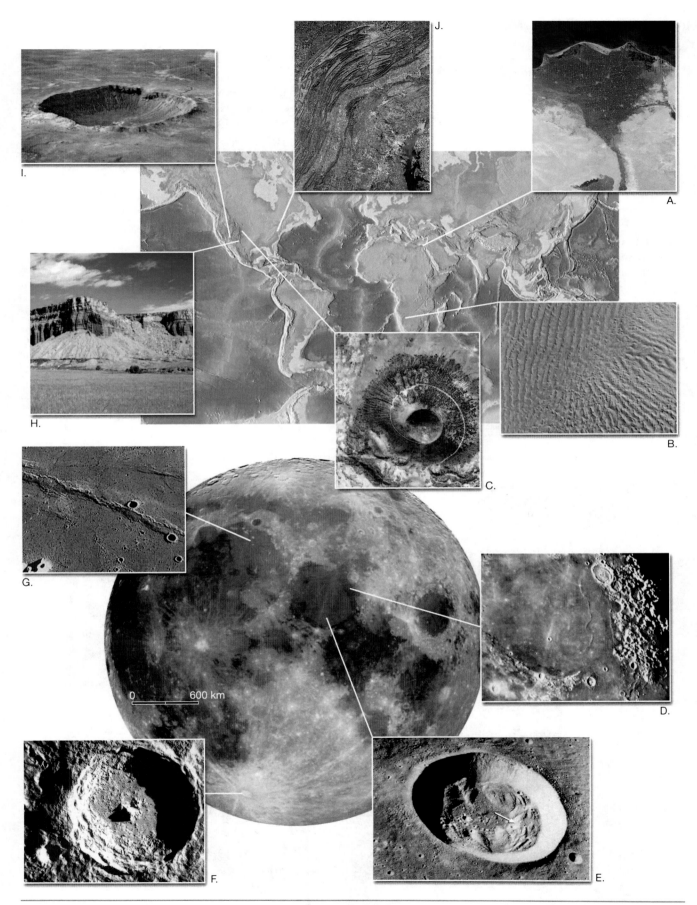

Figure 2 Geologic processes on the Earth and Moon. (A. and J. NASA/GSFC/JPL, MISR Team; B. Image provided by the USGS EROS Data Center Satellite Branch; C. Courtesy of U.S. Geological Survey; D. Lunar and Planetary Institute/Universities Research Association; E.-G. Courtesy of NASA; Moon, Courtesy of NASA/JPL-Caltech; H. Courtesy of USGS; I. Photograph by David Roddy, USGS)

7. Which lunar feature (Figure 2d, e, f, or g) most resembles Meteor Crater? Describe its appearance and probable origin.

_____

_____

8. Locate and label the lava flow at the base of Mt. Capulin (Figure 2c). Is it smooth or rough?

_____

9. The large, smooth, dark lunar feature represented in Figure 2d was most likely formed by (volcanism, gradation), whereas the feature inside the crater in 2e is most likely the result of gradation by (wind, water, gravity). Circle your answers.

10. Figure 2j, a portion of the folded Appalachian Mountains, is representative of tectonism on Earth. Which lunar photo best represents the same geologic process on the Moon? What may have produced the lunar feature?

_____

_____

Mercury

Mercury, the closest planet to the Sun, is only slightly larger than Earth's Moon. This smallest planet has no atmosphere and experiences a surface temperature range of 600° (−173°C–427°C). With noontime temperatures approaching 800°F (427°C), its exterior is one of the most extreme environments in the solar system. Use the images in Figure 3 to answer questions 11–13.

11. How does the surface of Mercury, Figure 3, compare to that of the Moon? What are the similarities? What are some differences?

_____

_____

_____

12. Of the four processes that alter a planet's surface, which is *least* effective on Mercury? Explain the reason for your choice.

_____

_____

_____

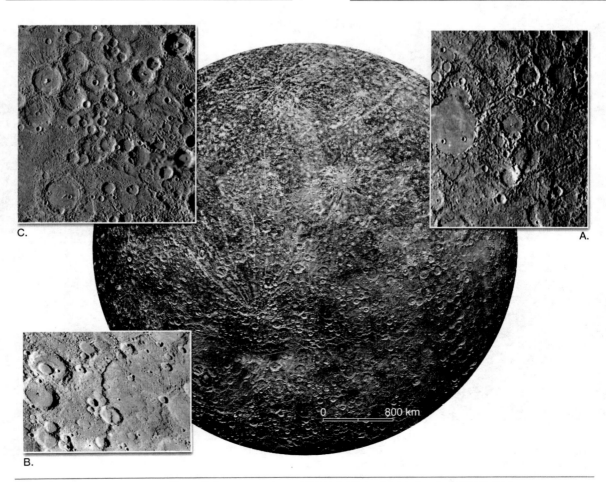

C.

A.

B.

Figure 3   Geologic processes on Mercury. (Images courtesy of NASA Jet Propulsion Laboratory, NASA-JPL)

13. Choosing from the geologic processes that act on a planet's surface, write the name of the process most likely responsible for the features in Figures 3a, b, and c next to the image.

14. The primary source of a planet's primitive atmosphere is the release of volcanic gases that are dissolved in molten rock. Suggest a reason(s) why Mercury, although it has numerous volcanic features, is devoid of an atmosphere.

_____

_____

_____

Venus

Venus, second only to the Moon in brilliance in the night sky, is similar to Earth in size, density, mass, and location in the solar system. The "enhanced greenhouse effect" of the Venusian atmosphere, consisting of 97% carbon dioxide with only a scant trace of water vapor, is responsible for surface temperatures near 475°C (900°F). Although strong above-surface winds exist on the planet, surface winds average only a few meters per second. The planet is shrouded in thick, opaque clouds that completely hide the surface from viewing by traditional visible light cameras. Nevertheless, using radar, which can penetrate through clouds, the unmanned *Magellan* spacecraft has provided hundreds of images of the surface that reveal a varied volcanic topography (Figure 4). In general, these radar images show rough topography (mountains, crater rims, ejecta, etc.) as bright regions, and smoother material as dark. With its high surface temperature, lack of water, and an atmospheric pressure that is 90 times that at Earth's surface, Venus is certainly one of the most uninviting places in the solar system. Use the Venusian images in Figure 4 to answer questions 15–25.

15. Using the full-disk image of Venus in Figure 4, write a brief, general description of the planet's surface.

_____

_____

_____

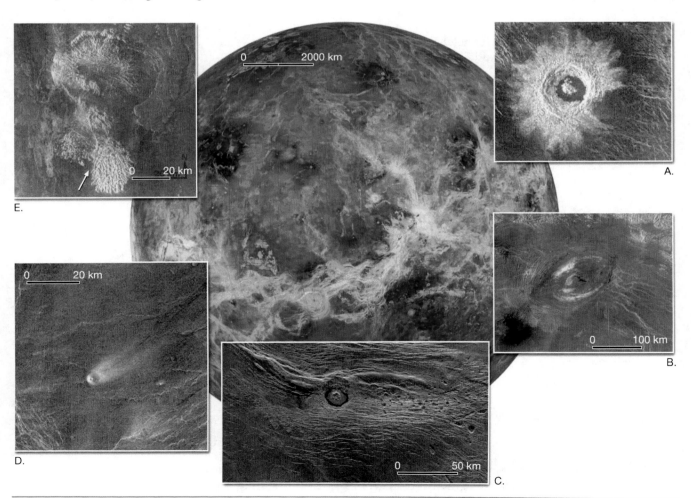

Figure 4 Geologic processes on Venus. (A.-E. Courtesy NASA/JPL-Caltech; Venus, Courtesy of NASA/JPL)

16. Choosing from the geologic processes that act on a planet's surface, write the name of the process most likely responsible for each feature in Figures 4a–e next to the image.

    Figure 4a is a radar image of Golubkina crater, a 34-kilometer (21-mile) wide impact crater.

17. Why are parts of the image in Figure 4a bright white?

    _____

    _____

18. Label the crater's central peak, crater floor, and ejecta on Figure 4a.

19. Is Golubkina crater younger or older than the surrounding landscape? How did you arrive at your conclusion?

    _____

    _____

    Figure 4b, Sacajawea, is a volcanic cone with a large summit caldera.

20. What is the approximate diameter in kilometers and miles of the summit caldera on Sacajawea?

    _____

21. Suggest a cause for the system of concentric lines that surround the caldera on Sacajawea.

    _____

    _____

22. The geologic process most likely responsible for producing the long, linear features in Figure 4c is (tectonism, gradation, impact cratering). Circle your answer.

23. The large crater in the upper left of center in Figure 4c is (older, younger, the same age) as the linear features. Circle your answer. How did you arrive at your conclusion?

    _____

    _____

    Figures 4d and e are of features produced by gradation.

24. The gradational agent responsible for the feature in Figure 4d is (running water, gravity, wind, ice),

whereas those landforms composed of unconsolidated volcanic debris on the side of the volcanic cone in Figure 4e are probably the result of (running water, gravity, wind, ice). Circle your answers.

25. Approximately how far do the landforms at the base of the volcano in Figure 4e extend beyond the summit of the cone? The features are most likely (glaciers, rivers, landslides). Circle your answer.

    _____

Mars

With its thin atmosphere, polar caps, and seasons, in many ways Mars is similar to Earth in that the same four geologic processes that shape our planet's surface have left their mark on Mars. The Martian surface is essentially volcanic. Although some of the largest volcanoes in the solar system are found on Mars, all are apparently extinct. However, numerous broad shield cones, vast lava flows, and plains of volcanic material all suggest an extensive volcanic history. Unlike Earth, Mars does not experience plate tectonics but does exhibit many tectonic features caused by compressional and extensional stresses. Furthermore, as on the Moon, Mercury, and Venus, impact craters are very evident on the Martian surface.

Gradation is the dominant geologic process altering the present-day surface of Mars. Gravity and wind are continuing agents responsible for frequent landslides and numerous dunes. Moreover, although extremely cold temperatures and low atmospheric pressures suppress the formation of liquid water on the surface of Mars today, many landforms suggest that, in the past, running water was an effective gradational agent.

After you examine the images of Mars in Figure 5, continue your investigation of the surfaces of the terrestrial planets by answering questions 26–33.

26. Selecting from the lettered photographs (Figure 5a–f), list the letter of one or more examples of features produced by each of the four geologic processes that modified the surface of Mars.

    Volcanism: _____

    Tectonism: _____

    Gradation: _____

    Impact cratering: _____

27. Using the full-disk image of Mars in Figure 5, write a brief, general description of the surface.

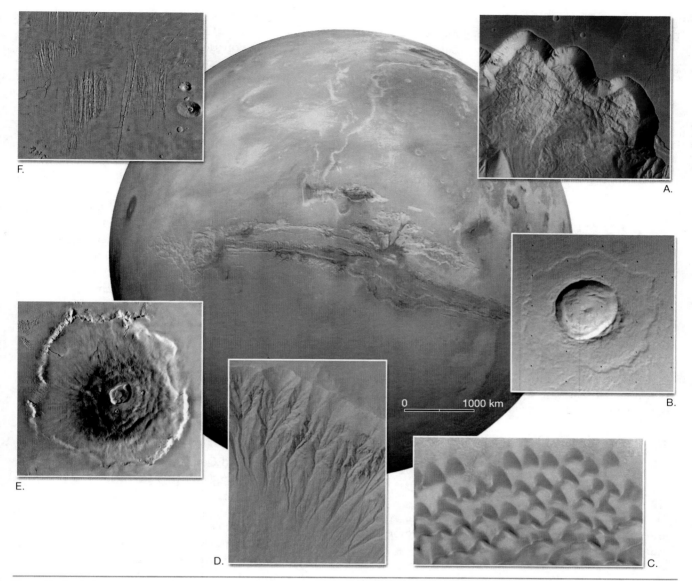

Figure 5 Geologic processes on Mars. (A. Courtesy NASA/JPL-Caltech; B: Courtesy of NASA/NSSDC; C. and F. Courtesy of NASA/Mars Orbiter Laser Altimeter (MOLA) Team; D. Courtesy of NASA/JPL/Malin Space Science Systems; E. Courtesy of the United States Geological Survey)

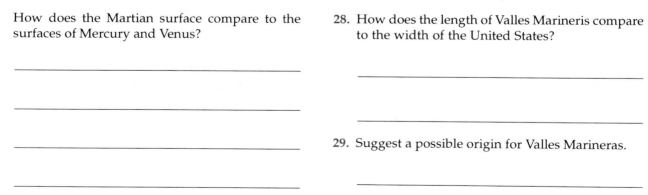

How does the Martian surface compare to the surfaces of Mercury and Venus?

_____

_____

_____

_____

The long linear feature near the center of the full-disk image of Mars is Valles Marineris, the longest canyon system in the solar system.

28. How does the length of Valles Marineris compare to the width of the United States?

_____

_____

29. Suggest a possible origin for Valles Marineras.

_____

30. Write the name of the gradational agent most likely responsible for producing the features illustrated in Figures 5a, c, and d by each image.

Figure 5e, Olympus Mons, one of four huge volcanoes in a region called Tharsis, is streaked down its sides by lava flows and has a caldera that measures approximately 50 × 80 kilometers.

31. What is the approximate width of Olympus Mons? How does the size of Olympus Mons compare to the distance across your home state?

_____

_____

32. When compared to the surface of Mercury and the lighter regions on the Moon, Olympus Mons is geologically (young, old, about the same age). Circle your answer and explain how you arrived at your conclusion.

_____

_____

The features in Figure 5d were most likely formed by water erosion. The barchan dunes illustrated in Figure 5c have been sculpted by wind.

33. Draw arrows on Figure 5d indicating the direction that the water that formed the channels flowed and on Figure 5c showing the prevailing wind direction in the region.

Figure 6 shows the Martian volcanic crater, Apollinaris Patera (letter A) and the surrounding region. Use Figure 6 to answer questions 34–38.

34. Compare Apollinaris Patera (letter A) to Olympus Mons (Figure 5e). How are the craters similar and how are they different?

_____

_____

_____

35. The landform marked B on Figure 6 consists of volcanic rock. What is the probable origin of the feature?

_____

_____

The landform marked C on Figure 6 is a large impact crater.

36. Assuming the same ratio between the width of a crater and the diameter of the object that produced it you determined for Meteor Crater in question 4, approximately how large was the object that formed the Martian crater?

_____

Ma'adim Vallis is the sinuous channel marked D in Figure 6.

37. The geologic process most likely responsible for Ma'adim Vallis is (tectonics, impact cratering, gradation). The agent that produced the feature was (ice, wind, running water). Circle your answers.

38. Considering your answers to question 37 and the fact that the floor of Gusev, the 160-km diameter crater lettered E, slopes toward the top of the photo, what type of material might comprise the floor of Gusev? What evidence supports your conclusion?

_____

_____

_____

Surface Ages and General Topography

Although the Moon and planets formed at the same time approximately 4.5 billion years ago, due to variations in the levels of geologic activity their current surfaces differ in age. Throughout time one or more of the four primary landform shaping processes has worked to alter each of the original surfaces.

In comparing planetary surfaces, impact craters provide a means for determining relative ages. In general, older surfaces show more craters per unit area, larger craters, and more degraded craters than younger surfaces.

Begin your investigation of the relative ages of surfaces by reexamining the photograph of the Moon in Figure 2. Then answer questions 39–42.

39. Notice that the surface of the Moon consists of two general types of regions. Describe the characteristics of each.

_____

_____

_____

_____

Figure 6   Apollinaris Patera (letter A) and surrounding region. (Courtesy NASA/JPL-Caltech. Produced by the U.S. Geological Survey)

40. The lighter areas on the Moon are referred to as *highlands,* and the darker areas are called *maria* (or plains). Which of the two is most densely cratered?

_____

41. Of the two regions, which is older—the highlands or maria? What fact(s) support your conclusion?

_____

_____

_____

42. Notice the craters that have bright ejecta deposits that form a star-like pattern of rays around them. Are these craters older or younger than the regions that surround them? How did you arrive at your conclusion?

_____

_____

_____

Use Figures 2–5 to answer questions 43–47.

43. Reexamine the full-disk image of Mercury in Figure 3. Describe the landforms and regions you observe.

_____

_____

_____

44. Based on the density of craters, the surface of Mercury is (older, younger, about the same age) as the maria on the Moon. Circle your answer.

45. Based on the density of craters, the surface of Venus (Figure 4) appears to be (older, younger, about the same age) as the Moon's highlands and (older, younger, about the same age) as the surface of Mercury. Circle your answers.

46. What are the similarities and differences in the surface of Mars (Figure 5) compared to the surfaces of the Moon (Figure 2) and Mercury (Figure 3)?

_____

_____

_____

_____

47. On a global scale, which planet looks more like Venus (Figure 4): Mercury or Mars? Explain the reason for your selection.

_____

_____

_____

    Use Figure 6, Apollinaris Patera (letter A) and the surrounding region, to answer questions 48–51.

48. Compare the southern half of the photograph to the northern half. Which surface is older? How did you arrive at your conclusion?

_____

_____

_____

49. What fact(s) supports the conclusion that the craters in the southern two-thirds of Figure 6 are of various ages?

_____

_____

50. In the following space, draw a sketch of the four craters in the vicinity of letter F. Label the craters in order of formation, with the number "1" being the oldest. Did you have any difficulty in assigning relative ages to the craters? If so, explain why.

_____

_____

51. Based on your observations of the features in Figure 6, what is the probable order of occurrence of features A, E, C, and D (first to last)? What evidence supports your answer?

_____

_____

_____

_____

    Although the surfaces of the terrestrial planets have various origins and evolutions, they do have similar large-scale features.

52. After you compare the elevation maps of Venus and Mars shown in Figure 7 with the global topography map of Earth in Figure 2, briefly list some of the similarities and differences among the general features depicted on the images of the three planets.

_____

_____

_____

Venus

Highest ▭ Lowest

Mars

Figure 7   Surface elevation maps of Venus and Mars. (Venus map courtesy of NASA/NSSDC; Mars map courtesy of NASA/Mars Orbiter Laser Altimeter (MOLA) Team)

Closing Observations

Use the information you have learned about the geologic processes that shape the Moon and terrestrial planets to answer questions 53–56.

53. Describe the similarities and differences between the landforms of Earth and

    Moon: _____

    _____

    _____

    Mercury: _____

    _____

    _____

    Venus: _____

    _____

    _____

    Mars: _____

    _____

    _____

54. Based on the density of craters, types of landforms, and the number of geologic processes evi-

dent, list the five surfaces you have investigated in order from youngest to oldest.

Youngest _____

_____

_____

_____

Oldest _____

55. Which of the five surfaces you have investigated has the most active geologic history? Which has the least active geologic history? Explain your choices.

_____

_____

_____

_____

56. List your thoughts concerning the future geologic evolution of

Mercury: _____

_____

Earth: _____

_____

_____

Mars: _____

_____

_____

Examining the Terrestrial Planets on the Internet

Continue your analysis of the topics presented in this exercise by completing the corresponding online activity on the *Applications & Investigations in Earth Science* website at http://prenhall.com/earthsciencelab

Examining the Terrestrial Planets

Date Due: _____

Name: _____

Date: _____

Class: _____

After you have finished this exercise, complete the following questions. You may have to refer to the exercise for assistance or to locate specific answers. Be prepared to submit this summary/report to your instructor at the designated time.

1. What are the four geologic processes that have shaped the surfaces of the terrestrial planets and the Moon? Give an example of a type of landform produced by each of the four processes.

   _____

   _____

   _____

   _____

2. The surface of the Moon most resembles the surface of (Mercury, Venus, Earth), whereas the surface of Venus is similar to that of (Earth, Mars). Circle your answers.

3. Which planet's surface has only been mapped using radar? Why has only radar been used?

   _____

   _____

4. List the most significant geologic process(es) that shape the surface of each terrestrial planet and the Moon.

   Mercury: _____

   Venus: _____

   Earth: _____

Moon: _____

Mars: _____

5. Of the major gradational agents, (running water, gravity, wind, ice) is the only one that alters the surface of all the terrestrial planets. Circle your answer.

6. Briefly describe how you can determine whether or not the age of one terrestrial planet's surface is older or younger than that of another terrestrial planet.

   _____

   _____

   _____

7. List the five surfaces you have investigated in this exercise in order from youngest to oldest.

   Youngest _____

   _____

   _____

   _____

   Oldest _____

8. Suggest a reason(s) as to why the surface of Mercury appears so much older than the surface of Venus.

   _____

   _____

   _____

239

9. On which planet, other than Earth, is it most likely that water-deposited sedimentary rocks, perhaps containing fossils, occur? Explain your choice.

_____

_____

_____

10. List and briefly describe the geologic processes that have acted on the Martian surface shown in Figure 8. Give specific examples of features in support of your conclusions.

_____

_____

_____

_____

_____

_____

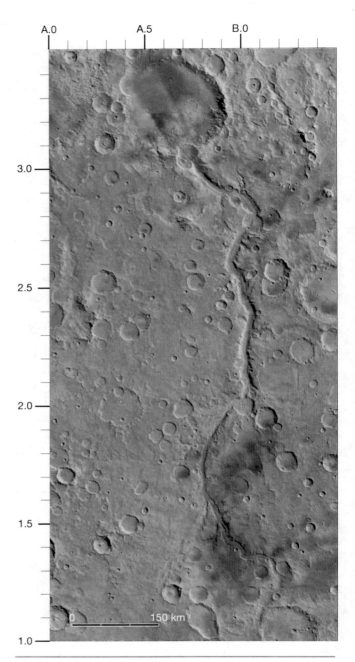

Figure 8   Photograph of the Martian surface to be used with question 10. (Courtesy NASA/JPL-Caltech. Produced by the U.S. Geological Survey)